622.182   K18g   FV
KARTSEV
GEOCHEMICAL METHODS OF PROSPECTING
AND EXPLORATION FOR PETROLEUM
AND NATURAL GAS
                              15.00

GEOCHEMICAL METHODS
OF PROSPECTING AND EXPLORATION
FOR PETROLEUM AND
NATURAL GAS

А. А. КАРЦЕВ, З. А. ТАБАСАРАНСКИЙ,
М. И. СУББОТА, Г. А. МОГИЛЕВСКИЙ

ГЕОХИМИЧЕСКИЕ МЕТОДЫ ПОИСКОВ И РАЗВЕДКИ НЕФТЯНЫХ И ГАЗОВЫХ МЕСТОРОЖДЕНИЙ

ГОСУДАРСТВЕННОЕ НАУЧНО-ТЕХНИЧЕСКОЕ ИЗДАТЕЛЬСТВО
НЕФТЯНОЙ И ГОРНО-ТОПЛИВНОЙ ЛИТЕРАТУРЫ
Москва 1954

A. A. KARTSEV, Z. A. TABASARANSKII,
M. I. SUBBOTA, and G. A. MOGILEVSKII

GEOCHEMICAL METHODS
OF PROSPECTING AND EXPLORATION
FOR PETROLEUM AND
NATURAL GAS

English Translation Edited by

PAUL A. WITHERSPOON and WILLIAM D. ROMEY

BERKELEY AND LOS ANGELES
UNIVERSITY OF CALIFORNIA PRESS
1959

UNIVERSITY OF CALIFORNIA PRESS
BERKELEY AND LOS ANGELES, CALIFORNIA

CAMBRIDGE UNIVERSITY PRESS
LONDON, ENGLAND

LIBRARY OF CONGRESS CATALOG CARD NUMBER: 59–11313

PRINTED BY OFFSET IN THE UNITED STATES OF AMERICA

Prefaces

EDITORS' PREFACE

California Research Corporation, a subsidiary of Standard Oil Company of California, became interested in this book because of its excellent and comprehensive coverage of the subject of geochemical prospecting for petroleum in the Soviet Union. After making a complete English translation, they decided that the petroleum industry in America and elsewhere would be interested in the many concepts presented and in the detailed descriptions of methodology and results. Accordingly, they kindly turned the translation over to the Minerals Research Laboratory of the Department of Mineral Technology, University of California, Berkeley.

This translation is an accurate reproduction of the authors' original and has been carefully checked for its scientific exactness. In several chapters, where sections seemed obscure, the original Russian has been retranslated. In this connection, we gratefully acknowledge the excellent work of Dr. W. D. Rosenfeld of California Research Corporation in editing Chapter XIII, "Microbiological Methods." His valuable assistance on this important chapter is especially deserving of recognition.

In some places, however, it was not feasible to redraft the entire text into literary English. Thus, although the translation is a faithful reproduction of the original, the reader may occasionally find the phraseology somewhat unfamiliar because of the differences between English and Russian syntax. Some unfamiliar data or terminology, however, is merely a reflection of the differences between petroleum technology in the Soviet Union and in the United States.

Most of the illustrations were adapted from the original publication, and the legends translated into English. A number of illustrations, however, could not be handled in this manner, and it was necessary either to eliminate them or to obtain the original drawings and photographs. When the authors were informed of this, they immediately provided all necessary materials through the Soviet agency, Mezhdunarodnaya Kniga, and thus made it possible to include illustrations that could not otherwise have been published. We should like to thank Mezhdunarodnaya Kniga and the authors for this generous assistance.

As might be expected in a technical translation, some words in Russian do not have exact equivalents in English. For example, "neftyanoe mestorozhdenie" has been translated as "petroleum formation" or "petroleum deposit" and has a much more general meaning than "neftyanaya zalezh'," which has been translated as "oil pool". As used by the authors, "petroleum formation" means a group of "oil pools" below a single region of the surface plus all intervening and overlying beds. Thus, a "formation" may include both productive and non-productive sections of strata. The authors also distinguish between the use of "poiskov," which has been translated as "prospecting," and "razvedka," which has been translated as

"exploration." "Prospecting" for petroleum should be understood to include the use of methods that are restricted to the earth's surface and are
largely carried out in undrilled areas. "Exploration" for petroleum, on
the other hand, should be understood as the work that is done after "prospecting" is finished, such as the examination of bore holes for evidences
of oil or gas.

The work "porod," which has been translated as "rock," is another
term that has a more general meaning in this book that it normally has in
English. As used by the authors, "rock" includes both consolidated and
unconsolidated forms. The work "glina," which has been translated as
"clay," apparently can also sometimes mean "shale," as will be evident
to the reader in Chapter VI. A number of other such terms occur at various places in the text. These are usually used only in a single chapter,
and, therefore, explanatory footnotes have been added at appropriate points.
The reader will also encounter a number of geologic names that are used
to describe the stratigraphy of those parts of the Soviet Union where oil is
produced. For those who are not familiar with this stratigraphy, a generalized geologic column is included as an Appendix. The original table of
contents of the Russian edition has been greatly expanded, and it is hoped
that it will serve as a guide to the details of the subject matter.

We should like to thank the authors for their great interest in this
translation. In addition to supplying the illustrative material mentioned
above, they have also contributed a preface to this edition. The emphasis
in geochemical prospecting in the Soviet Union has changed somewhat since
1954, when this book was first published. As the authors indicate, however,
the fundamental ideas and techniques have not changed. Certainly, nothing
comparable to this treatment of the subject has yet appeared in the English
language.

Finally, we want to express our sincere appreciation to Professor H.
E. Hawkes, University of California, for suggesting that we undertake the
publication of this translation. As director of a literature review project
on geochemical prospecting, Professor Hawkes was quick to appreciate the
value of this book and urged that it be published.

Berkeley   Paul A. Witherspoon
March 1, 1959   William D. Romey

AUTHORS' PREFACE TO AMERICAN EDITION

The Russian edition of this book was published in 1954. Naturally a great
many new developments have occurred in the field of geochemical prospecting and exploration for petroleum during the past four years. For the
most part, however, these changes have not affected the fundamental
methods or techniques described in this book. Rather, they have been concerned with the ways in which various geochemical procedures have been
applied. The possibilities of the various methods and logical ways of
combining them have been made clearer through practical applications.

It has been found that geochemical investigations involving horizons
close to the surface are effective in geologic provinces where the rocks are
considerably disturbed. Under some other conditions, they are relatively
ineffective. Geochemical investigations of horizons that have been cored
have been found to be particularly advantageous. Combining this type of

investigation with the drilling of shallow geologic structure tests is useful. The combined use of water-gas, hydrochemical, and bacterial surveys in studying aquifers has been widely developed. Consequently the relative significance of various parts of the book has changed somewhat.

We are greatly pleased that our work will be accessible to English-speaking readers. We would like to express our sincere gratitude to the people and institutions who have contributed to the translation and publication of this book in English, and especially to the workers at the Minerals Research Laboratory of the University of California and to Professor Paul A. Witherspoon.

Moscow	A. A. Kartsev
January 10, 1959	Z. A. Tabasaranskii
	M. I. Subbota
	G. A. Mogilevskii

AUTHORS' PREFACE TO RUSSIAN EDITION

All of the geochemical methods used in prospecting and exploration for petroleum and natural gas are described in this book. Theoretical principles, field methods, and techniques of geological interpretation are set forth. The geochemistry of petroleum and natural gas formations is also presented. The book is intended as a text for students of petroleum science and for petroleum geologists in their practical work. The introduction and chapters I, II, VII, VIII, IX, XI, XII, and XIV were written by A. A. Kartsev. Z. A. Tabasaranskii wrote chapter VI; M. I. Subbota, chapters III, IV, V, and X; and G. A. Mogilevskii, chapter XIII.

The manuscript was read entirely or in part by several people whose comments the authors greatly appreciated. The authors are especially grateful to the Head of the Central Petroleum and Gas Exploration Division (Glavneftegazrazvedka) G. L. Grishin, Professor M. V. Abramovich, Professor A. F. Dobryanskii, Professor S. I. Kuznetsov, Doctor of Geological-Mineralogical Sciences L. A. Gulyaeva, V. N. Florovskaya, Lecturer B. I. Sultanova, Lecturer B. S. Moldavskii, Candidate of Geological-Mineralogical Sciences E. A. Bars, and Candidate of Physical-Mathematical Sciences P. L. Antonov. The authors also express their thanks to Doctor of Biological Sciences S. V. Viktorov, who contributed a short section on geobotanical indicators of petroleum-bearing formations to the book.

Contents

[xiii]

Introduction

Geochemical methods are one of a group of ways of prospecting and exploring for petroleum and natural gas formations. Among these methods is the chemical analysis (as well as the physico-chemical and microbiological study) of gases, waters, rocks, and soils. The purpose of these analyses is to determine: (a) the presence of dispersed petroleum substances (petroleum, hydrocarbon gases, bitumens), (b) traces of the influence of petroleum substances on gases, waters, rocks, soils, and organisms, (c) substances or conditions which customarily accompany oil and gas pools.

Most geochemical methods of prospecting and exploration for petroleum are direct methods.[1] They directly indicate the actual presence of oil and gas. This is the main difference between geochemical and geophysical methods. The latter indicates only the presence of conditions favorable for petroleum accumulation. Herein lies the great value of geochemical prospecting methods. They are especially useful in the following two cases: (1) prospecting for stratigraphic and lithologic pools which are not associated with local structural features, (2) deciding whether a previously discovered structural trap contains petroleum or is "dry." Geochemical exploration methods are also effective in determining the presence of natural gas and petroleum in strata which have been drilled (geochemical well-logging).

Among geochemical methods there are indirect as well as direct methods of prospecting for petroleum. The problems posed by the indirect methods are similar to those in geophysical prospecting. Structural hydrochemical surveys are an example of the indirect approach.

Direct geochemical prospecting for petroleum is analogous to the oldest geological method which consisted of searching for and investigating oil and gas seeps. The difference between geochemical and geological methods is that the former are concerned with micro-concentrations of petroleum substances and microseeps, while the latter seek traces that are visible to the naked eye. None of the direct geochemical methods, however, can tell the investigator whether or not oil and gas pools are present. (Even less are they able to tell whether a pool is of economic proportions.) They can only verify the presence of petroleum hydrocarbons which may be present in a dispersed form.

Geochemical methods are used in prospecting and exploring for deposits of other useful minerals (especially ore deposits) as well as for petroleum. There are great differences between the methods used in petroleum work and the methods used in prospecting for ore deposits. These differences result basically from the peculiarities of petroleum and natural

---

[1] Using the term "exploration" in its strictest sense, exploration methods (not prospecting methods) can only be direct ones.

gas as minerals. The singularity of oil and gas is that the bond between them and the surrounding and containing rocks is weaker than it is for ores. Furthermore, tectonic factors play a decisive role in the formation of oil and gas pools. In prospecting and exploration for ore deposits, geochemical methods are so closely bound up with geological ones that it is practically impossible to separate them. On the other hand, in prospecting for petroleum, geological and geophysical methods may be separated from the geochemical ones to a large degree.[2] For this very reason, geochemical methods long occupied a subordinate place in searching for petroleum and natural gas formations. The presence of structure was considered decisive in prospecting for petroleum for a long time.

Recently, various other methods have come to be used more often, although structure still remains the most important feature in petroleum prospecting. Among these, geochemical methods occupy a larger and larger place. In the first stage of prospecting work (the finding of petroleum-bearing strata in a new district), geochemical methods play a very important role. This is also true in the last stage of exploration work — the discovery of productive horizons during drilling. These methods, however, are not being put to their fullest use at the present time.

Geochemical methods of prospecting for petroleum should be used only in close connection with the other prospecting work. The results should then be evaluated in the light of all available geological and geophysical data. The geologist examines the sum total of all facts obtained by the various methods and makes the final decision. The use of geochemical methods separately from other methods and evaluation of geochemical results without reference to geological data leads to incorrect conclusions.

Credit for the development of geochemical methods of prospecting for petroleum goes to Soviet scientists. The first development of such methods began in 1929 when V. A. Sokolov worked out and proposed the gas survey method. This method received extensive development and notoriety and also served as the basis for development of other geochemical methods. To V. A. Sokolov goes credit for development of the theory of movement of gases in the earth's crust which is the theoretical foundation for many other geochemical methods. He also developed methods of microanalysis of gases.

The core-gas survey and geomicrobiological method were first proposed by G. M. Mogilevskii in 1935 and 1937 respectively. Oil and gas well-logging, which at present is one of the most important geochemical methods, was proposed by M. V. Abramovich in 1933. All of these methods are based on the gas survey.

Bituminological research also was first developed in the USSR (in 1925). "Bituminology" is greatly developed in our country. N. A. Shlezinger and others in the USSR were the first to use luminescent-bituminous methods starting in 1939. Nowhere have luminescent-bitumenous methods received such development as in our country. V. N. Florovskaya's services in this field must be mentioned.

Starting in 1940, work on dissolved gases also began in the USSR.

---

[2]This does not mean that they should or can be used completely separately from geological and geophysical methods (see below).

Other methods which have been highly developed in the Soviet Union are
hydrochemical methods (V. A. Sulin and others), soil-genetic methods (V.
A. Kovda), and the oxidation-reduction potential method first proposed by
V. E. Levenson in 1936.

The Petroleum-Gas-Survey Bureau ("Neftegazos'emka") and, since
1950, the geochemical division of the Geochemical and Geophysical Exploration Scientific Research Institute (NIIGGR) of the Ministry for the Petroleum Industry have played an important role in the development of geochemical methods of prospecting for petroleum and natural gas. The following other organizations should also be mentioned: The Petroleum Institute (formerly the Institute of Combustible Resources) of the Academy of
Sciences of the USSR has played an important role in the development of
hydrochemical, bituminological, and oxidation-reduction potential methods.
The Soils Institute of the Academy of Sciences of the USSR has participated
in the development of soil-salt methods and soil-bitumen surveys. The
All-Union Geological Exploration Scientific Research Institute (VNIGRI)
has further developed bituminological and other methods.

As shown above, insufficient use is being made of geochemical methods
in the petroleum industry. Most of these methods require further refinement. There is still not sufficient correlation between geochemical and
other types of prospecting work. Not all petroleum geologists have a complete and correct understanding of the various geochemical methods of
searching for oil and gas. These deficiencies must be overcome in the
near future. The goal of this book is to help in that direction.

CHAPTER ONE

The Geochemistry
of Petroleum Formations

The geochemistry of petroleum formations is concerned with processes of chemical interaction between oil pools[1] and the medium surrounding them — gases, waters, rocks, organisms — and such chemical properties of crude oils, waters, gases, and rocks as are factors and consequences of these processes.

The geochemistry of petroleum is part of the geochemistry of oil formations and is concerned only with one aspect, the transformations and properties of crude oils themselves. The geochemistry of oil deposits, which encompasses these questions, also deals with another aspect, the environment of the oil pools. Oil pools, together with the medium surrounding them form polyphase systems. Among the phases of these systems, and also among the components of different chemical nature within the separate phases, chemical interaction takes place. Interchange of substances among phases also occurs as a result of physical and physicochemical processes (evaporation, adsorption, etc.); this also leads to chemical changes. As a result of all these processes, both the oils and the gases, waters, and rocks associated with them acquire new properties (which are subsequently changed). The study of this entire, very involved complex of phenomena constitutes the task of the geochemistry of oil formations.

The geochemistry of petroleum deposits is closely associated with questions of the origin of oil (oil genesis) and the formation of oil deposits (oil accumulation). Oil accumulation does not entirely end with the development of pools; it may proceed in several stages. Those chemical transformations of oils which proceed in the pools constitute the object of study of the geochemistry of oil formations. Herein lies its fundamental theoretical significance.

In the present work, however, the exposition of the fundamentals of the geochemistry of petroleum deposits mainly serves other purposes of a practical character. Some of these practical applications are described below.

1. The most important practical application of the geochemistry of oil formations is the use of the geochemical peculiarities of the environment of oil pools (gases, waters, rocks, organisms) as indices of oil-bearing character in exploration and prospecting. In this scheme, the geochemistry of oil formations provides the general theoretical basis of geochemical methods of exploration and prospecting for mineral resources of this type. The exposition of the fundamentals of the geochemistry of oil formations in the present work is primarily determined by these problems.

---

[1] By the word "pool" is here understood a single mass of oil; the words "formation" and "deposit" refer to a group of pools situated below a single region of the surface together with the non-oil-bearing rocks lying under, over, and between these pools.

2. An important application of the geochemistry of petroleum formations is the use of its data for the prognosis of the quality of oil and in prospecting for oil of predetermined quality. As yet, this problem can only be indicated; its solution is a matter for the future. Nevertheless, it would be improper to avoid all mention of this problem. Therefore, questions of the relation of the properties of crude oil to geological conditions are briefly stated below.

3. Data on the geochemistry of oil formations may also be used: (a) for the correlation of geologic strata (according to the properties of oils, waters); (b) for secondary methods of exploitation of oil pools (choice and preparation of water and gas for pumping into the reservoir); (c) in prospecting for several other mineral resources (ozokerite, iodine, sulfur, etc.).

In relation to all that has been stated, the present chapter is arranged in the following manner. Since the main fluid in the reservoir is oil, the characteristics of some crude oils are given at the beginning. Then, after a brief discussion of the external conditions affecting geochemical processes in oil formations, the character of these processes is given. After this, a summary is provided of conclusions on the relation of the properties of crude oils to the geological conditions of their deposition. Finally, those peculiarities of the environment of oil pools which are the consequences of the reaction of oil with the environment are characterized. This is followed by transition to the problem of geochemical indices of oil-bearing character. Of necessity, all questions are stated as briefly as possible. This chapter does not by any means attempt to give a complete account of the geochemistry of petroleum formations.

The geochemistry of natural gas formations is difficult to separate from that of oil formations; not only formations, but also individual pools usually have a "double content", i.e., oil and gas. Nevertheless, the geochemistry of purely gaseous formations has its special features. In this chapter only the geochemistry of oil formations is considered. Natural gases are included in the following manner: (1) as component parts of oil pools and (2) as part of the medium surrounding oil pools (gases in gas caps, marginal waters, etc.).[2]

PROPERTIES OF PETROLEUM

In this section are considered only those properties of crude oils which are important from the geochemical point of view. Before proceeding with the discussion of this problem, it is necessary to dwell briefly on the physical properties of petroleum.

The Physical State of Petroleum

The basic mass of petroleum in the usual conditions of oil pools consists of a mixture of liquid substances, normally containing a significant quantity of soluble gases (up to several hundred cu. m. of gases per ton of oil) and colloidally dissolved solid substances: tars, paraffins, etc. (up to 40%). The liquid substances are characterized by widely different boiling points.

---

[2]The elements of the general geochemistry of gases and of natural gas formations are given in Chapter III.

The physical state of the individual components may be changed under the conditions usual for pools. At pressures above 200 - 300 atm. under conditions of saturation by gas, oils may pass over into a single-phase state (so-called retrograde vaporization): in this case, however, solid substances separate.

TABLE 1. Fractional Composition of Petroleum

Boiling range at normal pressure, °C	Content, %	Technical names of fractions			
below 200	0 — 80	Gasoline[3] (to 150°) Ligroin } (light)	Light oils		Distillate
200 — 300	5 — 50	Kerosine			
300 — 550	0 — 80	Lubricating oils		Fuel oil	
above 550	0 — 70	Tar			Residue

A representation of the quantitative relations between the physically different components of oils gives their fractional composition (Table 1). This representation, however, is not exact, since gases are not represented therein. The temperature fractions, although they are of arbitrary, technical significance, are also essential for the evaluation of the composition of crude oils.

State of Knowledge on the Composition of Petroleum

The chemical composition of petroleum has not been adequately studied. Only the elementary composition has been completely studied. The group composition, i.e., the content of different groups (classes) of chemical compounds, has been studied only for the light fractions comprising on the average 15% of the oil mass. The group composition of kerosine and lubricating oil fractions is only approximately known, while that of the heavier fractions is practically unknown. The individual composition, i.e., the content in petroleum of individual chemical compounds, is known only for the gasolines.

The unsatisfactory state of knowledge of the heavy, high-molecular fractions is explained by the character of the method of analysis. At present, the separation of crude oil into fractions, necessary for analysis, is accomplished primarily by distillation and purification. The high temperatures used in these operations (for the higher fractions) destroy the natural compounds; the substances determined in this manner are newly formed in the analysis. Furthermore, the presence in the middle fractions of crude oils of an enormous number of compounds, isomers having nearly identical properties, makes it practically impossible at the present time to investigate the individual composition of any fractions, except the light ones.

---

[3] "Benzine" in original Russian has been translated as "gasoline." Ed.

Elemental Composition

The limits of variation of the elemental composition of petroleum are given in Table 2.[4]

TABLE 2. Elemental Composition of Petroleum[5]

%C	%H	%O	%S	%N	$\dfrac{C}{H}$	$\dfrac{C}{(O+S+N)}$	Generally, value (C+H) > 96%, content
83 — 87.5	11 — 14.5	0 — 2.5	0 — 5	0 — 1	5.7 — 7.7	12 — 870	O<1%, N<0.5%

If the elemental composition of crude oils is compared with the average elemental composition of sedimentary rock, the following is established: (1) carbon is concentrated in oils by a factor of 20 or more (the average percentage of C for sedimentary rocks ≈ 4, including carbonate C) and hydrogen by a factor of 25 (the average percentage of H ≈ 0.5); (2) dispersion of oxygen occurs in oils to the extent of 50 times or more; (3) a significant concentration of sulfur is sometimes observed in oil, up to tenfold (the average percentage of S in sedimentary rocks ≈ 0.5). Nitrogen may also be concentrated up to twofold (the average percentage of N for sediments ≈ 0.05). The very insignificant content of oxygen in the oils in comparison with the surrounding medium clearly expresses their geochemical nature.

Hydrocarbon Composition

The extremely widespread idea that petroleum is simply a hydrocarbon mixture is incorrect. Even in the case in which O+S+N = 3%, the non-hydrocarbon compounds may comprise as much as 30% of the oil mass; sometimes, indeed, they outweigh the hydrocarbons. Non-hydrocarbon compounds form the heaviest portion of crude oil and are concentrated upon distillation in the residue (not boiling below 550°C). The distillate of the oil, for which only the group composition is known, actually consists almost entirely of hydrocarbons of three kinds: paraffin, polymethylene (naphthenic), and aromatic. By the group composition of an oil is usually understood the correlation of paraffin (saturated), naphthenic, and aromatic hydrocarbons in its distillate (up to 550°C). This correlation basically determines the chemistry of petroleum.

Extreme and average values of the content of paraffin, naphthenic, and aromatic hydrocarbons in the distillates of all the crude oils of the world are given in Table 3.

---

[4]In the table doubtful and borderline cases are not used, specifically those cases with abnormally high percentages of O (the latter are usually explained by errors of analysis or "aerated" samples).

[5]The data are based on analyses of practically degassed oils and consequently, do not correspond to their natural state (1). When allowance is made for dissolved gases, the H content (in percent) must increase.

TABLE 3. Hydrocarbon Composition of Petroleum

	Content of hydrocarbons, per cent		
	paraffin	naphthenic	aromatic
Extreme values	0 — 75	20 — 80	5 — 60
Usual values	5 — 55	25 — 75	10 — 40
"Average world oil" according to A. F. Dobryanskii[6] . . .	30	46	24

The chemical classification of petroleum is established by the predominance of any one or two or three hydrocarbon groups. As follows from Table 3, the major component group usually consists of naphthenic hydrocarbons; less often it consists of paraffins. Aromatic hydrocarbons constitute the predominant group only in special cases.

Oils of anomalous hydrocarbon composition are of great geochemical interest. Such, for example, is naphthalenic medicinal oil, which is completely devoid of paraffin hydrocarbons; Ildokanian oil, on the contrary, is three-fourths saturated; Chusovian oil contains 60% aromatic hydrocarbons.

The reported data do not give a complete account of the hydrocarbon composition, even for the distillates of the oils for the following reasons, which are rooted in the existing methods of analysis.

1. Solid hydrocarbons comprise solid paraffins (or waxes) and ceresins, which sometimes constitute as much as 10% of the oil (in the more paraffinic oils); in the calculation of group composition these are all classed with the paraffin hydrocarbons. It is known, however, that they are, in part, cyclic (naphthenic). In the opinion of N. I. Chernozhukov (3), the naphthenic hydrocarbons are all ceresins; i.e., the high-molecular portion of the solid hydrocarbons (C_{37} and higher). This question remains unsolved.

2. Cyclic hydrocarbons contain side-chains of a saturated nature, which are sometimes very long. This is not taken into account in the calculation of group composition. If it were, the content of the "paraffinic element" in oils would be much greater than the content of paraffin hydrocarbons given in Table 3 (very often over 59%).

3. Complex polycyclic hydrocarbons containing both naphthenic and aromatic rings (naphtheno-aromatic hydrocarbons); in the calculation of group composition these are all classed with the aromatics. Separate determination of naphthenic and aromatic rings and "alkyl" side-chains only makes possible the so-called ring analysis. Data on ring composition alone are not sufficient for complete characterization of oils. On conversion to ring composition, however, the percent of aromatic rings must decrease.[7]

---

[6]These averages may be in error, as A. F. Dobryanskii (2) did not take into account the quantitative distribution of reserves of the particular crude oils, the analyses of which he used.

[7]A. Sachanen (4), on the basis of several derived assumptions, attempted to express the composition of oils by the data of ring analysis (in which he arbitrarily included tars). The content of saturated rings then approaches 80%, while the content of naphthenic rings does not exceed 30%.

Acids

The known oxygen compounds of definite structure in petroleum comprise acids and phenols. The total amount of acids in crude oils is 0 - 2%; exceptionally, it is sometimes as high as 3% (naphthalenic medicinal oil). The major part of the acids in oils consists of naphthenic acids. Therefore, as a rule, the more acids there are, the more naphthenic hydrocarbons there are. Besides this, a small quantity of aromatic and naphtheno-aromatic acids (5) are encountered, as well as the so-called asphaltogenic acids, which appear to be oxyacids (3). Finally, oils rich in paraffin hydrocarbons and solid paraffins sometimes contain aliphatic acids. Acids, despite their low concentration in petroleum, are of great importance in prospecting.

Compounds of Sulfur and Nitrogen

Sulfur is distributed very unevenly in petroleum. Besides the enormous mass of practically sulfur-free oils (%S<0.3), there are very many sulfurous oils (%S>1), some of which contain more than 4% sulfur: Chusovian, Termez, Mexican. The major portion of the sulfur and nitrogen in oil is concentrated in the tar. Besides tar, the following forms of sulfur are known with certainty: (a) elementary sulfur, present in the form of a colloidal solution (up to 1% of the oil), and (b) thiophenes (naphthenic sulfides). The remainder of the sulfur is distributed among substances of unknown structure.

The content of nitrogen in oils is usually directly related to their tarriness. Apart from tars, the nitrogen-containing substances in oils have been shown (spectroscopically) to contain porphyrins ($C_{32}H_{36}N_4$ et al.), which are the object of much attention from the point of view of the problem of petroleum genesis. Of equal interest are other complex nitrogen bases, the nature of which remains unknown, since they decompose on distillation. According to the data of V. V. Getseu, the nitrogen bases of oils include derivatives of pyridine and quinoline (determined by luminescent chromatography (6).

Tars and Asphaltenes

Tars (and asphaltenes) are substances of indefinite chemical structure. They are the heaviest components of crude oils, being concentrated to the extent of 80 - 90% in the residue of distillation. Precipitated tars are not the same as silicagel tars (true tars). The distinction between them is based on the method of their separation. The precipitation (or sulfuric acid) method comprises the following: 100 ml. of gasoline (benzine) and 10 ml. of H_2SO_4 (sp. gr. 1.84) are added to 50 ml. of oil in a settling vessel, the mixture is shaken and allowed to stand one hour, and the increase in volume of the H_2SO_4 layer, i.e., the volume of precipitated tars, is observed. The silica-gel (or adsorption) method consists of the adsorption of tars by silica-gel from benzene or chloroform extract.

The quantity of precipitated tars in oil is about twice as great as that of silica-gel tars. It usually varies from 10 to 40%, but sometimes falls nearly to zero (some Jurassio Emba oils and Devonian Pennsylvania oils) or rises to 70% (Termez oils). Apart from true tars (basically corresponding to silica-gel tars), precipitated tars also contain a large amount of very high-molecular hydrocarbons, mainly aromatic. The tarriest oils usually contain the greatest amount of aromatic hydrocarbons.

True tars apparently consist basically: (a) of polycyclic aromatic (and naphtheno-aromatic) groups containing O, S, and N atoms in rings and "bridge" bonds; (b) of side-chains. The molecular weight of tars lies between 300 and 1000. The general formula of tars is $C_nH_{2n-m}O_2$, where n = 18 - 65 and m = 10 - 12. True tars are also inhomogeneous. According to N. I. Chernozhukov tars with short side-chains are quite markedly different from tars with long side-chains (3). The question as to the differences within a group of tars is still unsolved.

Asphaltenes differ from tars in that although they dissolve, like tars, in benzene and chloroform, they are insoluble (in contrast to tars) in petroleum ether. The content of asphaltenes in oils is usually insignificant, less than 1%, but in exceptional cases may be as high as 3 - 5%. The asphaltene content is usually, but not always, related to the tarriness of the oil; the highest asphaltene contents are often observed in oils of the highest paraffin (wax) content. Structurally, asphaltenes are usually considered to be condensed tars of molecular weight 1000. This question, however, has been investigated very little. Apparently, there are also differences among the asphaltenes (7).

Elements of the Ash

The elements of the ash (incombustible residue) of greatest geochemical interest are vanadium and nickel. The V content of some crude oils is as much as 30% of the ash and more than $3 \times 10^{-3}\%$ of the oil (Ishimbai) or even higher. The Ni content may be as high as 12% of the ash or $10^{-3}\%$ of the oil. This means that in the ash of some oils (mainly those of the Ural-Volga region) these elements are highly concentrated in comparison with rocks: V up to 1000 times and Ni up to 500 times. The distribution of V and Ni in oils has been studied in great detail by L. A. Gulyaeva and I. I. Romm. The vanadium and nickel in oils is related to the tars and present in them, apparently, in the form of some complex compounds, the exact nature of which is unknown.

Specific Gravity

The specific gravity of crude oils varies from 0.77 to 0.98;[8] the values usually encountered are from 0.82 to 0.92. The variation in specific gravity of oil depends mainly on its content of tars. Inherent values of the specific gravities of crude oils, as a rule, are somewhat less than measured values owing to the presence in them of dissolved gases.

Optical Activity

The ability to rotate the plane of polarization of light rays is a property of nearly all crude oils (with the exception of distillates which are practically

----

[8] In exceptional cases crude oils are encountered with specific gravities outside these limits, but these, as a rule, are not oils in the strict meaning of the word, but products of the natural fractionation of petroleum (distillates or residues).

devoid of high-boiling fractions). The optical activity of petroleum is apparently related primarily to polycyclic naphthenes and, to a lesser extent, to aromatics (8).[9]

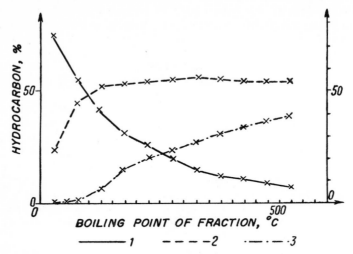

Fig. 1. Hydrocarbon composition of petroleum fractions.
1 —paraffins; 2 —napthenes; 3 —aromatics.

Physiological Activity

The physiological properties of petroleum consist of the hormonal effect (similar to the effect of folliculin), well known in the case of naphthalenic medicinal oil. To a lesser extent, this activity is inherent in other oils (as well as asphalts and coals): the measured activities of Rumanian, Indonesian, and naphthalenic oils are 1000, 2000, and 8000 "mouse units", respectively (9). The physiological properties of naphthalenic oil are due to polycyclic naphtheno-aromatic hydrocarbons similar to sterane (the oxyketone of which is folliculin) (10).

Regularities in the Chemistry of Petroleum

Among the different properties (and components) of oils there are definite, regular correlations. Oils are regular systems from the chemical point of view. This idea was set forth in great detail by A. F. Dobryanskii (2). The following correlations are of fundamental significance: (a) the distribution of different hydrocarbon groups among the oil fractions; (b) the paragenetic correlation among different properties for various types of oils.
    The first regularity is illustrated by the diagram shown in Figure 1. The diagram gives the following information: (a) the content of aromatic hydrocarbons increases steadily in the direction from lower (lighter) fractions to higher (heavier) ones; (b) the naphthene content increases at first in this direction, but on transition to the lubricating oil fractions it usually begins to decrease; (c) the content of paraffin hydrocarbons

---

[9]The luminescence of petroleum is described in Chapter VIII.

decreases in the same direction (in lubricating oils this group is represented only by solid hydrocarbons).[10] Thus, higher content of paraffins is
correlated with a greater degree of saturation by hydrogen of the light
fractions of oils, while higher content of cyclics is correlated with a more
pronounced deficiency of hydrogen in the higher fractions (especially those
not shown in the diagram, in which the oxygen, sulfur, and nitrogen are
concentrated).

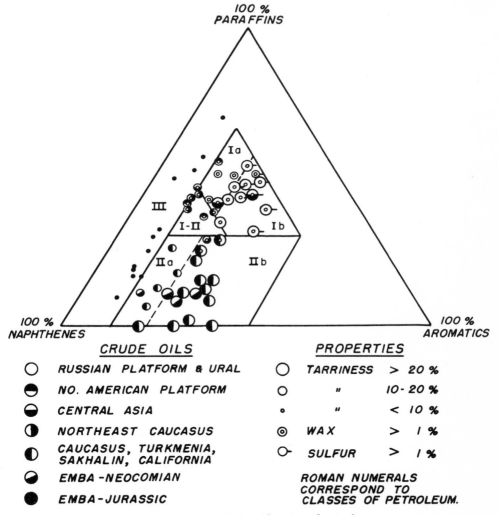

Fig. 2. Geochemical classification of petroleum.

---

[10]The slight increase sometimes observed in the percent of paraffins on transition
to lubricating oils is explained by the peculiarities of transition from liquid to solid
hydrocarbons.

The following characteristic paragenetic correlations between the different chemical properties of oils must be stated.

1. The more paraffin hydrocarbons in the light fractions of an oil: (a) the more aromatics there are; (b) the less branched-chain paraffins (isomers); (c) the more naphthenes with five-membered rings (derivatives of cyclopentane) in comparison with naphthenes with six-membered rings (derivatives of cyclohexane); (d) finally, the more solid hydrocarbons (waxes) in the lubricating oil fractions.

Consequently, there is a definite relation between the various hydrocarbon groups: The content of one of the groups in a crude oil is related not only to the content, but also to the structural type of the other groups.

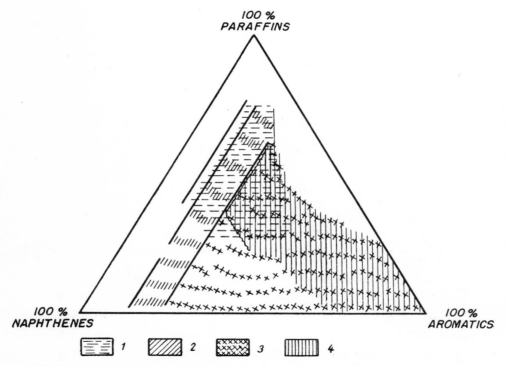

Fig. 3. Relation between the hydrocarbon composition of petroleum and its other chemical properties. 1—wax content over 1%; 2—tar content, 10-20%; 3—tar content over 20%; 4—sulfur content over 1%.

The paragenesis of aromatic and paraffin hydrocarbons in light fractions is of particular interest. These simple aromatic hydrocarbons (homologs of benzene) are genetically distinct from the more complex main body of aromatic hydrocarbons concentrated in higher fractions. They are characteristic for the most paraffinic methanic oils.

2. The more tar there is in a crude oil: (a) the more aromatic hydrocarbons there are; (b) the more polycyclic lubricating oil fractions there are (regardless of the character of the light fractions). Consequently, a definite relation exists between the hydrocarbon and non-hydrocarbon

portions of petroleum.[11] Thus, the differences among crude oils are not
determined by their fractional composition alone. Fractions with the same
boiling range may be chemically different in different oils.

According to the geochemical classification of petroleum suggested by
A. A. Kartsev (Fig. 2), two basic classes of oils are recognized: (1) aromatic paraffinic, waxy, tarry, sulfurous oils (typical representatives, the
paleozoic oils of the Ural-Volga region); (2) aromatic-naphthenic, non-
waxy, non-sulfurous oils (typical representatives, the majority of the Baku
oils). The relation between the hydrocarbon composition and other properties of oils is shown schematically in another diagram (Fig. 3).

PHYSICAL AND CHEMICAL CONDITIONS IN PETROLEUM FORMATIONS

In this section are considered only those conditions which exist in formations independently of petroleum; i.e., conditions which are not due to
reaction of the crude oils with the surrounding medium, but may in themselves be important factors of geochemical processes.

Temperature

Measured temperatures in oil beds vary from 10 to 180°C. It is quite
possible, however, that lower temperatures as well as much higher ones
exist: at a geothermal gradient of 1° per 20 m., usual for many formations,
the temperature at a depth of 5 km. must reach 250°C. The geochemical
effect of temperature in oil formations appears in the following form.

1. As the temperature increases, decomposition of some components
of petroleum may occur. For example, several complex sulfur compounds
in oils break down at a temperature below 100°C, forming hydrogen sulfide
and mercaptans; several nitrogen compounds break down at a temperature
below 200°C, forming quinolines and the like. Several other chemical
processes are accelerated.[12]

2. Elevated (and also, possibly, reduced) temperatures may arrest
biochemical processes which lead to oxidation of the oils; even at 70°C,
bacterial activity in oil-bearing strata ceases.

3. Temperature affects the physical state of the oil components, thus
changing the composition of petroleum. For example, at temperatures
below 30 - 40°C solid paraffins may separate out as a precipitate, etc.

---

[11] The relations between the content of naphthenic hydrocarbons and the acid content,
between the aromaticity of the lubricating oils and the sulfur content of the crude oils, etc.,
may be mentioned.

[12] Besides the substances mentioned above and the well-known porphyrins, the correlation among several hydrocarbons may be used as "geochemical thermometers" in
the opinion of S. N. Obryadchikov (11) and A. V. Frost (12). According to these authors,
the ratio of cyclopentane to methyl cyclohexane in oil increases as the temperature at
which the oil has been maintained decreases. These ideas, however, are not in accord
with geological facts: it is known that oils from a platform, as a rule, have undergone
higher temperatures than oils from folded regions (see the table at the end of the article
by Frost (12)).

Press' re

Hydrostatic pressure in the strata is also a geochemical factor. For oil
formations its magnitude may lie between a few units and several hundred
atmospheres. When the pressure exceeds 200 - 300 atm. and the strata
are saturated with gas, evaporation of liquid hydrocarbons (the so-called
retrograde vaporization) is observed. This sometimes extends down to the
lubricating oil fractions, which results in a change in the composition of
the crude oils.

In the presence of a hydraulic connection between an oil-bearing
stratum and another natural reservoir (particularly, the atmosphere), the
pressure drop leads primarily to removal from the crude oil of gases and
the lightest fractions.

Motion of Subterranean Waters

The rate of motion of water in oil-bearing strata may be extremely variable:
from 10 m. per year with significant water exchange (for example, in the
Grozny region)[13] to 10^{-8} m. per year in a static regime (for example, in
parts of the Ural-Volga region according to the calculations of A. I. Silin-
Bekchurin (13)). As a geochemical factor, the velocity of subterranean
waters is important because it insures the entry of a greater or lesser
quantity of substances which react with oils (primarily sulfates). Therefore, the greater this quantity is, the more change in the composition of the
oil there may be as a result of reaction with substances dissolved in the
water.

Physicochemical and Chemical Properties of Rocks and Waters

The properties of rocks, as collectors of hydrocarbons and as rocks constituting the roof and floor of oil-bearing reservoirs, may have a substantial effect on geochemical processes in petroleum formations. These
include sorption, catalytic, and reactive properties.

The sorption and catalytic properties of rocks are closely related.
Rocks may adsorb primarily asphaltenes and tars from crude oils. The
sorption capacity of rocks is usually the greater, the more colloidal fractions they contain and the more hydroaluminosilicate minerals of the type
of montmorillonite, etc., there are in the composition of these fractions.
Hence the greatest sorption capacity (except for coals) is found in several
fine clays such as Fuller's earth and bentonites, while the least is found in
quartz gravels and coarsely crystalline rocks.

First of all, these minerals may have a catalytic effect on some of the
chemical transformations of hydrocarbons and other components of petroleum: redistribution of hydrogen, hydrogenation, and the like. Very great
catalytic activity is also found in rocks of the type of bentonites. There
are no systematic investigations of these properties of the rocks of oil
formations on record. Therefore, it is impossible at the present time to
characterize either the activity of natural catalysts, or the specific effects
of various representatives thereof.

---

[13]Under natural conditions; that is, before processing.

The effect of sorption and catalysis on the properties of crude oils is apparently very great. For example, on the one hand, in the formation of Kettleman Hills (California), oil consisting entirely of clear fractions is found in thin, sandy beds in a stratum of nearly pure bentonites (14). On the other hand, an oil of very uncommon type, consisting of heavy, black oil resembling petroleum residue, is found in the purely siliceous Athabaska (Canada) sandstone (15).

Apparently, an effect similar to that of aluminosilicates may result from the radioactivity of rocks. The radioactivity of sedimentary rocks is associated with the finest fragmented particles thereof. Therefore, the most radioactive rocks are also fine clays.

The reactivity of rocks toward crude oils amounts mainly to their oxidizing action. The main mass of oxygen in sedimentary rocks (silica, silicates, and carbonates) is inert. Only the oxygen of sulfates, free oxides of iron, and some rarer minerals can be active. In the case of large accumulations of these substances, crude oils may acquire particular properties. For instance, very tarry oils are found in the gypsum-bearing Kungurian stratum.

Much more important is the oxidizing action of the sulfates dissolved in subterranean waters. It is, however, very difficult to estimate the effect of the sulfate content of the waters, since values of the sulfate content of waters may be "secondary", i.e., they themselves may depend chiefly on the reaction of petroleum with the waters. Also important are such physicochemical quantities as the pH of the water. According to the data of S. G. Movsesyan, alkaline waters have the ability to penetrate oil deposits in depth, so that their effect on crude oil is increased. The alkalinity of the waters, however, may itself be changed by the reaction with oil.

GEOCHEMICAL PROCESSES IN PETROLEUM FORMATIONS

Of the geochemical processes occurring in petroleum formations, only those will be considered in this section in which either the oils themselves or substances derived from them take part. The majority of these processes have not been sufficiently studied up to the present time. Three kinds of processes may be distinguished: (1) metamorphism of crude oils, proceeding parallel to the metamorphism of sedimentary rocks and subterranean waters; (2) oxidation of crude oils[14] with accompanying processes having the character of consequences; (3) processes of a physical character (evaporation, sorption) leading to changes in the chemistry of petroleum.

Metamorphism of Petroleum

Processes which occur when crude oils migrate to a greater depth with increase of temperature and pressure are called metamorphism of petroleum. These processes are very little known. The metamorphism of

---

[14]For rocks, as well as subterranean waters, oxidation and, in general, processes related to influences "from above" (the earth's surface) may not be called "Metamorphism"; the latter concept presupposes the action of plutonic factors.

petroleum may be considered the direct continuation of the process of its formation: the general tendency is toward reduction of the original substances.[15] The chief factors in the metamorphism of crude oils are temperature and catalysis. The process of metamorphism consists of redistribution of hydrogen among the components of oil according to the following scheme:

$$C_{m+n}H_p \rightarrow C_mH_q + C_nH_{p-q}; \ [q > (p-q)] \hspace{2cm} (1)$$

$$\text{A} \hspace{3cm} \text{B} \hspace{1.5cm} \text{C}$$

Here substance B may finally pass over to the gaseous phase (in the limit m = O; i.e., B is pure hydrogen), while substance C may go over to the solid phase (in the limit p = q; i.e., C is pure carbon), and in the end, liquid oil ceases to exist.

The chemistry of these processes was investigated by A. F. Dobryanskii. He showed that the redistribution of hydrogen within a crude oil is basically tantamount to the accumulation in the oil of low-molecular weight paraffins (B) and (in lesser quantity) low-molecular weight aromatic hydrocarbons (C) as a result of decomposition of high-molecular aromatic, naphthenic, and naphtheno-aromatic hydrocarbons (A). Complex molecules are broken down into simple ones; the detachment of side-chains gives paraffinic hydrocarbons, thus converting isomeric hydrocarbons to simple forms. Polycyclic groups are broken down into separate rings of the benzene type. Thus, the lower fractions of crude oils originate from the higher fractions (and, in the final analysis, from complex non-hydrocarbon compounds).

On the basis of these processes a number of regularities observed in the composition of petroleum may be explained: the concentration of paraffin hydrocarbons in the low fractions, their paragenesis with the simplest aromatic hydrocarbons and gasolines, the paragenesis of paraffinic hydrocarbons with naphthenes, etc. The explanation of the second phenomenon is especially important.

The overall results of the conversion of large molecules into smaller ones are depolymerization and decrease of the specific gravity of crude oils. A. F. Dobrysnskii and co-workers were able artificially to produce similar conversions of petroleum in 20 hours at a temperature of 250°C and in a longer time at 175°C, using natural clays as catalysts (16). These experiments show that the given processes are possible in nature.

The actual occurrence of the conversions described above are not disputed by anyone. Up to the present time, however, they have received little attention. In view of this, it is in order to point out several facts which can only be explained by processes of the metamorphism of petroleum. Besides purely chemical facts such as the previously mentioned paragenesis of saturates and aromatics in gasoline, geological facts are also important. Thus, on the Apsheron peninsula according to data from

---

[15]Metamorphism of crude oils ought not, however, to be called the process of their reduction: during the main stage of existence of oils in deposits true reduction, i.e., loss of oxygen and gain of hydrogen, is not an essential part of the process of metamorphism of oils.

the investigations of A. A. Kartsev, the vertical distribution of the properties of crude oils in individual pools can be explained only by metamorphism
(changes from one formation to another are not included here). With increase in depth (consequently, with increase of temperature), the specific
gravity regularly decreases and the content of light fractions increases.
The effect of other factors (oxidation, evaporation) is excluded, because
the effect should differ with change in depth, whereas according to observations, these factors remain the same throughout the entire section.

For the Kulsara formation (Emba), comparison of the detailed characteristics of the oils with geological conditions leads to the same conclusion
(17). Similar facts may be pointed out in connection with American formations (18, etc.). In Tuimazy, as the calculations of A. F. Dobryanskii
(2) indicate, the quantity of lighter aromatic hydrocarbons increases
relatively with depth; in Carboniferous oils the ratio of aromatics boiling
at temperatures over 400° to aromatics boiling at temperatures below 250°
($\underline{a} > 400^{\circ}/\underline{a} < 250^{\circ}$) is above 4, while in Devonian oils this quantity is less
than 2. These correlations, i.e., the major role of the simplest aromatics
in the lower strata, indicate the conversion of the simplest aromatic hydrocarbons from heavier ones in the deepest formations. In an analogous way,
the content of aromatic hydrocarbons in the light fractions also increases
with depth in the formations of Yablonov Ravine, Zol'noe, and Krasnokamsk.

The scheme of A. F. Dobryanskii given above apparently does not
entirely correspond to the actual course of metamorphism of petroleum.
Thus, the lower aromatic hydrocarbons are probably not the only "reservoir
of carbon" (as A. F. Dobryanskii expressed it) taking part in the redistribution of elements among the components of the oils. Among the hydrogen-
poor substances formed (in equation (1)) may also be high molecular compounds such as asphaltenes. Possibly, part of the asphaltenes were formed
by the decomposition of tars according to the scheme of equation (1) (if
processes of polymerization occur simultaneously). This is confirmed by
the high content of asphaltenes in many "paraffinic" oils (e.g., in high-wax
Grozny oils, up to 2%) and the linear relation between the solid paraffin
content of the oils and the value of the ratio of asphaltenes to tars (silica-
gel type) contained in them (Fig. 4). This problem must be studied very
carefully. Asphaltenes may readily be deposited from solution (in crude
oils) and sorbed by rocks. In this case a general enrichment of the oils in
hydrogen occurs, i.e., reduction. At the same time, the medium surrounding the deposit will be enriched by new components.[16] Unfortunately,
establishment of the presence of these products of decomposition of petroleum in rocks is hindered by their similarity to organic substances syngenetic to the rocks. Therefore, there are no firmly established facts in
this field at the present time.

It is quite possible that the course of the conversion of petroleum
under the influence of temperature, catalysis, and time may be qualitatively dependent on the manner in which these three basic factors are
combined. This question is quite obscure. The question of isomerization
is also obscure.

---

[16]This enrichment of the medium may also occur as a result of the evolution of
gases (CH_4, C_2H_6, H_2S, NH_3, N_2, etc.) upon decomposition of the more complex compounds.

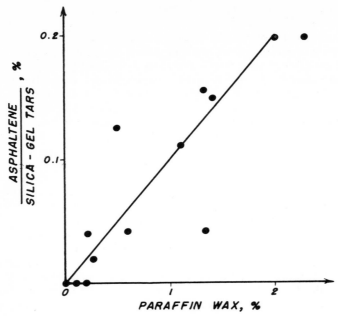

Fig. 4. Relation between the wax content of crude oils and the
ratio of asphaltenes to silica-gel tars.

For example, A. S. Velikovskii assumes that isomerization of hydrocarbons proceeds under the catalytic influence of aluminosilicates; hence,
in limestones, where there is less of the latter than in sandstones, crude
oils are less isomerized (19). This point of view does not agree with the
aforementioned arguments of A. F. Dobryanskii on the conversion of
isoparaffin hydrocarbons to simple forms by decomposition.

Finally, the possibility of hydrogenation of oils by free hydrogen
should be mentioned. The latter is formed upon decomposition of water
under the influence of radioactivity in the rocks (20). In this case the
process consists of the migration into the crude oils of substances from
the surrounding medium and, consequently, leads to the absolute enrichment of the oils in one of the elements. The extent of this process and
the part played by it, however, are in all probability insignificant.

Oxidation of Petroleum

In contrast to the conversions discussed above, oxidative processes in
petroleum formations have attracted attention for a long time. Even today,
however, much in this field is not clear. Important features distinguishing
oxidation from the processes considered above include: (a) the participation in them of organisms, and (b) significant changes in the medium surrounding the oil. The latter circumstance is of great significance in
prospecting for petroleum.

The oxidation of petroleum within the reservoir occurs because of
bound oxygen. The role of free oxygen (in the form of gaseous O_2 dissolved
in water) can only be appreciable in the immediate vicinity of the earth's
surface and, consequently, is important only in those rare cases where an

oil pool still exists at very shallow depths.[17] Salts dissolved in water, primarily sulfates,[18] are of basic significance. Such components of rocks are sulfate minerals and those of the limonite group may have some effect. The effect of water is pronounced owing to its mobility, which sharply increases the amount of reacting substance.

There is no doubt as to the actual occurrence of the process of interaction of crude oils with the sulfates in water: the well-known fact of the absence of sulfates in water in contact with oil pools is sufficient evidence of this. Also, the participation of microbes in this process is not disputed by anyone today. The question as to the possibility of nonbiochemical oxidation of oil in strata remains open. The basis of the process, regardless of its biochemical or nonbiochemical character, is the reaction expressed by the following scheme:

$$C_mH_p + \underline{R}SO_4 \rightarrow (C_{m+n}H_{p+q}) + (C_{m+n}H_{p+q}O_r) + CO_2 + H_2O + \underline{R}S$$

$$[\frac{m+n}{p+q} > \frac{m}{p}] \tag{2}$$

The parentheses enclosing the substances $C_{m+n}H_{p+q}$ and $C_{m+n}H_{p+q}O_r$ indicate that these compounds are intermediate products of the reaction and may also be converted in the end of CO_2 and H_2O. This means that the given process can completely destroy the oil. In reality, however, the reaction does not always go to completion.

The chemistry of the entire oxidation transformation is more complex than that expressed by equation (2), and many aspects of it are still obscure. The oxidation of crude oils by free O_2 has been studied experimentally. Anaerobic oxidation was experimentally investigated by V. A. Uspenskii and co-workers (21); thermodynamic calculations were performed by V. O. Tauson (22). Taking into account the data obtained by them, microbiological observations (23, etc.), several facts related to the distribution of the properties of crude oils in formations, and finally, several facts related to the oxidation of oils by free O_2 (3, 24), it may be concluded that in the oxidation of petroleum by sulfates the following phenomena occur.

1. Several hydrocarbons, mainly paraffinic (and including solid paraffins), are immediately oxidized to CO_2 and H_2O. In this case, owing to the elimination of paraffin hydrocarbons, the oils are relatively enriched in cyclic components.

2. Other hydrocarbons, mainly cyclic, yield on oxidation oxygen compounds of the type $C_{m+n}H_{p+q}O_r$. These are mainly acids and tars. Naphthenic hydrocarbons on oxidation form more acidic products, largely naphthenic acids, while aromatics form products of less acidic nature, chiefly tars. As a result of true oxidation crude oil is enriched in tars and acids.

3. True oxidation of hydrocarbons is accompanied by their dehydrogenation and polymerization, as well as cyclization to some extent. The hydrocarbon $C_{m+n}H_{p+q}$ in equation (2) is one product of the oxidative

---

[17]For example, in such exposed formations as Mirzaani.

[18]Apparently, nitrates also play some part.

dehydrogenation and polymerization of the hydrocarbon C_mH_p: its molecular weight is greater than that of C_mH_p (polymerization), and the C/H ratio is also greater (dehydrogenation). Naphthenes on dehydrogenation may give aromatic hydrocarbons, paraffin hydrocarbons, and apparently, naphthenes (i.e., cyclization occurs). The overall result of dehydrogenation and polymerization must be the enrichment of crude oil in heavier components.

It is possible that in anaerobic processes, dehydrogenation and polymerization of oils play an even greater part than true oxidation. It may be that a very important part is played by reactions following this scheme:

$$C_mH_p + \underline{R}SO_4 \longrightarrow C_{m+n}H_{p+q} + 4H_2O + \underline{R}S \qquad (3)$$

$$[\ \frac{m+n}{p+q} > \frac{m}{p}\ ]$$

4. Oxidation, dehydrogenation, and the like, are accompanied to some extent by antagonistic processes: as a rule oxidation leads to the formation of the lightest hydrocarbon—methane. It is this product (along with water) to which the hydrogen goes upon complete dehydrogenation of crude oil.

5. The substance of bacteria also takes part in the reactions. To a certain extent, the remains of dead bacteria combine with those tarry substances which are the chief products of oxidation.

Summarizing the above discussion, it must be concluded that the result of the action of sulfates is the enrichment of petroleum in heavy, more polymerized, mainly cyclic components, especially tars; at the same time, however, natural gas is formed.

The reality of these transformations in nature is shown by the existence in oil pools of zones of relatively heavy oils in those regions which are in contact with water. This is a well known phenomenon. The mechanism of propagation of the process throughout the reservoir is not entirely clear. The possibility that alkaline water percolates to the depths of the oil pool in a dispersed state should be considered.

The limits of biochemical oxidation of crude oils are determined by the temperature conditions. Thus, according to data from the investigations of V. M. Nikolaev in the Grozny formations in strata with temperatures over $70^{\circ}C$ the water contains sulfates, while in strata with lower temperatures the water is practically free of sulfates. Therefore, in the first case reduction proceeds much less vigorously.

Very low temperatures, apparently, also inhibit bacterial activity. Thus, according to the data of N. T. Lindtrop, in one of the formations of the Second Baku the water underlying the oil-bearing stratum at temperatures under $15^{\circ}C$ contains sulfates (25).

It is quite probable that the reaction between crude oils and sulfates can go to a certain extent even without the participation of organisms. Indirect confirmation of the occurrence of this process is furnished by cases in which the water is free of sulfates at high temperatures. For example, on the Apsheron peninsula, according to D. V. Zhabrev, there is no SO_4 in the waters adjacent to oil pools (though SO_4 is present at a sufficient distance from the pool in the same stratum), even in those strata in which the temperature reaches $100^{\circ}C$. The non-biochemical process may be catalyzed by such substances as the salts (soaps) of naphthenic acids in an alkaline medium (as in the industrial oxidation of hydrocarbons (26, 27). If the sulfates are solid minerals, the process apparently occurs in the same way as it does when the sulfates are in solution. Therefore, there are no particular differences in this case.

The character of the oxidation of petroleum is not fully established, and the course of the process may vary depending on conditions. In some cases the oxidation of saturated hydrocarbons may go preferentially to CO_2 and H_2O, while in others, the chief product may be tars, etc. These questions still require clarification.

Consequences of the Oxidation of Petroleum by Sulfates

The reactions discussed above may be accompanied by a number of processes in the medium surrounding the petroleum. First of all, the following kinds of substances may be evolved from the crude oils: (a) tars[19] formed upon oxidation and deposited from solution or sorbed by rocks; (b) acids, also formed upon oxidation and dissolved in water; (c) methane, obtained upon dehydrogenation of oil hydrocarbons and forming a gas phase.

Besides this a number of additional reactions may occur. The character of these depends in part on the kind of sulfate taking part in the basic reaction. In alkaline waters, where the given processes are usually observed, this will be sodium sulfate (the latter is not limited to alkaline waters). In this case the course of the reactions will be as follows:

$$C_nH_m + Na_2SO_4 \rightarrow Na_2S[20] + CO_2 + \tag{4}$$

$$H_2O \rightarrow NaHCO_3 + H_2S \; (+ \; CO_2 + H_2O)$$

As a result, soda appears, dissolved in the water, and consequently, the alkalinity of the water increases; the gases H_2S and CO_2 also appear and may remain in solution.[21]

In alkaline waters the evolution of acids from the petroleum may play a significant role. They form alkali metal salts (soaps) according to the reactions:

$$2C_nH_mCOOH + Na_2S \rightarrow 2C_nH_mCOONa + H_2S, \tag{5}$$

$$C_nH_mCOOH + NaHCO_3 \rightarrow C_nH_mCOONa + CO_2 + H_2O \tag{5'}$$

---

[19] These (secondary) tars must be distinguished from "primary" tars present in the oils. The character of the difference is as yet obscure.

[20] The intermediate products include Na_2SO_3 and Na_2SO_4. In alkaline waters NaHS is a relatively stable compound. According to the data of S. A. Shchukarev the content of HS ions may exceed that of free H_2S (28). The content of hydrosulfides in the waters of oil-bearing reservoirs has received little attention.

[21] In the case of oxidation of crude oils as a result not of sulfates, but of nitrates, the process apparently follows this course:

$$C_nH_m + 2NaNO_3 \rightarrow 2NaHCO_3 + N_2.$$

Owing to the inertness of nitrogen, this reaction does not occur. N_2O may appear as an intermediate product.

These sodium soaps also enter into the composition of the alkalinity of water. Sometimes they accumulate in water in such quantities that they may be used in industry (29).

If the water is hard owing to contact with gypsum, the reduction of sulfates may lead to rather different results. When the reaction occurs with the participation of calcium sulfate, it may be expressed by the following scheme:

$$(6)$$

$$C_nH_m + CaSO_4 \rightarrow CaS + CO_2 + H_2O \rightarrow CaCO_3 + H_2S (+ CO_2 + H_2O)$$

In this case the difficultly soluble calcium carbonate appears as a precipitate and, consequently, enters into the composition of the rocks. Thus, depending on the reacting sulfate, changes occur in the water, either alone or in the presence of rocks. The simultaneous action of Na and Ca sulfates is also possible in sodium sulfate-type waters.

The carbon dioxide gas formed in every case may react with several rock components. Several investigators (D. V. Zhabrev et al.) believe that under the influence of CO_2 in oil-bearing strata, even silicates may decompose; this effect is similar to the weathering of the earth's crust. There are, however, no firmly established facts known at present which prove the occurrence of these processes. Present knowledge of the action of hydrogen sulfide, to which is related the formation of sulfur and the sulfuring of oil, is more reliable.

Paragenesis of Petroleum and Sulfur. Sulfuring of Petroleum

Hydrogen sulfide is usually found in oil-bearing strata, in which is appears as a result of reduction of sulfates. It may also be formed in several other ways. Thus, at high temperatures (above 100°C) some sulfurous components of crude oils may decompose. It is possible that formation of hydrogen sulfide also occurs as a result of hydrolysis at normal temperatures (30). Hydrogen sulfide is a very active reducing agent. In oil-bearing reservoirs it must act primarily on ferric oxide minerals. The course of these reactions is represented by the following scheme:

$$H_2S + Fe_2O_3 \rightarrow S + 2FeO + H_2O , \qquad (7)$$

$$2H_2S + Fe_2O_3 \rightarrow FeS_2 + FeO + 2H_2O \qquad (8)$$

The substances formed—sulfur, pyrite, ferrous oxide—remain in the rocks,[22] although crystallization of pyrite in oil pools has never been recorded (32). Usually, the relations between H_2S and Fe_2O_3 are characterized by an excess of the first substance; hence, the reaction proceeds according to equation (8), and H_2S may continue to be present in the gases. Sulfur is formed on a large scale in the presence of free oxygen by the reaction:

$$2H_2S + O_2 \rightarrow 2S + 2H_2O \qquad (9)$$

---

[22]Ferrous oxide may form siderite under the influence of carbonic acid. Agglomerations of this mineral have been observed in oil deposits (31).

This process occurs near the surface of the earth, where O_2 is dissolved in the waters. It may result in the formation of industrial sulfur deposits. In these cases sulfur takes the form of the "cap" of an oil formation (33).

The sulfur (and hydrogen sulfide) formed may also react with hydrocarbons:

$$C_nH_m + S \rightarrow C_nH_mS \tag{10}$$

In this way a number of sulfur compounds may be formed and this leads to sulfuring of petroleum. The sulfur may also act as a catalyst, promoting polymerization and tar formation.

According to A. S. Velikovskii (19), V. A. Uspenskii, and O. A. Radchenko (34), the sulfuring of crude oils is closely related to their oxidation. According to Uspenskii and Radchenko, the sulfuring of oils occurs only in carbonate reservoirs, since in sandstone-clay rocks all of the H_2S formed in the oxidation of the crude oils is bound with iron to form pyrite. This confirms the following hypotheses: (a) in the waters or carbonate reservoirs hydrogen sulfide is common, while in brecciated reservoirs it is rare; (b) sulfurous oils, as well as masses of sulfur, are encountered as a rule in limestones and dolomites but not in brecciated rocks.

The hypothesis of the great richness in iron of brecciated rocks in comparison with carbonate rocks, based on the data of F. Clark concerning total Fe content (including silicate Fe) and applied to the phenomenon described above, is not proved. The fact of the matter is that to speak of the reduction of iron silicates by hydrogen sulfide is inadmissible. Only reduction by the latter of free oxides and hydroxides is conceivable and there are hardly any data on the content of these in rocks. The investigations of A. A. Kartsev and V. N. Kholodov for the West Ferghana formations reveal that there is no difference in non-silicate iron content between the sandstone and carbonate reservoirs there. At the same time, the differences in the sulfur content of the crude oils in these strata and the hydrogen sulfide content of the waters are quite marked.

Taking these facts into account, it must be concluded that the question of the sulfuring of petroleum is not fully clarified as yet. It may be that the sulfur content of the oils of carbonate rocks is partly explained by primary factors, as V. A. Sokolov (20) suggests. In this case the accumulation of H_2S in carbonate rocks is partly related to its evolution from sulfurous oils. It may also be that certain other, unknown causes are acting here.

Physical Processes

One of the most common physical processes affecting the properties of crude oils is gravitational differentiation. This phenomenon was investigated in great detail by M. V. Abramovich (35). As separation of gas, oil, and water occurs in a stratum, so stratification according to specific gravity takes place in an oil pool. The greater part of the dissolved gas collects in the upper parts of the reservoir, while the heavier portion of the dissolved tars accumulates in the lower parts. The greater the height of the reservoir, the more stratification occurs. When the height of a pool is a maximum, very light distillates may form at the top—from some light fractions. This phenomenon is apparently observed in the Kympin formations in Rumania (36) and those at Ventura in California (37). When the height of the reservoirs is small, differentiation is slight. Thus, in the formations of Tuimaz and East Texas, the oils in these fields are very homogeneous in spite of their great size.

Another physical process which is important in the geochemistry of petroleum is the partial evaporation of crude oils, which is especially rapid when there is a hydraulic outlet from the deposit to the atmosphere. At first, dissolved gases are evolved from the oils; they are followed by all the light fractions. The remaining crude oil is enriched in heavy components,[23] and these oils are extremely common. The light fractions may migrate not only to the atmosphere but also to other reservoirs. Then either new deposits of very light oils are formed, or these light "distillates" are mixed with other crude oils. It is not as yet possible to develop similar cases with confidence. At very great depths (greater than 3,000 m.) separation of heavier fractions from the oils may also occur.

Filtration fractionation of crude oils upon their passage through a layer of clay was long ago pointed out as a process leading to great changes in the properties of the oils. Here adsorption of the heavy components by the rocks plays the chief role. N. A. Eremenko attaches great importance to this process (38). In the opinion of most investigators, however, this phenomenon is not widespread. Most of the cases in which it has been suggested can be explained in other ways. For example, on the Apsheron peninsula, according to data from the investigations of A. A. Kartsev, filtration fractionation of the oils did not play any substantial part.

Among other physical processes, deposition from petroleum of solid paraffins and ceresins on decrease of temperature is worthy of note. This phenomenon is related to the formation of ozokerites. The problem of the formation of ozokerites is still far from solution. Apparently, the formation of ozokerites is not purely a physical process but also involves chemical changes of solid hydrocarbons (39).

Such are the fundamental geochemical processes taking place in petroleum formations. It should be kept in mind that different processes can occur in a given place simultaneously. It is even possible that transformations, opposite in kind, may occur simultaneously. Such is the case for metamorphism and oxidation. Oils contain chemically different substances, susceptible to change in different directions.

CAUSES OF PETROLEUM VARIABILITY

In their composition and properties crude oils are very diverse, because petroleum is not a single mineral form but an entire family of minerals related by gradual transitions. The diversity of crude oils is of three kinds: (1) the difference among oils of various geological provinces, usually of different age; (2) the differences between oils of various levels within the boundaries of a single formation; (3) the differences within the individual pools. These differences often have a regular character. These regularities were first noticed by A. K. Sorokin in Baku (40). The

---

[23]This process is not in itself related to oxidation. Therefore, to call all heavy oils oxidized, as is often done, is quite incorrect.

explanation of these regularities and their causes is very important for the understanding of the geochemical processes occurring in petroleum formations and for the development of a method of prognosis of the quality of crude oils.

The third kind of differences in the properties of oils—within pools—is chiefly explained by gravitational differentiation. This phenomenon is sufficiently clear and is not considered below. It remains to discuss the first two kinds of differences. The processes discussed above can greatly change crude oils and create sharp differences in their properties. It may be, however, that the nature of the original substances also affects these properties.

Role of the Initial Composition

There are several quite contradictory viewpoints on the evaluation of the role of the initial composition on the properties of petroleum. Thus, A. F. Dobryanskii, V. A. Uspenskii, and others deny the importance of the nature of the initial substances and consider that the observed differences among crude oils are wholly determined by their recent history. A number of investigators, generally admitting that the initial composition plays some part, relegate it to quite an insignificant place (15, 16).

Sharply differing views were developed by H. Hlauschek (41, 42), V. A. Sokolov, and several other authors. H. Hlauschek, proceeding from the previously observed relation between the character of crude oils and the age of the surrounding rock, attempted to establish the presence of evolution, related to the evolution of the organic world. However, the factual foundation for this hypothesis is very weak.

A more plausible hypothesis was advanced by V. A. Sokolov (20). This was based on the differences between the Baku and Second Baku crudes (see above). The association of Ural-Volga oils with carbonate reservoirs, and Baku oils with brecciated ones is related by V. A. Sokolov to the environmental character of the petroleum formation. In carbonate environments, where the land has contributed little, the main source of petroleum consists of the albumins and fats of plankton, which gives large amounts of saturates, paraffin, sulfur, and nitrogen; whereas, in sandy, argillaceous environments, where the land has furnished a large amount of lignin and humus residues from surface vegetation, the initial material is distinguished by its high cyclicity and low sulfur content.

V. A. Sokolov admits that this hypothesis cannot lay claim to universality. Its inadequacy is shown by the following. In the first place, a very great number of paraffinic oils lie, not in carbonate reservoirs, but in sandstone ones. At the same time, as the author himself observes, there are crude oils of the most saturated character (in fact, non-sulfurous) lying in sandstones; i.e., Pennsylvania oils. In the second place, V. A. Sokolov has only taken into account the composition of the light fractions. If the lubricating oil fractions are also considered, to say nothing of the tars, it is seen that the crudes of the Second Baku, as a rule, are not less but more cyclic than the oils of Baku and similar ones. In general, it appears that oils in limestone are distinguished by somewhat greater tarriness; this phenomenon has never been recorded.

Thus, the hypothesis of the primary environmental nature of oil hydrocarbons (in the form advanced by V. A. Sokolov) proves on closer

examination of the facts to be untenable. The primary nature of the sulfur
content in petroleum is more probable. But even here, possibly, it is not
the nature of the initial material that is playing a part but the character of
the evolution of the crude oils; the latter may not be the same in limestones and sandstones (owing to differences in the catalytic and oxidative
properties of rocks, and the like).

"Primary" hypotheses promoting the idea of differences in composition of the initial substances have recently been widely disseminated
abroad (42, 43, etc.). However, not one authentic instance can be adduced
of the evident influence of the initial composition of crude oils on the observed differences in their properties. This does not mean that such influence cannot exist in general, but it does mean that all "primary"
hypotheses are at present devoid of any solid foundation. To promote the
first plan, and therefore, to deny the processes of change in petroleum and
to admit that crude oils are completely stable and immune to changes by
other substances, is therefore impossible. This road will lead to the realm
of speculation and to the negation of progress.

For an explanation of the diversity of crude oils in nature, let us turn
to the phenomena of transformation of petroleum.

Significance of Physical Processes

The effect of evaporation of light fractions is apparently very substantial.
It especially affects the distribution of properties vertically in the section.
In the upper strata, where there is insufficient thickness of cover, the oils
are often impoverished in the light fractions in comparison with oils from
lower levels. Evaporation may also have taken place during the ancient
epochs of denudation. The relation between crude oils that have lost the
light fractions and the discontinuities and unconformities in the section was
established and studied in detail by Z. A. Tabasaranskii in the Western
Kuban. This has also been noted by A. A. Kartsev in Western Azerbaijan.
A similar, but more pronounced phenomenon, occurs at the Paleozoic-
Mesozoic boundary in the Rocky Mountains (44).

However, neither the physical processes nor the natural fractionation
of crude oils can explain the differences in the chemical composition of
narrow fractions of the same boiling range from different oils. Yet, such
differences are observed not only for different provinces but also for different levels of individual formations. This inevitably leads to the concept
of the great significance of chemical processes in the geochemical transformation of petroleum.[24]

Significance of Geochemical Transformations of Petroleum

The decisive significance of geochemical processes of change in petroleum
is acknowledged today by the majority of investigators working in this field.
On the question of the character of these processes, however, opinions

---

[24]Processes of mixing of crude oils cannot explain the observed facts of regular
distribution of the properties of the oils in the depths. They can only lead to special cases
of deviations from these regularities.

sharply differ. Thus, A. F. Dobryanskii favors the first plan of meta-morphism, denying the role of oxidation (2, 45, 46, et al.)[25]

V. A. Uspenskii and O. A. Radchenko adhere to a contrary position, considering that the main process of change of petroleum is biochemical, anaerobic oxidation at the expense of sulfates in the waters (34, 50, et al.)[26] According to the first point of view, light oils are formed from heavy ones, while lower fractions of oils are formed from higher fractions and tars. According to the second point of view, heavy crudes are formed from light oils, while higher fractions and tars are formed from lower fractions.

Identical regularities in the distribution of the properties of petroleum in formations are explained in each hypothesis by contradictory assumptions. Thus, the most common of these regularities in formations containing many strata are the decrease in specific gravity of crude oils and the decrease in their tarriness with depth. According to data from the investigations of A. A. Kartsev on 250 formations in various countries of the world, decrease in specific gravity and tarriness with depth are observed in 172 cases, while the opposite phenomenon is seen in only 30 cases (changes with depth in the remaining cases are absent or irregular). A. F. Dobryanskii explains this by the assertion that the crudes at lower levels are more metamorphosed on account of their greater age and higher temperatures. V. A. Uspenskii and O. A. Radchenko explain the same phenomenon by the assertion that the oils lying at lesser depths are more oxidized on account of the greater activity and higher sulfate content of the waters of the upper strata.

The one-sided character of any given point of view was pointed out by V. A. Sulin, A. A. Kartsev, and Acad. S. I. Mironov (52). If one adheres to the theory of metamorphism consistently, one will be obliged to acknowledge as accidental coincidences the many cases of regular relation between the properties of oils and waters, i.e., between the quantities that characterize the activity of the waters (the total mineralization Σ and the indicators of metamorphism, which are the secondary salinity S_2 and the primary alkalinity A_1) and the specific gravity and tarriness of the oils. Cases are known in which these and other quantities are not related to depth or are anomalously related thereto. Examples of this relation are given in diagrams (Fig. 5).

Besides this, regular diminution in the specific gravity of crude oils with depth is often observed with such slight differences in the ages and temperatures of the strata and at such low temperatures that to speak of the effect of metamorphism is impossible [e.g., the formations at Dossor, Tschiebü, and Witze in Germany (53) and at Sansa-Santa in Borneo (41)]. Finally, within the limits of the theory of A. F. Dobryanskii, the existence of crude oils which are high in tars and also high in paraffins, such as the typical oils of the Second Baku, cannot be explained. Thus, the theory of A. F. Dobryanskii cannot be considered universal.

Still less can the universality of the oxidation theory be admitted. Besides the facts given above in this connection, the following should be

---

[25]Similar views have been expressed by a number of authors (47, 48, 49, et al.) in less developed form.

[26]Similar views have also been expressed by other authors (38, 51, et al.).

pointed out. If one consistently applies the basic concept of the oxidation theory one is obliged to assume that all components of petroleum are derivatives of paraffinic hydrocarbons. This conclusion is completely inadmissible. It leads to an improbably high estimate of bacterial activity, because all nitrogen compounds in petroleum can be regarded in this case as conversion products of the substance of bacteria.[27] This conclusion clears the way for a perfectly admissible inorganic theory of oil formation, i.e., that in the final reckoning the formation of paraffinic hydrocarbons may result in the simplest of these—methane. Thus, the consistent development of one oxidation theory leads to a geochemical and geological absurdity. Today the authors of this theory admit that it is impossible to explain the origin of all oil tars by the oxidation of hydrocarbons (55). Consequently, here again one must deal with the problem of the heterogeneity of tars. This problem is very serious in petroleum geochemistry, but it cannot be solved owing to the lack of adequate methods.

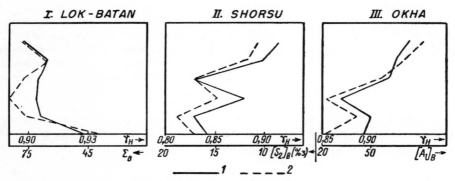

Fig. 5. Relation between the properties of crude oils and waters (distribution within the formation cross-section). 1—properties of oils (sp. gr., γ_H); 2—properties of waters (Σ - I; S_2 - II; A_1 - III).

    If it were possible to separate "primary" and "secondary" tars, the investigation of the causes of diversity among crude oils would take a long step forward. Valuable assistance can be rendered here by a detailed investigation of the chemical composition of oils in their changes within the bounds of particular formations. Such data are very meager at present.
    Thus, it must be concluded that the role of the different geochemical processes that cause the natural variations in petroleum is extremely important, but it is evidently not possible to attribute all differences to any one of these processes.

---

[27]The hypothesis, advanced by several authors, that nitrogenous substances, including porphyrins, in crude oils are accidental admixtures, should be considered invalid: the regular relation between these substances and the remaining portions of the oils, as well as the type of oils (see above, and also (2), especially the section on porphyrins (54). Note that distillates, which are regarded as "filtrates" and therefore must extract porphyrins from the rocks, are devoid of them.

Conclusions

Consideration of the entire complex of facts related to the geochemistry of petroleum in the light of the methodology of dialectical materialism leads to the following conclusions. The diversity in the properties of crude oils in nature is mainly the result of geochemical transformations of petroleum under the influence of external conditions. The observed properties of every oil are the result of its history. The composition of the initial substances probably has some effect, but this is only a minor influence which cannot be demonstrated as yet.

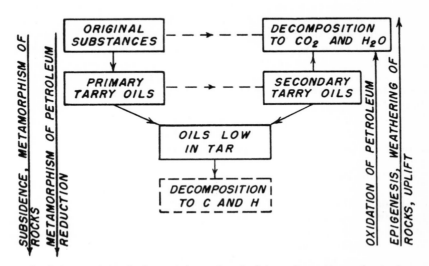

Fig. 6. Scheme of the fundamental geochemical transformations of petroleum.

Of the geochemical processes leading to conversions of crude oils, two groups, which are oppositely directed for the most part, are of decisive importance. This is determined by the close relation between the history of the oils and the general manner of "life" on the earth's crust. The metamorphism of petroleum is related to the settling and metamorphism of rocks. Oxidative transformations, the epigenesis of oils, are related to rising and epigenesis. The decomposition of oils may be the final result of both processes, upon the passage of the crude oils beyond the limits of the "field" of their geochemical being.

A scheme of the fundamental directions of the conversions of petroleum on the background of general geological processes is shown graphically (Fig. 6).[28] This scheme reveals that in nature at least two genetically distinct forms of heavy tarry oils are encountered (the residues from evaporation constitute a third). Unfortunately, the state of knowledge concerning the composition of crudes in relation to the conditions of their deposition

[28]This scheme is similar to that suggested by D. I. Vydrin (56), but was developed independently. Recently, N. B. Vassoevich and G. A. Amosov (57) arrived at the same conception.

does not permit an accurate elucidation of the geochemical history of
particular oils.

The given scheme characterizes only the most fundamental features of
the geochemical evolution of petroleum. In reality, there are a number of
complications, which have been described above in different connection.
Briefly, the basic hypotheses on these complicating factors may be summarized in the following form.

1. The character (and therefore, results) of metamorphism as well
as oxidation may vary in dependence on a combination of such conditions
as time, temperature, catalysts, form of reagent, and the like.

2. Metamorphism and oxidation may proceed simultaneously and in
the same place, since crude oil contains chemically dissimilar components.

3. In the course of geological history one direction of transformation
may shift to the reverse direction as a result of changes in sign of fluctu-
ating movements of the earth's crust of great amplitude.

4. On chemical processes may be superimposed physical ones; the
combination of evaporation of light fractions and oxidation is especially
probable.

As a result the overall picture becomes very complex. Interpretation
of the enumerated correlations requires careful study of many geological
and chemical indices for each particular case.

Practical Importance of the Question

Elucidation of the relation between the properties of crude oils and the geological conditions of their existence should make possible the solution of
the problem of prognosis of the quality of petroleum; it may make such a
problem as prospecting for oil of definite quality the order of the day.
These problems are extremely important, since the economic value of
various crudes may be different, for example, for oils without gasoline
and those high in this component. Therefore, attempts at predicting the
quality of crude oils have been made for a long time, but they bore a
primitively empirical character. More scientific were the prognoses of
B. M. Sarkisyan for the Apsheron peninsula (58). It is characteristic that
all these prognoses depend on the previously noted predominant regularity,
i.e., the increase in gasoline content of petroleum with the depth of the
deposit. However, this regularity is not universal. Furthermore, besides
the gasoline content, the primary interest lies in the prediction of such
properties as the hydrocarbon composition of the light fractions (which
determines their octane number) and the like. Therefore, it must be
admitted that no method of predicting the quality of crude oils has been
developed as yet. The necessity of work in this direction should be perfectly obvious.

After gaining an acquaintance with the changes in crude oils themselves, it is in order to proceed to the effects of these processes on the
surrounding medium.

GEOCHEMICAL PECULIARITIES OF THE GASES, WATERS, AND
ROCKS OF PETROLEUM FORMATIONS

The environment of oil pools consists of gases, waters, and rocks. As a
special factor of the environment organisms may be distinguished, such

as bacteria living in the waters.[29]

The geochemical peculiarities of gases, waters, and rocks of petroleum formations are of three kinds. To the first kind belongs the content in the gases, waters, and rocks of the products of the direct dispersion of the main substance of the oil pool: hydrocarbon gases, bitumens, and the like. To the second kind belong those properties which are the result of chemical reactions between hydrocarbons and the surrounding substance (for example, soda formed in the oxidation of oil). Finally, the third kind of peculiarity has no direct, genetic relation to petroleum. An example is the phenomenon of the presence of calcium chloride in reservoir waters, which is characteristic for certain formations only because of a combination of conditions favoring the simultaneous accumulation of the crude oils and these substances. The relation between oil pools and the associated geochemical peculiarities of gases, waters, and rocks is paragenesis. In accordance with the preceding statements, three kinds of paragenesis are distinguished.

Natural Gases

The natural gases of oil formations are, in part, a transitional link between the crude oils and the surrounding medium; the gases dissolved in oil constitute a part of the oils themselves, and it is impossible to draw a sharp line between them and the free gases.

According to the conditions of their location in petroleum formations, the following forms of gases may be distinguished: (1) dissolved in oils; (2) free (in gas caps); (3) dissolved in waters; (4) sorbed by rocks. Transition from one of these forms to another is relatively easy. This transition is a physical process. In the latter a decisive role is played by pressure, especially the correlation between the pressure of the gas and the hydrostatic pressure in the reservoir. The chemical properties of the gases, oils, waters, and rocks themselves are also important. The composition of each of the four forms also depends on the solubility of particular kinds of gases; in a gas cap, gases of much lower solubility (e.g., CH_4, N_2) will predominate, while in the waters, the role of the most water-soluble gases (CO_2) will become more important, etc.

In Table 4 data are given on the composition of the natural gases of oil formations, i.e., the composition of free gases, as well as those partly dissolved in oils and waters (that portion of them which is evolved upon penetrating the strata).[30] In this table C_2H_6+ refers to hydrocarbons from ethane up; $C_5H_{12}+$ refers to hydrocarbons from pentane up. The most abundant gases of oil formations, as Table 4 reveals, are methane, the heavier gases as a group, carbon dioxide, and nitrogen. These four components can therefore be used as a basis of classification.

---

[29]The following factors may be distinguished by their spatial relation to the oil pool: (1) internal factors of the environment—oil-saturated rocks with bound water occluded therein; (2) external factors of the environment—the outer portion of the reservoir, saturated with gases and waters, basement and cap rocks, etc.

[30]It should be kept in mind that data on the CO_2 content of freely evolved gases are not entirely indicative, owing to its great solubility.

TABLE 4. Composition of Natural Gases from Petroleum

% CH_4	% C_2H_6	% C_3H_8	% C_4H_{10}	% C_5H_{12+}	% C_2H_{6+}	$\dfrac{CH_4}{C_2H_{6+}}$	% total C_nH_m	% CO_2	% N_2	% H_2S
1 – 99	0.2 – 34	0.01 – 35	0 – 18	0.2 – 15	1 – 66	0.2 – 99	5 – 100	0 – 95	0 – 60	0 – 12

The geochemical classification of the natural gases of oil formations must be compatible with chemical as well as geological characteristics. An example of such a classification is presented here. For the preparation of this classification, a double trigonogram (Fig. 7) similar to that suggested by S. A. Durov for waters (59) is used. The upper triangle gives the total composition of the natural gas; and its vertices correspond to values of the total gas content (comprising hydrocarbons, carbon dioxide, and nitrogen) equal to 100%. The triangle to the left gives the composition of the carbonaceous part of the gas; and its vertices correspond to values of the gas content (comprising methane, the heavier hydrocarbons, and carbon dioxide, computed on the basis of these three components without N_2, etc.). The triangle to the left is necessary for the development of a correlation among hydrocarbons that is of great significance. The data of both triangles are projected onto a square. A point on the square shows the classification position of the gas from a given pool.[31]

TABLE 5. Geochemical Classification of Natural Gases from Petroleum

Class	Composition					Geological region of origin of typical representatives
	% total C_nH_m	% CH_4	% C_2H_6	% CO_2	% N_2	
1. Hydrocarbon, dry	> 95	> 75	< 25	< 5	< 5	Emba, Gulf Coast, Rocky Mountains
2. Hydrocarbon, oily	> 95	< 75	> 25	< 5	< 5	Northern Caucasus
3. Carbon dioxide, dry	< 95	25 – 95	< 25	> 5	< 5	Baku, California, Mexico
4. Carbon dioxide, oily[32]	< 95	< 75	25 – 75	> 5	< 5	Southern Mexico
5. Nitrogenous, dry	< 95	25 – 95	< 25	< 5	> 5	North American Platform
6. Nitrogenous, oily	< 95	< 75	25 – 75	< 5	> 5	Russian platform, Permian basin of the U.S.A.

[31]Other gases, the content of which is usually insignificant (H_2S, H_2, etc.), are ignored.

[32]Apparently, a rare class.

More than a hundred analyses of the most typical gases from petroleum formations are plotted in the diagram (Fig. 7). Consideration of the
latter leads to the conclusion that a relation exists between chemical and
geological indices. The diagram renders it possible to distinguish six
classes, the characteristics of which are listed in Table 5.

As is shown in the diagram (Fig. 7), transitions among classes occur.
However, no transitions between the carbon dioxide and nitrogen classes
have been observed. Consideration of Table 5 leads to the conclusion that
nitrogenous gases are associated with platforms, while all other natural
gases are associated with folded regions. Development of the geochemical
essence of the classification is possible only when the genesis of each individual component is known.

Hydrocarbons constitute the main part of the gases of oil formations.
Hydrocarbon gases (methane) are formed by metamorphism and oxidation
of crude oils. The very marked tendency of gases to migrate must also be
taken into account. Therefore, it is not surprising that the distribution of
gas saturations is complex. On one hand, the regular increase of gas
saturation with depth and age is observed [a shining example: Seal Beach

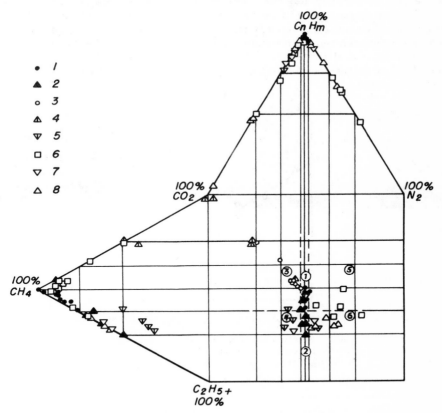

Fig. 7. Geochemical classification of natural gases from petroleum. 1—Emba,
Gulf Coast, Rocky Mountains; 2—Northern Caucasus; 3—Transcaucasia, California;
4—Northern Mexico; 5—Southern Mexico; 6—North American platform; 7—Permian basin of North America; 8—Russian platform and the near-Ural region.
Figures in circles correspond to the class numbers of Table 5.

in California (60)]. A. F. Dobryanskii believes that pools that are richer
in gas have undergone more transformation than paraffinic oils. In connection with this, the linear relation between the relative gas saturation
and clay content of reservoirs pointed out by V. S. Melik-Pashaev is of
interest. It may be that this dependence has a partially genetic character;
the great catalytic activity of clay particles increases gas formation
through the decomposition of hydrocarbons.

On the other hand, many cases are known of vast gas accumulations
with tarry oils (the PK group of the Apsheron peninsula, Shorsu, Sed' Iol',
etc.).

The ratio of methane to heavier hydrocarbons (CH_4/C_2H_6+) is related
to the character of the oil. It is inversely dependent on the content of
paraffinic hydrocarbons in the light fractions of crude oils of the same
strata (Fig. 8). The more saturated the gasoline fraction is, the more oily
the gas. The cause of this phenomenon is the high vapor pressure of the
lower paraffinic hydrocarbons in comparison with the lower naphthenes
(the content of the latter in natural gases is quite negligible). Thus, the
character of the hydrocarbon portion of natural gases, and hence, the class
of the gas, are paragenetically related to the type of crude oil.[33]

Carbon dioxide gas in petroleum formations is mainly a product of
oxidation of crude oils. Gases with a predominance of CO_2 in their composition are associated with crudes having a tarriness of 40% or more
[McKittrick in California (61), Panuco in Mexico (62),[34] et al.]. If the
oxidation of oils ceased. the CO_2, owing to its solubility and activity,
would vanish.

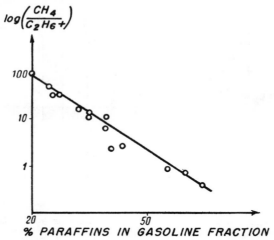

Fig. 8. Relation between the hydrocarbon composition of
natural gases and the content of paraffinic hydrocarbons
in the light fractions of crude oils from the same strata.

---

[33]Within gas-oil pools, gravitational stratification of gases is sometimes observed:
in the Chusovian formation the methane content decreases with depth on account of the
heavy hydrocarbons.

[34]In this formation the amount of CO_2 is so great that it has been utilized as a
mineral resource (production of dry ice).

Nitrogen is only partially genetically associated with petroleum. It may be evolved upon the decomposition of nitrogenous substances in oil, and also upon reduction of nitrates in the waters. The remainder of the nitrogen may be of atmospheric origin. Consequently, nitrogen may be genetically foreign to the oil formation, persisting there only because of its inertness. Upon oxidation of the hydrocarbons, the mole fraction of nitrogen in the gases may increase (63). Carbon dioxide and nitrogen are antagonists in the composition of natural gases.

Thus, the composition of the gases in oil formations is mainly determined by: (a) the composition of petroleum; (b) the presence or absence of processes of oxidation; (c) the geological and geochemical age of the deposits. The association of hydrogen sulfide with crude oils and rocks has been discussed above. A vast accumulation of this gas has been reported at Shorsu. The question of hydrogen is most obscure. As a rule, the content of this element is negligible. At Shorsu it reaches an anomalously high value, 12%.

Oxygen is a "forbidden" gas in petroleum formations. The absence of oxygen, however, is due not to the crude oils themselves but to the action of rock components; in deep strata there is no oxygen where there is no oil.

Summing up, the relations between the main gases and oils are as shown in the following form (Table 6). Only the origin of the main mass of the gases in oil formations is given. CH_4 and CO_2 may in some measure, also be of extraneous origin.

TABLE 6. Nature of the Relation of Natural Gases to Petroleum

Gas	Paragenesis		Absence of relation
	Type I	Type II	
C_2H_{6+} CH_4	Immediate evolution	Dehydrogenation of petroleum	—
CO_2	Decomposition of oxygen-containing substances	Oxidation of petroleum	—
N_2	Decomposition of nitrogenous substances	Reduction of nitrates	Atmospheric origin
H_2S	Decomposition of sulfur-containing substances	Reduction of sulfates	—

Waters

According to the conditions of their formation, the waters of petroleum formations are classified as: (a) bound (capillary, pendular) waters within the oil pools; (b) free waters in oil-bearing reservoirs, i.e., bottom waters within the productive limits and those beyond; (c) bound waters outside the pool in oil-bearing reservoirs, as well as cap and basement rocks; (d) free waters in reservoirs devoid of oil. The composition of bound waters has been studied very little. In Table 7 data are given on the chemical composition of the waters of oil formations, or more precisely, the salts dissolved

TABLE 7. Composition of the Waters of Petroleum Formations

Content	Total ions	Cl	Br	I	HCO$_3$	$C_nH_mO_2$ [35]
In mg. per 100 g. water . . .	20-30000	10-18000	0-200	0-12	0-1800	0-500
In % - equivalents . . .	100	1-50	0-0.3	0-0.01	0-49	0-8

Content	HS	SO$_4$	Na	K	NH$_4$	Ca	Mg
In mg. per 100 g. water . . .	0-20	0-450	10-9000	0.5-140	0-45	4-2000	0-600
In % - equivalents . . .	0-0.2	0-15	30-50	0.05-1	0-0.3	0.1-30	0-10

therein. The table refers only to the free waters of oil-bearing reservoirs.

Minimum values of total mineralization and content of chlorine, sodium, and calcium are encountered in very rare cases, in such formations as Binagady and Mirzaani, where the deposits are adjacent to waters which communicate with the earth's surface. The maximum quantities of organic anions (naphthenates) in the Maikop of Norio and of the weight content of SO$_4$ in the Kungura in the Chusovian formation are also unique.

The waters of petroleum formations belong, in the main, to two types: the alkaline sodium bicarbonate type and the hard calcium chloride type (the latter includes the magnesium chloride variety) (64). Maximum values of mineralization, absolute content of all ions (Table 7) except HCO$_3$, and the relative importance of Ca and Cl ions are inherent in the calcium chloride type. Maximum values of relative content of HCO$_3$, SO$_4$, and $C_nH_mO_2$ belong to the alkaline type. The types differ sharply in pH. For alkaline waters the pH is over 8, while for calcium chloride waters the pH lies between 4 and 6. This low pH in calcium chloride waters is explained by T. I. Kazmina on the basis of the great amount of CO$_2$ present in the form of dissolved gas (65). At the same time V. N. Ovchinnikov and others believe that the acidity of calcium chloride waters is the result of the hydrolysis of CaCl$_2$ and MgCl$_2$. This question requires further investigation.

The accumulation of the majority of components in the waters of an oil formation is not genetically related to petroleum. It is related to such a characteristic phenomenon as the formation of calcium chloride. V. A. Sulin proved that the latter is the final stage of metamorphism of the salt content of the waters of the earth's crust. The process consists mainly of the displacement of a calcium ion by one of sodium when the latter is sufficiently concentrated in the waters, and the absorption of the calcium by the rocks:

$$2NaCl + Ca^{++} \rightarrow CaCl_2 + 2Na^{+}$$

[35]Organic anions (chiefly naphthenate ions).

The absence of sulfate (or abnormally low concentration) in waters may be due to a chemical combination with the oil. This may be entirely true for alkaline waters and only partly true for calcium chloride waters. Soda in the waters of oil formations, for the most part, in any case, is the result of the reaction of crude oils with the surrounding medium. Soaps (naphthenates and the like) belong entirely to this category.

Iodine and ammonia may pass into waters from crude oils on decomsition of some components of the latter. Practically all of the iodine and ammonia in the waters of petroleum formations has this origin.

The nature of the relation between the components of waters, characteristic of oil formations, and crude oil is shown in Table 8. The table refers only to the main mass of the given substance under the conditions of oil formations.

TABLE 8. Nature of the Relation between the Components of Waters and Petroleum

Components of waters	Paragenesis type I	Paragenesis type II	Paragenesis type III
$C_nH_mO_2$	Evolution from petroleum	Oxidation of petroleum	—
I	Decomposition of iodine-containing substances	—	—
NH_4	Decomposition of nitrogenous substances	—	—
$NaHCO_3$	—	Formation on oxidation of petroleum	—
HS	Decomposition of sulfur-containing substances	Reduction of sulfates	—
$-(SO_4)$	—	Reduction of petroleum	Deposition at high concentration
$CaCl_2$	—	—	Cationic exchange at high concentration
Br	—	—	Concentration

Change of Properties of Waters in Oil-Bearing Strata

The phenomenon of variations in the composition of the waters within the boundaries of a single stratus in oil formations was first established by

B. I. Sultanov (66). This question is not adequately understood even today.
The inhomogeneity of the composition of waters in strata is characteristic
of folded regions. Two main regularities have been observed. According
to the data of the investigators, B. I. Sultanov, V. A. Sulin, A. A. Kartsev,
et al., the mineralization and chloride content of the waters, etc., on the
Apsheron peninsula increase both down dip into synclines and in zones of
structural closure. One or the other of these phenomena is observed in
many other cases; in a few cases, both are observed. The increase of
mineralization with depth was also noted in a number of other formations
(Kazan-bulag, Tashkala). The basic explanation of this phenomenon is the
gravitational stratification of the waters in the stratum (this also occurs
with crude oils). In the opinion of D. V. Zhabrev, as the deposit is approached, the mineralization falls off on account of desulfurization. This,
however, does not explain the absolute decrease of the chloride content.

The inverse phenomenon (i.e., the increase of mineralization in the
upper regions by reduction) was observed, aside from Baku (in PK) in the
Khadyzhia district, and also in the formation of Salt Creek (Rocky Mountains) (67). For the Eastern Kuban, V. A. Lashchenov explains the observed regularity by the increase in the rate of exchange of water with increase of depth. But in other cases, this explanation is not always possible.
It may well be that the increase of mineralization of the waters within
zones of structural closure is related to a reaction of the pools themselves.
Part of the water is carried away by gas that is evolved from the pool and
flows upward, and the salt content of the waters remaining in the stratum
increases (68).

Organisms

As is known, bacteria in oil-bearing strata were first observed in 1926 by
T. L. Ginzburg-Karagicheva. Several forms of anaerobic bacteria living
in the depths of petroleum formations are now known: desulfators, denitri-
fiers, and others (69). The desulfators Vibrio desulfuricans and V. thermo-
desulfuricans are of fundamental significance. They utilize for nourishment
various components of crude oils; as a source of oxygen, they use sulfates
dissolved in the waters. These organisms promote the oxidation of petroleum. Besides temperature, conditions limiting their development are low
pH (below 5), very high salt content (over 20°Bé), and high concentrations
of H_2S (23). The specifics of the nourishment of oil bacteria are as yet unknown. Apparently, some of them subsist on hydrocarbons and albumins—
the remains of other bacteria (21). The origin of bacteria in oil-bearing
reservoirs also remains obscure.

Besides living bacteria in the oils and waters of petroleum formations,
products of their vital processes have been observed, such as ferments
(catalase, proteinase) (70, 71). A. A. Maliyants and E. A. Reinfel'd in 1936
observed purple sulfur bacteria which oxidized H_2S to SO_4 in the waters of
the Baku formations (72). These organisms color the water a rose tint.
The quantity of these bacteria is directly related to the content in the waters
of naphthenates, which are utilized by them for nourishment (and also, possibly, as a source of oxygen). According to B. L. Isachenko the purple
sulfur bacteria can use O_2 formed in the decomposition of H_2O under the
influence of radioactive radiations; i.e., they are partially aerobic.

Rocks

Organic substances in the rocks of oil formations may contain a number of products originally formed from petroleum. These materials comprise: (a) sorbed and polymerized products of direct diffusion of hydrocarbons; (b) asphaltenes, tars, and solid paraffins and ceresins deposited from solution in crude oil (under the influence of different processes). Investigations of the organic substances in the rocks of oil formations (exclusive of large accumulations of such substances in the form of veins) were carried out by V. E. Levenson and A. T. Kochmarev in Baku, L. V. Khmelevskaya (73), V. N. Florovskaya (74), A. A. Kartsev (75), I. A. Yurkevich, P. Trask (76), and others. In view of the inadequacy of the methods used and the great similarity of substances originally formed from petroleum to other organic components of rocks, these investigations gave obscure and partly contradictory results. This problem requires further careful study.

Of the inorganic components of rocks, those paragenetic with crude oils are minerals consisting of reduced forms of S and Fe: pyrite, free sulfur, siderite, etc., and also $CaCO_3$, etc. The result of the transition of ferric oxide to ferrous oxide is a change in the color of the rocks from red to green; this is well known for the Baku formations and elsewhere. If the content of gypsum is not very great, the latter may vanish in the immediate vicinity of oil pools; this has also been observed on the Apsheron peninsula (66, 77).

The geochemical peculiarities of the gases, waters, and rocks of petroleum formations may be used as indications in prospecting. They are geochemical indices of oil-bearing character. Their significance is sharply increased because of the existence of aureoles of diffusion. The latter means that oil and gas in a diffused state spread beyond the boundaries of the pool. Waters adjacent to the crude oils migrate in the same manner.[36] The diffused oil components, including hydrocarbon gases, also react with the surrounding medium. Therefore the geochemical influence of the oil pool extends throughout an extremely large volume, even reaching the surface of the earth.

BIBLIOGRAPHY

1. V.A. Klubov. Geochemical classification of caustobiolites. Sb. geol. rabot, posvyashch. pamyati akad. I.M. Gubkina, Gostoptekhizdat, 1950.
2. A.F. Dobryanskii. Geochemistry of petroleum. Lengostoptekhizdat, 1948.
3. N.I. Chernozhukov, S.Z. Krein, B.V. Losikov. Chemistry of mineral oils. Gostoptekhizdat, 1951.
4. A.N. Sachanen. The Chemical Constituents of Petroleum. N. Y., 1945.
5. B.M. Rybak. Naphthenic acids. Gostoptekhizdat, 1948.
6. V.V. Getseu. Abstract of candidate's dissertation, "Investigation of Daghestan oils" (on the question of nitrogenous compounds). Publ. VNIGRI, 1954.

---

[36]The mechanism of diffusion is discussed in the appropriate chapters.

7. O.A. Radchenko and O.P. Bolotskaya. Toward the problem of the rela-
    tion between the character of the asphaltenes and the type of
    petroleum. Doklady Akad. Nauk SSSR, vol. 68, No. 4, 1949.

8. G.A. Amosov. Investigation of the optical rotation of crude oils. Tr.
    VNIGRI, No. 57 (Geokhim. sb., No. 203) Lengostoptekhizdat, 1951.

9. S. Ascheim and W. Hohlweg. Über das Vorkommen östrogener
    Wirkstoffe in Bitumen. Deutsche Mediz., Wochenschr., vol. 59,
    No. 1, 1933.

10. Yu.G. Mamedaliev. Toward the theory of the mechanism of the action
    of naphthalenic oil. Izvestiya Akad. Nauk SSSR, ser. khim., No. 5,
    1946.

11. S.N. Obryadchikov. Temperature conditions of the formation of petro-
    leum in nature. Sb. "Origin of petroleum and natural gas", Publ.
    TsIMT - nefti, M., 1947.

12. A.V. Frost and L.K. Osnitskaya. Toward the problem of the origin of
    petroleum. Sb. "Pam. akad. I.M. Gubkina", Akad. Nauk SSSR,
    1951.

13. A.I. Silin-Bekchurin. Formation of the subterranean waters of the
    northeastern part of the Russian platform and the western slope
    of the Urals. Tr. Lab. gidrogeol. problem Akad. Nauk SSSR, v.
    4, 1949.

14. J.A. Taff. Physical Properties of Petroleum in California. Problems
    of Petroleum Geology, Tulsa, 1934.

15. B.T. Brooks Active-surface catalysts in the formation of petroleum.
    Bull. Am. Assn. Petrol. Geol., vol. 33, No. 9, 1942.

16. A.F. Dobryanskii, A.I. Bogomolov, and I.V. Sklyar. Catalytic influence
    on rocks on change of composition of petroleum. ZhPKh, v. 22,
    No. 10, 1949.

17. A.I. Bogomolov and F.B. Indebom. Experimental geochemical investi-
    gation of crude oils along the section of rocks of the South Emba
    region. Tr. VNIGRI, No. 57 (Geokhim. sb., No. 2-3) Lengostop-
    tekhizdat, 1951.

18. D.C. Barton. Evolution of Gulf Coast crude oil. Bull. Am. Assn.
    Petrol. Geol., vol. 21, No. 7, 1937.

19. Soviet petroleum. Gostoptekhizdat, 1949.

20. V.A. Sokolov, Outlines of the genesis of petroleum. Gostoptekhizdat,
    1948.

21. V.A. Uspenskii, A.I. Gorskaya, and I.P. Karpova. Genesis of algarites
    and processes of anaerobic oxidation of petroleum. Izvestiya Akad.
    Nauk SSR, ser. geol., No. 4, 1947.

22. V.O. Tauson. On the reduction of sulfates by bacteria in the presence
    of hydrocarbons. Mikrobiologiya, vd. 1, No. 3, 1932.

23. L.D. Shturm. Role of sulfate reducing bacteria in the life and history
    of oil formations. Sb. "Pam. akad. I.M. Gubkina", Akad. Nauk
    SSSR, 1951.

24. A.F. Plate. Catalytic aromatization of paraffin hydrocarbons. Akad.
    Nauk SSSR, 1951.

25. N.T. Lindtrop, Role of water in the formation and disintegration of oil
    pools, sb. "Pam. akad. I.M. Gubkina". Akad. Nauk SSSR, 1951.

26. G.S. Petrov. Synthetic fatty acids. Pishchepromizdat, 1951.

27. V.K. Tsyskovskii. Oxidation of petrolatum and paraffin.
    Gostoptekhizdat, 1948.

28. A.N. Ovchinnikov. Mineral waters. Gosgeolizdat, 1947.

29. N.I. Butorin and Z.P. Buks. Naphthenic acids in the stratum waters of the Old - and New - Grozny regions. Groznen. neftyanik. No. 5-6, 1935.

30. C. Palmer. California oil-field waters. Econ. Geol., vol. 19, No. 7, 1924.

31. T.I. Kazmina. Geochemical investigation of the Maikop and Khadum deposits of the Khadyzhian and Neftyano-Shirvanian formations. Tr. NGRI, No. 104. ONTI, 1938.

32. Oil formations of Azerbaijan. Tr. 17 - i sessii Mezhd. geol. kongr., v. 4. Gostoptekhizdat, 1940.

33. A.S. Uklonskii. Paragenesis of sulfur and petroleum. Publ. UzFAN SSR, 1940.

34. V.A. Uspenskii and O.A. Radchenko. Toward the problem of the genesis of types of crude oils. Lengostoptekhizdat, 1947.

35. M.V. Abramovich. Change of the properties of petroleum in an oil-bearing stratum in relation to the conditions of its deposition. Tr. Geol. instituta AzFAN, v. 19, AzFAN SSR, 1939.

36. K. Kreichi-Graf. Fundamental questions of petroleum geology (transl. from German). ONTI, 1934.

37. D.C. Barton. Variation and migration of crude oil at Spindletop. Bull. Am. Assn. Petrol. Geol., v. 19, No. 5, 1935.

38. N.A. Eremenko. Change of several properties of crude oils in a formation in dependence on the conditions of establishment of the pools. Vestnik Moskov. Univ., No. 9, 1948.

39. Yu.N. Petrova and N.F. Kasatkina. Comparative study of solid hydrocarbons, ozokerites, and paraffinic oils. Tr. VNIGRI, No. 57 (Geokhim. sb., No. 2-3), Lengostoptekhizdat, 1951.

40. A. Konchine. Guide des excursions du VII Congrés Géologique Internationale, 24. S Pb., 1897.

41. H. Hlauschek. Naphten — und Methanöle. Stuttgart, 1937.

42. H. Hlauschek. Roumanian crude oils. Bull. Am. Assn. Petrol. Geol., vol. 34, No. 4, 1950.

43. K.W. Barr, F. Morton, A. Richards, and R. Young. The crude oils of Trinidad. Jour. Inst. Petrol. Technol., vol. 35, No. 310, 1949.

44. C.E. Dobbin. Carbon ratios and oil gravities in the Rocky Mountain region. Bull. Am. Assn. Petrol. Geol., v. 13, No. 10, 1929.

45. A.F. Dobryanskii and A.I. Bogomolov. Attempt at analysis of several positions of the hypothesis of transformation of petroleum with data on the Second Baku, Tr. VNIGRI, No. 28 (Geokhim, sb., No. 1). Lengostoptekhizdat, 1949.

46. A.F. Dobryanskii. Transformation of petroleum in nature as a cause of the variety of its properties. Vestnik Leningrad. Univ., No. 4, 1950.

47. H. Höfer. Die Entstehung der Erdöle. Petrol. Zeitschr., vol. 18, No. 31, 1922.

48. W.E. Pratt. Hydrogenation and the origin of petroleum. Prob. of Petrol. Geology, Tulsa, 1934.

49. D.C. Barton. Natural history of the Gulf Coast crude oil. Probl. of Petrol. Geology, Tulsa, 1934.

50. O.A. Radchenko. Contemporary views on the genesis of petroleum and the processes of its transformation and disintegration. Sb. ''Pam akad. I.M. Gubkina''. Akad. Nauk SSSR, 1951.

51. C. Washburne. Some physical principles of the origin of petroleum. Bull. Am. Assn. Petrol. Geol., vol. 3, 1919.

52. S.I. Mironov. The problem of the origin of petroleum and methods of its solution. Izvestiya Akad. Nauk SSSR, ser. geol., No. 2, 1952.

53. H. Steinbrecher and O. Stutzer. Chemische Untersetzung deutscher Erdöle. Stuttgart, 1934.

54. F.M. Efendiev and M.A. Dzhafarov. Spectroscopic investigation of Apsheron crude oils with respect to their porphyrin content. Izvestiya Akad. Nauk AzSSR, No. 10, 1951.

55. O.A. Radchenko, A.S. Chernysheva, and O.P. Bolotskaya. Toward the problem of the chemical character of the products of weathering of petroleum, Tr. VNIGRI, No. 57 (Geokhim. sb., No. 2-3), Lengostoptekhizdat, 1951.

56. D.I. Vydrin. Geological conditions of formation and conversion of petroleum and natural gases. Tr. Grozn. neft. instituta, sb. 5., Grozoblizdat, 1948.

57. N.B. Vassoevich and G.A. Amosov. Alteration of petroleum in the earth's crust. Geol. sb. NITO VNIGRI, II (V), Lengostoptekhizdat, 1953.

58. B.M. Sarkisyan. Dependence of the quality of petroleum on geological conditions. Aznefteizdat, 1947.

59. S.A. Durov. Toward the problem of the genesis of natural waters. Tr. Lab. gidrogeol. problem Akad. Nauk SSSR, v. III. M., 1948.

60. Geologic formations and economic development of the oil and gas fields of California. Sacramento, 1943.

61. Sh. Rogers. Helium-bearing natural gases (Transl. from English). ONTI, 1935.

62. J.M. Muir. Occurrence of natural gas in Mexican oil fields. Geology of Natural Gas. USA, 1935.

63. A.L. Kozlov. Problems of the geochemistry of natural gases. Gostoptekhizdat, 1950.

64. V.A. Sulin. Waters of oil formations in the system of natural waters. Gostoptekhizdat, 1946.

65. T.I. Kazmina. Devonian waters of the eastern part of the Russian platform. Tr. VNIGRI, No. 57 (Geokhim. sb., No. 2-3), Lengostoptekhizdat, 1951.

66. B.I. Sultanov. Change of the chemical composition of the waters of petroleum formations resulting from the reaction of gas and oil therewith. Aznefteizdat, 1936.

67. W.H. Emmons. Geology of Petroleum. N. Y., No. 9, 1931.

68. Van Mills and R.S. Wells. The evaporation and concentration of waters associated with petroleum and natural gas. U. S. Geol. Survey Bull., No. 693, 1919.

69. L.O. Shturm. Microbiological investigation of the waters of oil-bearing strata. Mikrobiologiya, v. 19, No. 1, 1950.

70. M.A. Messineva, New data on biochemical factors of transformation of organic material in the genesis of petroleum. Sb. "Origin of petroleum and natural gas". Publ. TsIMT nefti, 1947.

71. D.Z. Babaev. Toward the problem of the nature of the catalysis of the crude oils and underlying waters of an oil stratum. Izvestiya Akad. Nauk AzSSR, No. 2, 1950.

72. B.L. Isachenko. Purple sulfur bacteria from the lower limits of the biosphere. Izbr. tr., vol. 2. Akad. Nauk SSSR, 1951.
73. L.V. Khmelevskaya. Toward a method of lithological study of sedimentary rocks in oil-bearing regions. Tr. 17 - i sessii Mezhd. geol. kongr., v. 4. Gostoptekhizdat, 1940.
74. V.N. Florovskaya and V.G. Melkov. Introduction to luminescent bituminology. Gosgeolizdat, 1946.
75. A.A. Kartsev. The organic matter of the rocks of the Kirovabad oil-bearing region. Koklady Akad. Nauk SSSR, v. 65, No. 3, 1949.
76. P.D. Trask and H.W. Patnode. Source beds of petroleum, Tulsa, 1942.
77. V.E. Levenson and N.G. Utshtein. Sulfur in sedimentary formations in the immediate vicinity of petroleum and other bitumens. Tr. AzNII, No. 25. Aznefteizdat, 1934.

CHAPTER TWO

Classification of
Geochemical Prospecting Methods

GEOCHEMICAL INDICES OF PETROLEUM

Geochemical indices of petroleum are those chemical characteristics (properties) of gases, waters, and rocks (including soils) which are related in their origin to crude oil or which indicate conditions favorable to the existence of oil pools. Among these indicators are arbitrarily included geomicrobiological ones, i.e., analogous characteristics in the world of microbes.

All geochemical indices of petroleum can be classified as direct and indirect. Among the direct indices should be included such a characteristic of gases, waters, rocks, and soils as the presence in them of dispersed oil components in the form of liquid and solid bitumens and hydrocarbon gases.[1] The direct geochemical indices are the immediate derivatives of petroleum (including the products of their polymerization. For example, solid bitumens may form as a result of the polymerization of liquid substances and gases): their connection with crude oil is paragenesis of type I. All other indicators should be considered indirect.

Indirect geochemical indices of petroleum can be grouped into two categories. To the first belong those characteristics of gases, waters, rocks, and soils which appear as a result of processes of chemical reaction of an oil component (including hydrocarbon gases) with the surrounding medium (waters and rocks). These indirect indicators of type I are vestiges of the effect of crude oil on its surroundings. Their connection with petroleum is paragenesis of type II. Examples of indirect indices include the presence of hydrogen sulfide in some gases, that of soda in certain waters, and the like.

Indirect geochemical indices of petroleum of type II are those characteristics of gases, waters, and the like, which indicate conditions favorable to the existence of oil pools but not to the presence of oil or gas itself. Indirect indices of type II are substances or conditions usually associated with crude oil. Their connection with petroleum is paragenesis of type III. An example of this group of indices is the presence of calcium chloride in waters.

Such is the division of the geochemical indices of oil-bearing character according to the nature of their connection with petroleum. It should be kept in mind that the same indications may in different cases belong to different groups. Thus, for example, hydrogen sulfide may be a direct product of an oil pool, and it also may be formed in the reaction between crude oil and sulfates. In the first case, it may belong to the direct indices; in the second case, it may belong to the indirect group.

---

[1] Also components evolved from them, such as iodine and ammonia.

[42]

Since geochemical indices are the characteristics of gases in some cases, water in others, and rocks or soils in still others, they may be subdivided according to this feature. It is necessary, however, to place the oil bitumens located in rocks and soils in a special group called bituminous indices. As a result, the following kinds of indices may be distinguished: (1) gaseous; (2) bituminous; (3) hydrochemical; (4) soil-salt; (5) lithochemical. The following should be grouped separately: (6) physicochemical indices (E_H) and (7) geomicrobiological indices.

Finally, still another subdivision of these geochemical indices is possible. Some of the indices may be considered as well-defined indicators of the presence of petroleum (but not necessarily in commercial quantities). An example of this kind of index is the content of soaps (naphthenates) in waters. Such indices have an independent significance. Other indicators are not in themselves sufficient for judging as to the presence of petroleum because they may be of entirely different origin. An example of such an ambiguous index is methane. Such indices do not have an independent significance and they are in the majority. Very often in the evaluation of some indicator, the quantitative aspect plays the main role. This question is not considered in the present chapter.

The classification of most geochemical indices of petroleum is given in Table 9. In view of the ambiguous significance of many indices, as

TABLE 9. Classification of Geochemical Indices of Petroleum

Direct indices

gaseous	bituminous	hydrochemical	soil-salt
C_2H_{6+} CH_4	oil bitumens	soaps I NH_4	I

Indirect indices

Type I (vestiges of the effect of petroleum)					Type II (usually associated substances and conditions)		
gaseous	hydro-chemical	soil-salt	litho-chemical	geo-micro-biolog-ical	gaseous	hydro-chemical	physico-chemical
H_2S CO_2 N_2	HS $NaHCO_3$ $-(SO_4)$	$CaCO_3$ SiO_2	FeS_2 $FeCO_3$ $-(Fe_2O_3)$	hydro-carbon bac-teria	$-(O_2)$	$CaCl_2$ Br	Low E_H

stated above, the classification given is arbitrary. Furthermore, the degree of importance of particular indices therein is not stated. This question is considered in the corresponding individual chapters that follow. Since these indicators are the basis of geochemical methods of prospecting for oil and gas formations, they can also serve as a basis for classifying these methods.

CLASSIFICATION OF GEOCHEMICAL METHODS ACCORDING TO INDICES USED

Geochemical methods of prospecting for oil and gas formations may be subdivided into direct and indirect methods. Direct geochemical methods are based on the use of direct indications of petroleum, while indirect methods are correspondingly based on direct indices. Further subdivision of methods should be done according to the kind of natural bodies (gases, waters, rocks, soils) with which the given method deals. Such a subdivision is practical and uniquely possible.

Further, it is necessary to take the following into account. Firstly, among the gaseous indices there are no indirect indicators of independent significance. Therefore, all geochemical methods based on gases may be regarded as direct methods. Gas methods may be divided into three types according to the form in which the gases exist: free, sorbed, or in aqueous solution.

Secondly, among hydrochemical and soil-salt indices, on the contrary, direct indices of oil-bearing character have practically no independent significance. Therefore, hydrochemical and soil-salt methods may be considered as belonging entirely to the indirect methods (although this will not be quite correct). It should be pointed out that these methods include those which are not used for the immediate purpose of prospecting for petroleum but only for the elucidation of the geological structure, the so-called structural hydrochemical and soil-salt surveys, and the like. Those methods which are indirect in the full sense of the word use several indices which are generally not indicators of oil-bearing character.

Thirdly and lastly, the "lithochemical" methods in general have no independent existence as yet.

From the above considerations, the classification of geochemical methods of prospecting for oil and gas formations according to the indices used may be represented in the following scheme (Table 10).

TABLE 10. Classification of Geochemical Methods According to the Indices Used

Direct		Indirect			
Gas	Bitumen	Hydrochemical	Soil-salt	Physico-chemical	Microbi-ological

CLASSIFICATION OF GEOCHEMICAL METHODS BY OBJECTIVE AND BY ORGANIZATION

Geochemical methods may be divided by objective into: (1) reconnaissance prospecting; (2) detailed prospecting; (3) exploration. To prospecting belong those methods which are used prior to the discovery of a productive formation. Reconnaissance prospecting methods are used for the general evaluation of new districts and regions and prospecting for oil-bearing strata; detailed prospecting methods are used for selection and evaluation of particular areas. Exploration methods are used on known oil formations for locating productive levels within the stratigraphic section, correlation of these intervals, etc.

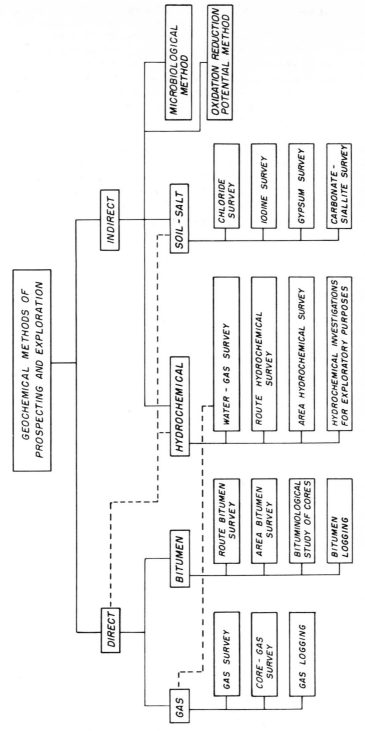

Fig. 9. Classification of geochemical methods of prospecting and exploration for oil and gas formations.

Methods may be divided by organization into (1) geochemical surveys; (2) geochemical well logging; (3) various special (topical) investigations. Surveying methods are divided into route surveys and area surveys and are conducted only for the purpose of prospecting. Route surveys are for reconnaissance, while area surveys are for more detailed prospecting. Various kinds of geochemical well logging operations are done chiefly for the purpose of exploration, i.e., detecting productive zones during drilling operations. Special investigations are made for various subsidiary purposes in prospecting in exploration, and even in the operation of completed wells.

The general scheme of the classification of methods is shown graphically in Figure 9, shown on the preceding page. The explanation of the details of this scheme follows in the corresponding chapters. Further description of the methods is given according to the classification: (1) gas; (2) bitumen; (3) hydrochemical, etc. A description of gas methods is presented in a special chapter, "Fundamentals of the geochemistry of gases".

CHAPTER THREE

The Geochemistry of Gases

INTRODUCTION

Volatile substances having either a low critical temperature or a high critical pressure that do not pass into the liquid state under the normal conditions at the earth's surface are called gases. Substances having critical temperatures and pressures such that they may pass into a finely-divided liquid state under atmospheric conditions are called vapors. The concentration of a vapor at the earth's surface depends on temperature and pressure.

Gaseous Minerals

Gases are minerals of a unique type. Minerals are natural chemical compounds or native elements formed as a result of various geological processes occurring in the earth's crust. Minerals are found in the solid, liquid, and gaseous states depending on the geochemical circumstances of their formation. Gaseous minerals differ from ordinary ones mainly in that they do not have a definite crystalline form and therefore cannot be determined by the methods used in mineralogy.

Many gaseous minerals consist of atoms of a single kind, i.e., they are elements. Such, for example, are hydrogen (H_2), nitrogen (N_2), oxygen (O_2), ozone (O_3), helium (He), neon (Ne), krypton (Kr), xenon (Xe), argon (A), iodine (I), chlorine (Cl), etc. Some gaseous minerals are quite simple chemical compounds, such as carbon monoxide (CO), carbon dioxide (CO_2), hydrogen sulfide (H_2S), ammonia (NH_3), nitric oxide (NO), nitrogen dioxide (NO_2), methane (CH_4), ethane (C_2H_6), propane (C_3H_8), butane (C_4H_{10}), ethylene (C_2H_4), etc. A large group of gaseous minerals, usually found in low concentrations in a specific geochemical situation, have a very complex composition. They are genetically associated with biochemical processes occurring in that part of the crust adjacent to the surface.

The number of gaseous minerals in the earth's crust is enormous. There is an especially large number of gaseous minerals in the soil air. Unfortunately, the gaseous minerals have, as yet, scarcely been studied. This is graphically demonstrated by existing courses in mineralogy, many of which do not mention gaseous minerals at all. In the voluminous work of A. G. Betekhtin (1), consisting of 928 pages, not more than 10 pages are devoted to gaseous minerals. Even at the present time a mineralogy of gases has not been established.

Of the enormous number of minerals in the earth's crust, a very few constitute the greater part of the earth's atmosphere and the gases penetrating the rock masses. These include nitrogen, oxygen, carbon dioxide, and methane. Other gaseous minerals play a subordinate role, occupying a small volume and rarely forming gas accumulations. Among these may be included hydrogen, helium, volatile heavy hydrocarbons, and hydrogen sulfide.

Finally, there is a group of rather abundant gaseous minerals which usually do not form accumulations. They exist in a rarefied state or else form temporary accumulations at the moment of their generation and are quickly dissipated. Among such minerals are included ammonia, carbon monoxide, nitrous oxide, nitric oxide, nitrogen dioxide, argon, krypton, xenon, radon, and also chlorine, bromine, iodine, fluorine, and sulfur vapor (emitted from volcanoes).

A number of gaseous minerals are found in negligibly small concentrations and correspond to the biosphere; they appear as a result of the emanations of plants, animals, and microorganisms and their metabolism. V. I. Vernadskii thought that there must be thousands of different varieties of gaseous minerals in the troposphere. He stated that there were an especially great number of biogenic organic minerals; the terpenes alone number over two thousand, whereas the total number of known solid, natural minerals does not exceed fifteen hundred (2). The study of organic gases is a field of enormous difficulty. Here estremely sensitive and accurate methods are indispensable because it is necessary in analysis to deal with concentrations of dispersed gases lying between 10^{-5} and $10^{-10}\%$.

Gaseous Associations

By gaseous associations are meant natural mixtures of different gaseous minerals (or condensed gases). Accumulations of any one gas in nature are encountered very rarely; even in this rare case, the content of the main gas is not over 99.9%, while the remaining 0.1% consists of admixtures, sometimes quite varied. Gaseous associations are usually called natural gases.

PROPERTIES OF GASES

Gaseous minerals are distinguished by physical and chemical properties, such as molecular weight, specific weight and specific gravity, solubility, color, odor, boiling point, melting point, combustibility, chemical activity, etc.

Specific weight. The weight of one liter of the gas at 0° and 760 mm. pressure. By specific gravity is meant the ratio of the weight of the gas to the weight of an equal volume of air, reduced to 0° and 760 mm. pressure. The weight of one liter of dry air, freed from carbon dioxide, is equal to 1.2928 g. under standard conditions. The specific gravities of different gases are quite varied. A table of specific weights and specific gravities for various gases is given on the following page.

The specific weight of gases is of enormous significance in the geochemical history of the earth. It is believed that hydrogen, being the lightest gas, readily passes out of the earth's atmosphere into interplanetary space. Argon, krypton, xenon, and other gases, being much heavier, were retained by the earth from the moment of their appearance. The exceptional inertness of the rare gases contributed to this.

Coefficient of solubility. This is the volume of gas which can be dissolved in unit volume of liquid when the pressure of the gas over the liquid is 760 mm. Hg. The solubility of a gas at constant temperature and pressure depends on the composition of the gas and the properties of the liquid. Oxygen is more soluble than nitrogen, and carbon dioxide is more soluble

TABLE 11. Specific Weight and Specific Gravity of Various Gases

Gas	Specific weight, g./l.	Specific gravity
Nitrogen	1.2505	0.9674
Oxygen	1.429	1.1053
Carbon dioxide	1.9767	1.529
Methane	0.7168	0.5545
Ethane	1.3562	1.049
Propane	2.02	1.562
Butane	2.673	2.067
Hydrogen	0.08987	0.0695
Carbon monoxide	1.2504	0.968
Nitrous oxide	1.9777	---
Helium	0.1785	0.1381
Argon	1.783	1.378
Krypton	3.708	---
Xenon	5.851	---
Hydrogen sulfide	1.5392	1.1906

than either. The volatile, heavy hydrocarbons are more soluble than methane. Gases are more soluble in distilled water than in salt water.

Color of gases. Most gases are colorless. Nitrogen dioxide is orange, while iodine vapor has a very characteristic color. The gases emitted in volcanic eruptions are often colored.

Odor of gases. The presence of a number of gases is determined by characteristic odor. For example, hydrogen sulfide is detected in air through the sense of smell by its odor of rotten eggs when its concentration is less than 0.00001% (a hydrogen sulfide concentration in the air equal to 0.01 - 0.03% is dangerous to life, while 0.07% is lethal). The presence of ammonia, ozone, ethylene, and various esters is easily determined by odor. Many gases emitted by flowering plants are detected by odor. Nitrogen, oxygen, hydrogen, methane, ethane, and the inert gases (helium, argon, and others) are odorless.

Boiling point. The temperature of transition of the liquefied gas to the gaseous state at a pressure of 760 mm. Hg. is called the boiling point. Methane has a boiling point of -161.13° C; ethane, -89.0° C; propane, -49.11° C; isobutane, -10.2° C; n-butane, +0.6° C, etc. The "heavier" the hydrocarbon, the higher the temperature at which it passes into liquid.

Combustibility of gases. There exist combustible gases, which may be ignited with a match, incombustible gases, and gases which prevent combustion. Among the combustible gases are included all hydrocarbons and hydrogen. Among incombustible gases are included nitrogen and the inert gases, and among those which hinder combustion is included carbon dioxide.

Chemical activity. Oxygen, hydrogen, ammonia, carbon dioxide, and others are chemically active, i.e., they enter easily into chemical combination under ordinary conditions. Helium, neon, argon, krypton, xenon, and in part, nitrogen are inert gases. Hydrocarbon gases are quite stable; however, under certain conditions they enter into various chemical reactions. Depending on the chemical activity of gases, there are chemical and physical methods of gas analysis, as well as combinations of these and other methods, i.e., physicochemical methods. Gases which enter actively into chemical reaction are determined by chemical methods, while those which do not react chemically are determined through their physical properties.

Determination of Gases

Gases may be subjected to general gas analysis, complete gas analysis, and special analysis (3, 4). By general gas analysis is meant determination of the most often encountered gases: oxygen, carbon dioxide, nitrogen (+ inert gases), total combustible gases, carbon monoxide, and hydrogen. The analysis is conducted by a chemical method in an ORS type apparatus (e.g., VTI) with an accuracy not usually exceeding 0.2%.

In complete gas analysis all gaseous components entering into the composition of natural gas, including inert gases and hydrocarbon gas, are determined. For this analysis a great variety of methods is required, including spectral analysis and fractional distillation of gases with the aid of liquid air. Sometimes the elementary composition of the gas is determined.

In special analysis one or several gaseous components that are necessary for a particular purpose are studied. For example, with the aid of special apparatus and methods of investigation, traces of hydrocarbon gas in soil air are determined with an accuracy from 10^{-5} to 10^{-6}%; traces of mercury vapor in the atmosphere, traces of the deadly hydrogen sulfide in the air, etc., are also determined.

TYPES OF GASES

Gases in the Atmosphere

The atmosphere consists of gases and vapors, as well as a certain amount of dust and microorganisms. Water vapor is found only in the lower part of the atmosphere, the troposphere; at higher levels, it is observed very rarely and in negligible amounts and apparently reaches those heights only during powerful volcanic eruptions. Only in the troposphere are encountered microorganisms and surface dust. In the stratosphere, only meteoritic dust and, sometimes, dust of volcanic origin are observed.

As a result of continual agitation, the gaseous composition of the atmosphere is remarkably constant. The atmosphere consists of nitrogen (78.05 vol. %), oxygen (20.90%), carbon dioxide (0.03% on the average), argon (0.932%), helium (0.0005%), neon (0.0018%), krypton (0.0001%), and xenon (0.000008%) (5). In the atmosphere there are traces of hydrogen (apparently less than 0.001%), traces of methane (usually below 0.0001%), traces of ammonia and radon; and near the sea the air contains iodine.

Air always contains ozone in a concentration of 0.02 - 0.03 mg./m.^{3}, and the quantity of ozone always increases sharply after storms. In the stratosphere the quantity of ozone increases and it forms a peculiar "ozone screen". This prevents the passage of a great amount of ultraviolet radiation to the earth's surface and thus protects organisms from destruction (5). The ozone in the stratosphere is formed from oxygen as a result of the action of the ultraviolet radiation of the sun. Nitric oxide and nitrogen dioxide formed during lightning discharges are sometimes observed in the atmosphere.

The amount of carbon dioxide at the earth's surface is subject to fluctuations. Carbon dioxide is released into the atmosphere in the respiration of animals and plants (in the dark), and it is also formed in the course of biochemical processes in the soil. Large amounts of carbon dioxide are expelled into the atmosphere by volcanoes and evolved in metamorphic processes occurring in the depths of the earth. Much hydrocarbon gas accumulates in large cities and near factories. Large amounts of carbon dioxide are absorbed in the photosynthesis of plants and dissolved in the waters of the seas and oceans.

The most characteristic feature of the atmosphere is the presence in it of oxygen and nitrogen. V. I. Vernadskii (6) maintained that the free oxygen of the troposphere and oxygen dissolved in the surface waters make up more than a fifth of the troposphere. Life on earth depends on this oxygen. According to Vernadskii an analogous phenomenon is also observed for the free nitrogen of the troposphere, and in general, the gaseous envelope of the earth, our air, is the basis of life.

However, even though considerable amounts of oxygen and nitrogen are formed by living organisms, this cannot be considered the only method of formation of these gases. The earth's crust contains almost 49% (by weight) oxygen, while the earth as a whole contains about 28%. This indicates that oxygen is produced not only by biochemical means but in other ways as well, and it was already present in the atmosphere, as was nitrogen, before the development of life.

Gases in the Hydrosphere

The waters of the earth's surface, which form the hydrosphere, contain various dissolved gases. The amount of gas dissolved in water depends on the temperature of the water, its salt content, and the composition of the dissolved salts. The solubility decreases with an increase in temperature or an increase in salt content.

Gases dissolved in the water of open reservoirs come to it chiefly from the atmosphere. Dissolved gases also result from biochemical processes of conversion and decomposition of organic matter in the water masses and at the bottom of the reservoir (7). The gaseous composition of the hydrosphere varies depending on the intensity of biochemical processes in water which lead, on the one hand, to the absorption of CO_2 and O_2 and, on the other hand, to the evolution of H_2S, CH_4, O_2, etc. The composition of the gases of the hydrosphere differs from that of the atmosphere in that the water contains relatively more oxygen and carbon dioxide and less nitrogen. This is due in part to the fact that oxygen and carbon dioxide are more soluble in water than is nitrogen. Air extracted from aqueous solution usually contains about 35% oxygen and 65% nitrogen.

At a considerable depth in the seas and oceans, the oxygen decreases in amount and is sometimes completely absent. Then, however, a greater amount of hydrogen sulfide is developed; this is especially characteristic of the Black Sea. In the Black Sea, beginning at a depth near 200 m., a large amount of H_2S, formed by the reduction of sulfates with the aid of microorganisms, appears in the water (8, 9). The presence of a high concentration of hydrogen sulfide limits the zone of life for animals which require free oxygen and are killed by hydrogen sulfide. Only anaerobic microorganisms live in the zone of hydrogen sulfide contamination (10). Sometimes there is observed a sharp diminution of oxygen in lakes even at the very surface. This case, which is due to the absorption of oxygen by organic matter, was observed in Belorussian lakes (11). The waters at the surface contained 0.31 mg./1. of oxygen, while the waters at a depth of 1 m. contained still less.

On the other hand, in some lakes a high concentration of dissolved oxygen in the water is found; this oxygen is evolved by seaweed. So much oxygen is produced that it accumulates in the form of bubbles on the leaves of plants and is dislodged by ripples on the surface of the lake.

Gases in the Lithosphere

The lithosphere is permeated by gases down to depths at which the pressure is so great that gases exist only in the liquid or solid state. V. I. Vernadskii wrote that soil without gases is not soil. The same may be said of rock. Gases in rock exist in the following three types of associations.

1. Free gases occupying all cavities in the rock not occupied by water. Free gases may be present in dispersed form in the pores of the rock, in free fissures, in caverns, or in the form of bubbles in mineral crystals. If a stratum containing free gas is markedly porous, covered at the top by a relatively impermeable cap, and contorted into a fold favorable for the accumulation, the gas may collect in a much greater part of the stratum and form a gaseous accumulation or gas pool. If the gas is trapped in an aquiter, it will be under greater pressure.

2. Gases sorbed by rock are held on the surface of all the particles of the rock (adsorption) and permeate the entire mass of the dense parts of every particle of sand (internal absorption), apparently including even the crystal lattice of minerals. Various rocks differ in their sorption capacity. For example, hydrocarbon gas is best sorbed by coal, then by brown coal, clays, and casting sand, and is least sorbed by limestone and, especially, sorted sand. Different gases are sorbed in different amounts by rock. Of the hydrocarbon gases, methane is the least well sorbed, and the best sorbed are propane, butane, and ethane.

3. Gases dissolved in the waters and oil which permeate the rock. Part of the gases evolved in eruptions is formed in a short interval preceding the ejection of magma and is caused by various processes in the magma chamber which occur as a result of changes in pressure. Specific types of gaseous associations are characteristic of various parts of the lithosphere. Compared with the atmosphere, soil gas (or the soil atmosphere) is characterized by: a reduced content of oxygen, which is consumed in the oxidation of organic remains and by bacteria; an increased content of carbon dioxide (usually 0.1 - 0.5%, often 1 - 2%, rarely 5%); and a relatively high content of nitrogen. Methane is usually found in the form of traces. The presence of volatile organic substances and nitrous oxide is characteristic.

With increase of depth the quantity of oxygen decreases and at a depth of several hundred meters it disappears altogether, being consumed in the oxidative processes that transform organic matter and combined with various minerals. In place of oxygen, methane or purely nitrogenous gas appears with an admixture of inert gases. For example, in the Central region of the Donbas in an interval between the surface and a depth of 500 - 700 m., a zone of carbon dioxide-nitrogen and nitrogen gases is observed (12).

Down from this level to a depth of 1,000 - 1,200 m. lies the so-called transition zone which is characterized by nitrogen-methane gases. At still
greater depths lies the methane zone.

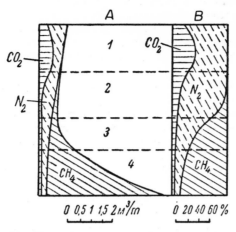

Fig. 10. General variation in the composition of the
gases of coal strata with depth. A — composition of
gases in m.^{3} per ton of coal; B — composition of gases
in volume percent; 1 — zone of nitrogen-carbon dioxide gases; 2 — zone of nitrogen gases; 3 — zone of
nitrogen-methane gases; 4 — zone of methane gases.
(According to G. D. Lidin and I. L. Ettinger.)

In Figure 10 is shown the general variation in the composition of the
gases of coal strata with depth proposed by G. D. Lidin and I. L. Ettinger
(13). Four zones were distinguished by them; carbon dioxide-nitrogen
gases predominate in the upper zone, nitrogen gases in the second zone,
nitrogen-methane gases in the third zone, and methane gases in the deepest
zone. Here the methane is of biogenic and metamorphic origin and has
been formed as a result of processes of metamorphism of coal which lead
to carbonization accompanied by evolution of methane and several other
gases.

In regions of oil formations, the following rule is found to be generally
applicable: the nitrogen-oxygen gases of the soil and subsoil are gradually
replaced first by carbon dioxide-nitrogen gases and then, in turn, by
nitrogen-methane and the hydrocarbon gases associated with gas migrations from oil and gas reservoirs.

ORIGIN OF GASES AND THEIR GENETIC CLASSIFICATION

Gases are formed as a result of a great variety of processes: chemical
reactions, the action of high temperatures on rock, radioactive disintegration, biochemical transformations of substances etc. A particularly great
variety of gases is evolved in biochemical reactions. The first fully complete classification of natural gases belongs Academician V. I. Vernadskii
(1912 - 1914).

V. I. Vernadskii (14, 15) divided all gases into the following three
groups.

1. Gases of the earth's surface, which enter into the composition of the atmosphere.

2. Gases associated with high temperature. To this group belong gases from magma chambers, which are, for the most part, expelled to the surface through volcanoes.

3. Gases which penetrate the earth's crust. To this group belong all gases of the earth's crust which form gaseous accumulations or penetrate all rocks. The third group was divided by V. I. Vernadskii into two sub-groups, namely:

     a. gases of the atmosphere which penetrate into the lithosphere;

     b. gases from "tectonic streams" that are formed within the rock itself and migrate to the surface along tectonic dislocations.

In this classification the natural gases of petroleum formations belong to the subgroup of the gases of tectonic streams. These gases were in turn divided by V. I. Vernadskii into a number of types according to chemical composition: nitrogen, carbon dioxide, methane, hydrogen, hydrogen sulfide, etc.

In 1937 V. V. Belousov suggested a more orderly classification of the natural gases of the lighosphere (16). In this system Belousov proceeded on the basis of the principle of the genesis of gases and not according to their location or formation. All gases are divided by him into the following four types.

1. Gases of biochemical origin that are formed in the decomposition of dying organic matter by microorganisms (hydrocarbon gases, carbon dioxide, hydrogen sulfide, nitrogen, etc.).

2. Gases of atmospheric origin which pass into the lithosphere from the atmosphere.

3. Gases of chemical origin, which in turn are divided into gases:

     a. originating during metamorphic action under the influence of high temperatures and pressures in rocks;

     b. produced in natural reactions occurring at ordinary temperatures.

4. Gases of radioactive origin.

Although it is basically sound, the classification of V. V. Belousov has several shortcomings. This classification does not consider gaseous associations that must be dealt with in any natural situation but only individual gases, i.e., gaseous minerals. For example, nitrogen may be of biochemical, atmospheric, or chemical origin. In regarding nitrogen as a mineral, it is impossible to determine its genesis if all the other gaseous components found with it are discarded.

A. A. Saukov (5) holds that segregation of gases of atmospheric origin into a separate group is unjustified since the gases of the air are, in the main, the basis of life. Another shortcoming of the classification is the absence of subgroups in the group of gases of biochemical origin, which are of enormous practical significance. It might be necessary to distinguish separately gases of oil formations, gases of purely gaseous formations, gases of coal formations, etc. These are considered in the text of the book but were not included in the classification.

In 1950 A. L. Kozlov (17) broadened V. V. Belousov's classification of gases to some extent. However, this did not make the classification any better for practical purposes and it is only of theoretical interest. For example, Kozlov distinguishes specific groups of gases of radioactive origin, radiochemical origin, and nuclear reactions. It is practically impossible to determine to which of the three stated groups a natural gas belongs. From this point of view, the earlier classification of gases proposed by V. V. Belousov, which did not subdivide gases of radioactive origin better answered the needs of practice.

In view of what has been stated, the following classification of natural gaseous associations, based on the classifications of V. V. Belousov (16) and A. L. Kozlov (17), is proposed (Table 12 and Figure 11). In the table, only the most typical gaseous associations are given. Countless varieties of gas mixtures are found in nature because gases are very mobile minerals, and, therefore, all such accumulations consist to a greater or lesser extent of mixtures of gases of various genetic groups. In this suggested classification are given those components that are most important and, in the final analysis, that determine the type of the gas and the properties of the mixture.

TABLE 12. Classification of Natural Gaseous Associations

Gases according to origin	Component composition (most typical)
Type I. Gases of Mainly Biochemical Origin	
Group 1. Gases originating in the depths	
Class 1. Gases from petroleum	Methane-ethane-propane-butane (CH_4 from 40 to 90%, heavy hydrocarbon gases from 0.5 to 50%, traces of N_2, CO_2, He, and sometimes H_2S). Part of hydrocarbons metamorphic in origin. Subclasses of chiefly methane, chiefly ethane, propane, butane, and hydrogen sulfide-containing gases are distinguished
Class 2. Gases from purely gaseous formations	Methane (CH_4 from 80 to 99.9%, admixtures of N_2 and CO_2, sometimes traces or low concentrations (up to 1–3%) of heavy hydrocarbons, H_2S). Part of the methane may be of metamorphic origin. Gases containing hydrogen sulfide and methane are evolved in desulfation processes (H_2S up to 5%)
Class 3. Gases from mud volcanoes (gas-petroleum)	1. Methane (CH_4 90–99%, traces of heavy hydrocarbons, traces of N_2, CO_2, sometimes H_2S) 2. Methane-carbon dioxide (CH_4 from 50 to 60%, CO_2 20–40%, traces of heavy hydrocarbons, N_2, rarely H_2S) 3. Hydrocarbon (CH_4 80–90%, heavy hydrocarbons up to 5%, admixtures of N_2, CO_2) 4. Nitrogen (rare) (N_2 60–80%, CH_4, CO_2). All gases of biochemical or metamorphic origin

(continued)

TABLE 12. Classification of Natural Gaseous Associations (Cont'd)

Gases according to origin	Component composition (most typical)
Type I. Gases of Mainly Biochemical Origin	

Group 1. Gases originating in the depths

Class 4. Gases from coal formations	Methane and methane-nitrogen (CH_4 from 60 to 95%, N_2 up to 15%, traces of H_2; sometimes traces of heavy hydrocarbons in the sorbed state). Part of the CH_4 is of metamorphic origin
Class 5. Gases from salt strata	Nitrogen-methane-carbon dioxide (N_2, CH_4, CO_2; hydrogen and heavy hydrocarbons are encountered). Gases are syngenetic, absorbed, or in pores. Present in small quantities

Group 2. Gases of surface origin (zone of aeration)

Class 1. Gases formed in marshes	Methane-nitrogen, nitrogen-methane, and nitrogen (CH_4 usually 20–65%, N_2 15–90%, CO_2 2–10%, rarely traces of H_2S, N_2O; heavy hydrocarbons always absent). Admixtures of N_2 of atmospheric origin are possible
Class 2. Peat gases	Nitrogen and nitrogen-methane (N_2 up to 99%, CH_4 up to 40%, admixtures of CO_2; heavy hydrocarbons are absent). Part of the N_2 is of atmospheric origin
Class 3. Gases from photosynthesis	Oxygen (O_2 up to 90%). Given off by aqueous plants

Group 3. Gases of the atmosphere and of atmospheric origin

Class 1. Atmospheric air	Nitrogen-oxygen [N_2 78.05%, O_2 20.99%, CO_2 0.03%. Coefficient $(Ar \cdot 100)/N_2 = 1.18$]. O_2, N_2, and CO_2 are to a considerable extent produced biochemically
Class 2. Gases from the upper layers of the atmosphere	The same, with much ozone (O_3) which is not of biochemical origin
Class 3. Soil air	Nitrogen-oxygen-carbon dioxide (N_2 from 76 to 93%, O_2 from 5 to 18%, CO_2 from 0.1 to 5%, sometimes traces of NH_3, N_2S, CH_4,

(continued)

TABLE 12. Classification of Natural Gaseous Associations (Cont'd)

Gases according to origin	Component composition (most typical)
Type I. Gases of Mainly Biochemical Origin	
Group 3. Gases of the atmosphere and of atmospheric origin	
Class 3. Soil air (Cont'd)	N_2O, volatile organic substances, etc.). The oxygen is derived from the atmosphere, the nitrogen comes partly from the atmosphere
Class 4. Gases from the depths, of atmospheric origin	Nitrogen [N_2 from 80 to 100%, admixtures of CH_4, sometimes CO_2, He, Ar. The coefficient $(Ar \cdot 100)/N_2$ is about 1.18]. Sometimes mixed with biochemical methane
Type II. Gases of Metamorphic Origin (Natural Chemical Reactions)	
Class 1. Volcanic gases	Gases and sublimate vapors (H_2O, CO_2, N_2, admixtures of H_2, CO, H_2S, O_2, traces of CH_4, vapors of HCl, Cl_2, HF, $B(OH)_3$, SO_2, NH_3, chlorides, inert gases)
Class 2. Gases from postvolcanic processes	Subclass 1. Gases from thermal springs. Nitrogen (N_2 80–99%, CO_2 up to 10%, inert gases, rarely admiztures of O_2 of surface origin). Often mixed with gases of atmospheric origin Subclass 2. Gases from cold springs. a. Carbon dioxide (CO_2 up to 99.9%, admixtures of CH_4, N_2, inert gases). Often discharged together with mineral water. Sometimes mixed with gases of biochemical origin (methane) b. Carbon dioxide-hydrogen sulfide (CO_2 up to 90%, always much H_2S, admixtures of N_2, CH_4, inert gases). Sometimes mixed with biochemical gases and gases of atmospheric origin. Often discharged together with mineral water
Class 3. Gases held in the cavities of metamorphic and magmatic rocks	Hydrogen-nitrogen (H_2 up to 80%, N_2 up to 60%, admixtures of CH_4 and inert gases)
Class 4. Gases from chemical reactions under normal conditions	CO_2, H_2S, H_2, etc. Always mixed with gases of different origin. Little studied.

(continued)

TABLE 12. Classification of Natural Gaseous Associations (Cont'd)

Gases according to origin	Component composition (most typical)
Type III.[1] Gases of Radioactive Origin	
Class 1. Gases from the spontaneous decomposition of radioactive elements	He, radon (Rn), Ar, Xe. Always mixed with gases of different origin
Class 2. Gases formed under the influence of radioactive radiation	H_2, O_2, CH_4, CO, C_nH_{2n}, CO_2, and others. Always mixed with gases of different origin
Class 3. Gases from nuclear reactions	All elementary gases. Usually, they are merely admixtures in gases of different origin

In view of the fact that the geochemical methods studied here are intended for oil and gas prospecting, detailed consideration is given in this discussion only to the natural gases associated with petroleum (including purely gaseous) formations.

Natural Gases of Purely Gaseous Formations

By purely gaseous formations are meant formations of natural gas consisting chiefly of methane and occurring in a layer without oil. The gas fields of Saratov, Melitopol', Mel'nikov, Dagestan, etc., may serve as examples of purely gaseous formations. The Saratov gas formations (Elshanka, Kurdyum) contain 91.1 - 93.2% methane, from 3.4 to 6% nitrogen, traces of hydrogen sulfide, and sometimes up to 4.2% heavy hydrocarbon gases. Carbon dioxide is practically absent (18). The heavy hydrocarbons were derived from the deeper levels where oil is found.

The purely gaseous formation of Melitopol' contains up to 98% methane, 1.8% nitrogen, and 0.2% CO_2. Heavy hydrocarbon gases are entirely absent. The Mel'nikov formation contains 88.0% methane, about 11.7% nitrogen, 0.1% carbon dioxide, and 0.2% heavy hydrocarbons. In natural gases from the western part of the Mel'nikov formation, heavy hydrocarbons are entirely absent.

The majority of gas formations are more or less associated with oil formations, and this circumstance is clearly reflected in the composition of the gas. The presence of heavy, volatile hydrocarbons indicates in most cases, the close connection between the gas formation and oil pools. Oil may lie either below a gas-bearing stratum or in adjacent areas at the same level. Thus, for example, in the Saratov and Stalingrad gas- and oil-bearing regions, the Devonian contains only oil pools, while the Tournaisian layer and coal-bearing strata contain individual accumulations of both oil

---

[1]In pure form, gases of Type III are encountered only in the cavities of minerals or in the sorbed state.

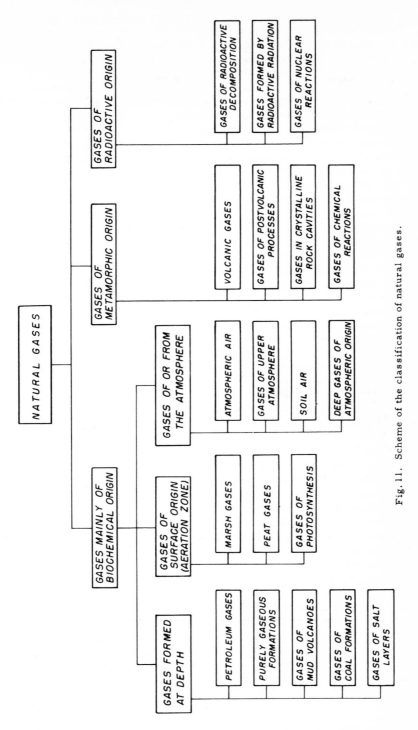

Fig. 11. Scheme of the classification of natural gases.

and gas. At higher levels, only purely gaseous pools are found (17).

V. A. Sokolov (18), in comparing gas formations of the Tertiary era with formations of the Paleozoic era, notes that the Paleozoic formations the CO_2 content is somewhat lower on the average than in Tertiary ones. At the same time the nitrogen content, which is quite insignificant in Tertiary formations, sharply increases upon transition to Paleozoic formations. The amount of hydrogen sulfide, which is negligible in Tertiary formations, sharply increases in Paleozoic ones. V. A. Sokolov (18) holds that the latter is connected with the higher content of sulfur in Paleozoic oils. A. L. Kozlov (17) explains the appearance of hydrogen sulfide by the phenomenon of bacterial desulfation occurring in the presence of hydrocarbons.

Genesis of Purely Gaseous Formations

The natural gases of purely gaseous formations consist mainly of methane, sometimes contain admixtures of heavy hydrocarbon gases, and are often genetically associated with oil formations. From this is may be concluded that the overwhelming majority of methane accumulations are of biochemical origin. However, the time of formation of methane in the pool itself is not clear.

It is known that dead organic matter, forming a sediment in a pond or lake, is immediately decomposed with the aid of bacteria. If the contiguous water layer and the upper ground layer are well aerated, the organic matter is decomposed under oxidizing conditions, whereupon carbon dioxide, nitrogen, and other gaseous substances are formed. If the contiguous layer is poorly aerated and hence constitutes a reducing medium which may often contain hydrogen sulfide, the decomposition of dead organic matter proceeds in an anaerobic or partially anaerobic medium. In this case methane, nitrogen, and some carbon dioxide are formed. The generated gas is evolved from the sediment into the atmosphere or dissolved in the water. There it is partially oxidized by methane-oxidizing bacteria.

The decomposition of dead organic matter (in the form of animal or plant remains or microorganisms) proceeds nonuniformly. At first the decomposition proceeds very intensely and the substances that decompose most easily are primarily changed to gases. V. I. Vernadskii (6) held that nearly all the matter of which organisms are made is composed of gases. These gases: O_2, CO_2, H_2O, NH_3, H_2S, SO_2, SO_3, H_2, CH_4, CO, HCHO, COS, and NO_2 go back into the atmosphere either after the death of the organisms (as they decay) or in the course of their vital processes.

The more difficulty decomposed substances of organisms are buried under new sediments, but their transformation continues. Under anaerobic conditions methane, nitrogen, carbon dioxide, and traces of hydrogen sulfide are mainly formed. The evolved gases accumulate in the sediment in the form of bubbles and upon change of atmospheric pressure or agitation of the sediment they escape to the surface. Besides the free evolution of gas, part of the latter is gradually dissipated by solution in the water and diffusion into the hydrosphere. Only a small part of the gas can remain in the sediment in the form of gas. At the same time oil-type bitumens are formed in the sediment. The formation of large accumulations of gas, as a result of primary decomposition of organic matter at the bottom of the pond, is impossible.

The formation of large gaseous accumulations apparently occurs as a result of the concentration of methane from one or more sources in natural reservoirs. The following processes lead to the formation of methane in the depths:

1. Biochemical transformation of stable organic matter and bitumen in argillaceous rocks covered by relatively impermeable strata. Radioactive elements may play a well-known role in the process of transformation of organic matter.

2. Biochemical transformation of petroleum (see also Chapter 1). E. N. Bokova (19) demonstrated that methane is formed in the decomposition of oil by microorganisms under anaerobic conditions. The experiments were conducted with heavy Sakhalin oil. In the course of the experiment, which lasted two years, 450 cm.^{3} of gas was collected. The composition of the gas proved to be as follows: 20.9% methane, 0.0080% heavy fraction (the composition of the heavy fraction may include nitrous oxide and heavy hydrocarbons), 0.6% hydrogen, 4.6% carbon dioxide and hydrogen sulfide, and 73.9% nitrogen. These investigations show that large quantities of methane may be formed in the decomposition of heavy oil under the conditions which prevail in oil pools.

3. Geochemical transformation of petroleum. A. F. Dobryanskii (20) holds that in this process the accumulation of the simplest paraffinic hydrocarbons occurs, "methane may be the final product of the transformation of petroleum." As a result, the gases of ancient sedimentary rocks are often richer in methane than those of young rocks.

4. Thermal formation of methane. In some cases as a result of tectonic processes, methane may be formed by the action of high temperature on bituminous rocks and coals buried in the depths of the earth.

The formation of the heavy, volatile hydrocarbons (ethane, propane, butane, isobutane), present as admixtures in the gases of many purely gaseous formations, has not been sufficiently studied. Analyses of marsh gases have shown that under these conditions neither ethane, propane, nor butane is formed. Studies of the products of the microbiological decomposition of various organic substances in artificial media has also been unable to solve completely the problem of the origin of heavy hydrocarbons. In these experiments traces of heavy hydrocarbons were observed only in rare cases, and these did not usually comprise more than 0.2% of the composition of the gas. However, it is known that the gases of oil formations contain a large amount of heavy hydrocarbons. Thus, for example, the gases of the Grozny formation contain up to 51.3% heavy hydrocarbons (18), those of Ishimbai contain 47.3%, and those of Tuimazy contain about 29.6% (here the reference is to the gas produced with the crude oil). From what were the heavy, volatile hydrocarbons in the formations derived? Apparently, the heavy, volatile hydrocarbons are the products of the metamorphism of oil and oil bitumens and of changes caused by microorganisms (see also Chapter 1).

Change in the Composition of Natural Gas Within a Formation

The composition of natural gas in a formation changes with time because of geochemical processes in the gas-bearing stratum and also as a result of the migration of gases of different origin into this stratum. Let us consider the process of this change in composition (see also Chapter 1).

Waters within a gas pool contain a large group of varied microorganisms which utilize gaseous and liquid hydrocarbons as a source of carbon. Hydrocarbon microorganisms which oxidize methane, ethane, etc., evolve carbon dioxide. In time a considerable amount of carbon dioxide may accumulate in a gas formation. Denitrifying bacteria observed in the waters of oil formations decompose nitrogen compounds and evolve free nitrogen. Desulfurizing bacteria which utilize methane and decompose sulfates evolve hydrogen sulfide. Desulfurizing bacteria oxidize hydrocarbons not only at the gas-water interface in a gas pool but also along the path of migration of the hydrocarbons to the surface (17).

A certain amount of nitrogen, inert gases, and oxygen may enter from the atmosphere owing to the movement of subterranean waters. The oxygen is thereupon consumed by microorganisms, while the nitrogen and helium may accumulate and become more concentrated. Sometimes helium may enter the gas formation from crystalline rocks as a result of radioactive decomposition.

The gas formation may be enriched by gases from deeper-lying accumulations having a different composition or that have formed in a zone of magmatic activity. Gases may enter as a result of migration along tectonic dislocations and fissures and as a result of diffusion through unbroken rocks.

The migration of gases of atmospheric origin through strata is generally known. Moving ground waters may dissolve part of the gases of a pool and carry them beyond the limits of the formation. This especially applies to easily soluble gases such as carbon dioxide and hydrogen sulfide. The composition of natural gas is also greatly changed during the process of oil field exploitation.

Dissipation of Gas Accumulations

The dissipation of gas accumulations occurs mainly as a result of the creation of ruptures in the earth's crust by tectonic movements. In some cases the process of erosion may promote the destruction of a gas pool lying at shallow depths. Dissipation of gas also occurs as a result of diffusion through continuous rock layers. Since diffusion proceeds very slowly, absolute depletion of a formation in this way is hardly to be expected.

The destruction of methane within a gas formation occurs as a result of the biochemical process of the reduction of sulfates by hydrocarbons. Without doubt, a considerable amount of methane is destroyed in the course of geological time (17).

BIBLIOGRAPHY

1. A.G. Betekhtin. Mineralogy. Gosgeolozdat, 1950.
2. V.I. Vernadskii. On the significance of the soil atmosphere and its biogenic structure. Pochvovedenie, No. 4-5, 1944.
3. V.A. Sokolov. Analysis of gases. Gostoptekhizdat, 1950.
4. A.A. Cherepennikov. Handbook on sampling and analysis of natural gases. Gosgeolizdat, 1951.
5. A.A. Saukov. Geochemistry. Gosgeolizdat, 1950.
6. V.I. Vernadskii. Essays on geochemistry. Gorgeonefteizdat, 1934.

7. V.I. Vernadskii. History of the minerals of the earth's crust: Volume II. History of natural waters. Goskhimtekhizdat, 1933.

8. A.E. Kriss. Microorganisms and the biological productivity of ponds (and lakes). Priroda, No. 5, 1953.

9. L.D. Shturm. First investigations by Russian scientists of hydrogen sulfide fermentation in the Black Sea. Mikrobiologiya, v. XX, No. 5, 1951.

10. A.E. Kriss, E.A. Rukina, and V.I. Biryuzova. Fate of dead organic matter in the Black Sea. Mikrobiologiya, v. XX, No. 2, 1951.

11. G.R. Vinberg. Case of freezing of fish in a lake in summer. Priroda, No. 3, 1951.

12. A.I. Kravtsov. Effect of geological conditions on the gas-bearing character of coal formations. Ugletekhizdat, 1950.

13. G.D. Lidin and I.L. Ettinger. Gases of coal formations. Priroda, No. 4, 1949.

14. V.I. Vernadskii. On the gas exchange of the earth's crust. Izvestiya Akad. Nauk, 1912.

15. V.I. Vernadskii. On the classification of natural gases. Sb. "Prirodnye gazy", No. 2, Geologo-razvedochnoe byuro gazovykh mesto-rozhdneii tresta Stroigaz, 1931.

16. V.V. Belousov. Essays on the geochemistry of natural gases. ONTI, L., 1937.

17. A.L. Kozlov. Problems of the geochemistry of natural gases. Gostoptekhizdat, 1950.

18. V.A. Sokolov. Essays on the genesis of petroleum. Gostoptekhizdat, 1950.

19. E.N. Bokova. Formation of methane in the microbial decomposition of petroleum. Polevaya i promyslovaya geokhimiya, No. 2, 1953, Gostoptekhizdat.

20. A.F. Dobryanskii. Geochemistry of petroleum. Gostoptekhizdat, 1948.

CHAPTER FOUR

Gas Surveys

The gas survey[1] is the most important and widespread geochemical method of prospecting for oil and gas. It is a direct method because it detects migrating hydrocarbon gases that are directly associated with an oil or gas pool.

The basis of the theory of the gas survey is the hypothesis that all gaseous accumulations tend to disperse; hence, over a gas or oil formation and for some distance around it higher concentrations of gas must be present. As the distance from the formation increases, the concentration of gas falls to zero or a negligibly small value. However, it shoud not be thought that dispersion of gases is the only process taking place in the depths of the earth.

The processes of dispersion and concentration occur simultaneously, but in some periods in the geological history of a region, one of these processes predominates, while in other periods the other prevails. The presence of a hydrocarbon accumulation indicates that, in the history of a given area, the process of concentration has predominated over that of dispersion.

In general outline, the method of the gas survey consists in taking a sample of subsoil air, analyzing it in order to detect microconcentrations of hydrocarbons, transferring the results of analysis to a chart, and making a geological interpretation of the data so obtained. The detection of traces of migrating hydrocarbons, i.e., microconcentrations thereof, is possible only with the aid of special, very sensitive apparatus.

BRIEF HISTORY OF GAS SURVEYING

The gas survey was suggested as a method of prospecting for oil and gas by V. A. Sokolov in 1929. He theoretically proved the possibility of diffusion of gas in the entire area over an oil formation and in 1930 showed experimentally that the subsoil air over oil formations contains a greater quantity of hydrocarbon gases than subsoil air located far from any formation (1, 2, 3, 4). For this purpose V. A. Sokolov constructed a special mercury apparatus, with which, microconcentrations of hydrocarbons as low as $10^{-5}\%$ could be determined.

In 1935-1936 gas surveys were conducted for experimental-industrial purposes by a number of organizations concerned with oil prospecting in the Northern Caucasus and in Azerbaijan (5 and 6). During the period from 1935 to 1940 the gas survey was continuously perfected; new, more convenient and productive microanalytical instruments were invented (7), methods of field work were improved (8, 9), and the theory was developed

---

[1] The method may also be used for the detection of coal deposits rich in methane.

(10, 11). In 1940 the specialized office Neftegazos'emka (Oil-gas-survey) was organized for prospecting work; the scientific director was V. A. Sokolov. Every year Neftegazos'emka sent 25-30 production and research parties to various parts of the Soviet Union. The wide industrial use of gas surveying revealed substantial shortcomings in the method and indicated the need for more profound theoretical investigations.

In 1943-1944 V. A. Sokolov, B. M. Nakashidze, and N. M. Turkel'taub developed the circulative mercury apparatus, with which the combustibility could be determined of the heavy fraction (it had already been shown that the heavy fraction consists not only of heavy hydrocarbons, but also of some incombustible gas, presumably nitrous oxide). In 1945 N. M. Turkel'taub constructed the field apparatus TG-1, which determined only combustible gases directly through the products of combustion; in 1946 he constructed the apparatus TG-5, which resolves combustible gases into methane and heavy hydrocarbons with the aid of activated charcoal. In 1945 major efforts to improve the field method of gas surveying were begun. At that time the first experimental work on gas surveying by accumulation of hydrocarbons on silica-gel was done. E. K. Gerling and B. M. Nakashidze then proved conclusively that the incombustible component of the heavy fraction consists of nitrous oxide and often constitutes 80 - 95% of the entire gas. Since nitrous oxide is mainly formed in the uppermost soil layer, it was decided to resort to the gas survey only for combustible gases.

However, it was found that the combustible gases consist not only of oil-type hydrocarbons, but also contain various admixtures of surface origin. In order to avoid the latter and obtain stable indices, independent of the season of the survey, development of a method for conducting gas surveys at greater depth was begun in 1947. The successful conclusion of this investigation made it possible to utilize the deeper survey method completely in one region in 1948.

Further investigations revealed that the main migration paths of hydrocarbons that are detected by the gas survey are zones of tectonic disturbances and areas of increased fracturing. Fissures in the rocks of several formations were studied, and it was found that in zones of increased fracturing, higher concentrations of hydrocarbons were observed. For this reason gaseous anomalies in the region of a platform are diffuse and indistinct. The reliability of detecting anomalies was increased by the use of complex geochemical methods of oil prospecting.

With the aid of the gas survey several oil formations were independently discovered. Several tens of formations were discovered by a combination of prospecting methods, among which the gas survey was not the least important. The great majority of gas anomalies have not yet been tested by drilling.

Gas surveying became firmly established in the general complex of oil prospecting work. However, it is not yet a perfect method; it requires further improvement. The possibilities of improving the gas survey are still far from exhausted (12).

In conclusion it should be stated that gas surveying was first used in Germany and Rumania two years after its introduction in the USSR, but was not further developed (13). In the USA the gas survey has been used for free gases, only since 1938 in the form of the so-called gasodynamic method (14, 15). Advertising articles published in the USA do not give any idea of the actual status of the method.

THEORETICAL BASIS OF THE GAS SURVEY

In this section will be considered the fundamental theory of gas surveying: the path of migration of the gas from the pool to the earth's surface, the physical basis of the phenomenon of gas diffusion, the change of composition of the gas in the process of migration, and the composition of the gas studied in the gas survey.

Migration of a Gas

By migration is understood any movement or displacement of a gas in the earth. Migration is a physical phenomenon, although some forms of migration depend on physicochemical conditions. Migration occurs either in free pores and fissures, zones of tectonic disturbance (free migration, effusion), or through an entire layer, including all crystalline rocks, as a result of the diffusion of molecules within matter (diffusion migration or diffusion). Migration of a gas may occur within a highly permeable rock (i.e., within a reservoir) as well as in other rocks regardless of their porosity or permeability.

In geochemical prospecting, the migration of gas by diffusion is very important, because the presence in depths of a source of hydrocarbons may be inferred from diffusion products. Migration of gas takes place in the following ways.

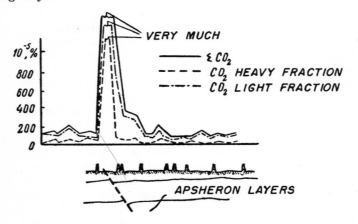

Fig. 12. Microgaseous seep along a fault.

1. Through zones of major tectonic disturbances. This type of migration is well known to all geologists and includes most gas seeps. However, paths through zones of disturbances gradually become filled with mineral deposits and the rate of migration sharply decreases. Gas continues to pass through the zones, but in such small quantity that it can only be detected with instruments—these are the so-called microgas seeps.

Microgas seeps may also originate in some other manner. For example, a certain tectonic disturbance does not reach the surface, but ceases to exist at a given depth. Then the gas migrates freely through the disrupted zone only to this depth, its further upward flow is hindered, and it diffuses into a rather small area and is found in the subsoil atmosphere in the form of a number of microgas seeps. As an example of a microgas seep discovered in a gas survey, a profile through one of the oil formations is shown (Fig. 12, after E. London).

2. Migration of a gas through tectonic fissures. All rocks are cut across by an enormous quantity of fissures of various forms.

All fissures are classified (according to Lazo) as endokinetic or exokinetic. To the first group belong expansion and shrinkage, or contraction, fissures resulting from cooling and drying. To the second group belong fissures caused by: (a) collapse and downfaulting, (b) uplift and overthrust, (c) folding and warping. Endokinetic fissures are usually of small size and are associated with specific rocks. Exokinetic fissures, on the other hand, often cut across whole series of strats. This group includes fissures associated with faulting.

Shrinkage fissures and expansion fissures differ. Shrinkage fissures, as a rule, cannot serve as paths for the migration of gas to the surface. The study of fissures under the microscope carried out by A. G. Mileshina (16) showed that fissures are encountered at all depths in deep wells. Most of the rocks studies were limestones and dolomites from formations located in the southeastern part of the Russian platform.

All fissures are classified as primary or secondary. Primary fissures are very fine (Fig. 13), highly branched and interconnected, and their origin is at the time of formation of the deposit. In recrystallized rocks there are no primary fissures. Secondary fissures are subdivided into fissures of tectonic origin and those of recrystallization. The breadth of tectonic fissures is usually 0.2 - 0.5 mm., rarely as much as 1 cm. In most cases they are filled with crystalline calcite, secondary deposits of silica, and more rarely, quartz. Open (empty) fissures are rarely encountered.

Recrystallization fissures are very widespread and are always filled with crystalline calcite. The coefficient of fissuring of rocks located in different parts of a structure was calculated. The "coefficient of fissuring" is the ratio of the total area of all fissures to the unit surface area of rock (16). The greatest degree of fissuring was found in rocks located in places where the folding of strata was greatest. A high degree of fracturing is also observed in the crests and troughs of structures. There are fewer fissures on the limbs of folds. The most pronounced gas anomalies are usually found in areas of maximum fracturing and fissuring of rocks (17).

Investigations of rock fissuring showed that the great majority of fissures are closed by secondary mineral deposits, so that they cannot serve as paths for the easy migration of gas. At the same time the facts also show that gas anomalies correspond to zones of fissuring. Here, evidently, the entire geological history of the region is of enormous and decisive significance. The fissures were not always closed by mineral deposits, and in such periods gas could easily migrate into and saturate the rocks with hydrocarbons that happen to be located in the path of the migrating gas. The fissures were gradually closed, but traces of gas remained in the entire section, and that gas continues to move slowly to the surface. At certain times oscillatory tectonic movements in the platform cause the formation of new fissures through which gas again flows more easily.

Thus, the process of gas migration is not absolutely stable with time; it is sometimes faster and sometimes slower, but it never ceases. The rate of movement of the gas varies depending on the nature of the tectonic movements. In folded regions where tens of seismic impulses are recorded daily, fissures arise more often, and this facilitates gas migration. A known example is the formation of gigantic fissures in the earth's crust at the time of the Ashkhabad earthquake of 1948, followed by the ejection of gas, water, and granular, clayey matter from the deeper fissures (18).

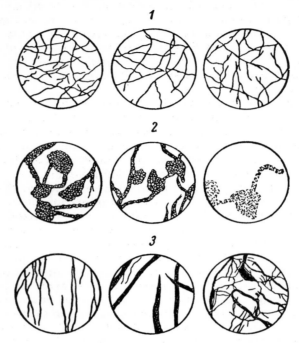

Fig. 13. Types of fissures in limestones and dolomites under the microscope. 1—primary fissures; 2—recrystallization fissures; 3—tectonic fissures.

This is the reason for the greater effectiveness of the gas survey in folded regions.

3. Migration of a hydrocarbon gas may occur as a result of solution of the gas in water during the movement of the latter in a rock stratum (19). The movement of the hydrocarbons coincides in direction with that of the water. Solution of gases in water and their joint migration are of great significance.

4. Penetration of gases through an unbroken rock layer. This variety of gas migration can theoretically occur anywhere in permeable, as well as relatively impermeable rocks. The latter are of the greatest significance since oil and gas pools are always covered by them.

Physical Forms of Gas Movement Through Rocks[2]

The geological aspect of the question of gas migration was considered above. However, this question also has a physical aspect closely associated

---

[2]Written by A. A. Kartsev.

with the geological and of great importance to the gas survey. The theory of the mass movement of a gas through the earth's crust was worked out in detail by V. A. Sokolov and P. L. Antonov (20). However, several of the conclusions of these authors are debatable in character. Here is given only the briefest, most elementary account of the physical nature of the migration of a gas in rock.

The mass transfer of a gas through the earth's crust can occur in various physical forms. The latter depend on geological conditions, as well as on the character of the paths of migration. The most important form is diffusion of the gas. Diffusion occurs when individual molecules of a specific gas move through a liquid or solid medium (or another gas) under the influence of a concentration gradient of the particular gas. Diffusion, consequently, leads to equalization of concentrations.

Diffusion obeys Fick's first law, which is expressed in the following equation:

$$dQ = -DdS\frac{dC}{dh}dt$$

where dQ is the mass of gas diffusing during time dt through cross-section dS; D is the coefficient of diffusion, measured by the amount of gas diffusing in unit time through unit area when the concentration gradient $dC/dh = 1$. The dimensions of the coefficient of diffusion in the absolute system of units are cm.^{2}/sec. The (-) sign in the Fick equation signifies that the gas molecules move in the direction of diminishing concentration.

The coefficient of diffusion D is a quantity which in the general case depends on the properties of the diffusing gas, the properties of the medium through which the diffusion takes place, and thermodynamic conditions. From the data given in Table 13, it may be seen that the coefficients of various gases in water are dependent on the molecular weights of the gases.

TABLE 13. Coefficients of Diffusion for Gases in Water

Gas	Molecular weight	D x 10^5, cm.^{2}/sec.
Methane	16	2.2
Ethane	30	1.6
Propane	44	1.3
Nitrogen	28	1.8
Oxygen	32	1.9
Carbon dioxide . . .	44	1.6
Nitrous oxide	44	1.5

Table 13 shows that the diffusion coefficients of gases in water decrease with increase of molecular weight. This dependence is most apparent for hydrocarbons and nitrogen since they are chemically inert;[3] it ceases to be applicable for oxygen-containing gases.

Several types of diffusion should be distinguished. The most important of these types are: (a) diffusion of gases through liquids; (b) diffusion of

---

[3]According to the latest data of P. L. Antonov, the diffusion coefficients of hydrocarbon gases are inversely proportional to the square roots of their molecular weights.

gases through continuous, solid bodies; (c) diffusion of gases along the interfaces of liquids and solid bodies. Within the earth's crust all these types of diffusion may occur.

As is well known, all pores and cavities in rocks below the ground water table, with the exception of the relatively insignificant volume occupied by oil and gas pools, are filled with water. Therefore, gas diffusion in the earth's crust proceeds, as a rule, through rocks saturated with water. However, the conditions of diffusion may be different. The presence of fissures (see above) is of the greatest importance. If openings of the fissures are large enough and extensive enough, diffusion of a gas through fissured rock saturated with water may proceed in practically the same way as through water; i.e., with the same coefficients of diffusion. This is an extreme case.

Another extreme case is that of an unbroken layer of halogen-containing rocks, for example, gypsum or salt. There a gas diffuses only through continuous solid matter, through a crystal lattice. The diffusion coefficients and diffusion rates depending on them will be much lower in this case. However, diffusion through a continuous, crystalline medium is a relatively rare case for a sedimentary stratum. It occurs less often than diffusion through water-filled fissures.

The intermediate cases are more important: diffusion of a gas through unbroken layers of water-saturated sedimentary rocks of the usual kinds — sandstone, clay, carbonate. Such diffusion is a more complex process. In this case gas molecules move: (1) through water-filled pores (molecules dissolved in water); (2) along the surfaces of mineral particles (adsorbed molecules); (3) finally, in part, through the crystal lattices of minerals. There are transitions among these three types of diffusion. Sorption processes play an enormous role in this process.

The average diffusion coefficients and, consequently, diffusion rates of gases through water-saturated rocks are considerably lower than in fissured rocks or in water. This is also shown by experimental determinations of the diffusion coefficients in rocks, conducted by V. A. Sokolov (21) and P. L. Antonov (22). Some of the results of Antonov's measurements are given in Table 14.

TABLE 14. Coefficients of Diffusion for Hexane Vapor in Rocks and Other Media

Medium	D, cm.^{2}/sec.
Distilled water	2.1×10^{-5}
Kudinov clay with moisture content $26-28\%$	1.55×10^{-6}
Mixture of clay with 15% quartz sand	2.5×10^{-6}
Mixture of clay with 50% quartz sand	1.2×10^{-6}
Mixture of clay with 70% quartz sand	1.7×10^{-7}
Quartz sand, completely saturated with water	6.1×10^{-7}

The data given in Table 14 show that diffusion coefficients in unfissured clays and sands are lower than in water by a factor of 8 - 100 or more. In the light of these facts, such a decrease of diffusion coefficients is quite understandable: firstly, the path of the gas molecules moving through the pores is not a straight line (owing to the tortuous nature of the pores);

secondly, part of the gas molecules are sorbed by mineral particles and only diffuse along their surfaces and through their crystal lattices; thirdly, there is the effect of non-interconnected pores, etc.

The diversity of diffusion coefficients in different rocks must be the result of such factors as breadth, form, and extent of rock channels, orientation of mineral grains, crystal structure, and the like. It should be noted that existing data on such diffusion coefficients are completely inadequate. Extensive investigations must be conducted in this field.

Thus, in a sedimentary layer there are observed two very important, fundamentally different cases of gas diffusion (not counting the relatively rare case of diffusion through a continuous crystalline medium): diffusion through fissured rocks and diffusion through continuous rocks. The rates of diffusion for the first case can evidently be tens of times greater than for the second. This difference is very important. Obviously, there are also intermediate cases corresponding to lesser degrees of fissuring.

Besides diffusion of gases, the bulk flow (effusion) of gases through rocks is also observed. Bulk flow of a gas is the movement of a continuous mass of gas along a pressure gradient in conformity with Darcy's Law. Such mass transfer may occur in gas pools (20). Another instance of this type of flow in sedimentary rocks may occur in water-filled fissures in the uppermost parts of the earth's crust, where, as a result of the decrease of hydrostatic pressure, gas which has risen from the depths in the dissolved state is evolved in the form of bubbles, thus existing as a separate free phase. It must be emphasized that Darcy-type movement of gases in rock layers is a relatively rare case and plays a subordinate role in comparison with movement by diffusion.

Questions concerning the physical forms of the movement of gases through rock layers require further treatment.

Alteration of a Gas During the Process of Migration

In the course of migration, a hydrocarbon gas undergoes various transformations. During migration through fissures, its composition is only slightly changed since its passage from the pool to the surface requires relatively little time.

In gas surveying practice there are many cases in which the composition of a hydrocarbon gas, determined in the subsoil atmosphere in a region of microgas outcrops, is very similar to that of the gas from the underlying pool. When there is a large amount of heavy hydrocarbons in the pool, these also predominate in the subsoil atmosphere; when the natural gas consists only of methane, heavy hydrocarbons are absent from the subsoil atmosphere.

As already indicated, the migragion of a gas through rocks that are low in porosity and dense (or impermeable) proceeds very slowly. The gas is situated in the path from the pool to the surface for hundreds of thousands and millions of years. It must pass through a great variety of rocks. It is perfectly natural that the composition of the gas cannot remain constant, because the rate of flow cannot remain unchanged. Let us consider this question in more detail.

In the process of migration, part of the gas is absorbed (sorbed) by rocks; the heavy hydrocarbons are sorbed more completely than methane. When the flow of migrating gas is not constant, the gas will gradually be enriched in methane owing to the loss of heavy hydrocarbons. However, as soon as equilibrium is reached, the sorption factor will no longer be able to regulate the flow of heavy hydrocarbons to the surface.

In passing through aquifers, the hydrocarbon gas dissolves in the water; the heavy hydrocarbons are dissolved more completely than methane. Since the waters at various levels above an oil formation are in continuous motion, any gas dissolved in these waters will be carried out of the sphere of influence of the gas field.

Migrating gas after passing through an aquifer is enriched in methane and will contain less of the heavy hydrocarbons than it did at first. Part of the hydrocarbon gas is consumed in reactions with mineral substances in the rocks and waters, leading to formation of a peculiar reducing zone over the oil formation (see Chapters I and III). For example, in some areas of the Kuibyshev Transvolga region, gray rocks predominate in the anticlines of the structures and dark-colored (brown) ones predominate in their peripheries. In this case the gray color of the rocks is not associated with any one horizon but cuts across all levels within the zone of uplift. This change in color of the rocks covering oil or gas pools confirms the theory of diffusion of hydrocarbons from their point of accumulation into the surrounding sedimentary layer and may in turn serve as an indicator of petroleum.

Various bacteria cause a substantial decrease in the amount of migrating hydrocarbon gases. As a result of the bacterial oxidation of methane, CO_2 and H_2O are formed, while the utilization of hydrocarbons in the process of reduction of sulfates leads to the generation of H_2S.

Exchange of gases between the subsoil atmosphere and the air above the earth's surface has an enormous effect on the concentration of hydrocarbons in the subsoil atmosphere. Gas-exchange consists essentially in the replacement of the soil air, which contains considerable amounts of CO_2 and other emanations and is poor in oxygen, by atmospheric air, which is rich in oxygen. Gas-exchange contributes to the diurnal variation of temperature and the change of atmospheric pressure (the so-called ''breathing of the soil'').

During the day, while the soil is being heated by the sun's rays, the soil air expands and part of it leaves the soil. At night, on the contrary, when the temperature falls, the soil air contracts and draws fresh, oxygen-rich air into the soil from the atmosphere. A decrease of atmospheric pressure promotes the efflux of soil air, while an increase leads to the influx of atmospheric air. Rains cause air to be squeezed out of the pores, hindering aeration, and this leads to the formation of anaerobic centers in the soil (especially in long periods of rainfall). Long-continued drying of the soil leads to cracks (often penetrating to a depth of 1 m. and even more), the freeing of the pores from moisture, and the rapid efflux of soil air to the atmosphere. Gas-exchange also occurs as a result of the alternate diffusion of gases and the expulsion of soil air.

The rate of gas-exchange is affected by the degree of heating of the soil surface, which depends on the time of day and year, plant cover, color of the soil, heat conductivity of the soil, etc. Gas-exchange proceeds most intensely in the top layers of the soil but persists even at a depth of 1 - 1.5 m. or more. Deeper-lying layers also experience the effect of gas-exchange but to a lesser degree.

Gas-exchange leads to the loss by the soil and subsoil of their characteristic gases, as well as the hydrocarbons migrating from the depths. The losses may be so great that in the case of a small quantity of migrating hydrocarbons it is difficult to detect a gas anomaly.

The sensitivity of the analytical apparatus TG-5A is rated at $10^{-5}\%$, however, the accuracy of determinations does not exceed $\pm\ 20 \times 10^{-5}\%$. The deviation of repeated analyses is assumed to be $\pm 40\%$ of the first analysis. The most typical concentrations of hydrocarbon gases in the sub-soil for regions which are not oil-bearing lie between 0.00020% and 0.00040%. Anomalous areas in oil-bearing regions are characterized by concentrations of 0.00070 - 0.00300%, or rarely 0.10000%. If the concentration of hydrocarbons in the subsoil is less than this, the gas survey should be applied very cautiously.

Gas anomalies may be detected by means of gas and bacterial surveys conducted by present-day methods, even when the main mas of hydrocarbons is intercepted by bacteria near the surface.

Composition of the Gas Detected in the Gas Survey

The problem of the composition of the gas detected in a gas survey is a fundamental one, being of great importance not only from the theoretical standpoint but also in field practice. It must be stated that this problem has not been completely solved at the present time.

When the gas survey was first developed, analysis was done by means of the mercury apparatus of Sokolov, which separated the gases by condensation at the temperature of liquid nitrogen into methane and heavy hydrocarbons. It was suggested that the gas condensed out by liquid nitrogen was composed solely of heavy hydrocarbons. It was explained later that among the heavy hydrocarbons there were certain other gases which did not ignite at the usual temperature of incandescence of platinum (900° C). Nitrous oxide proved to be such an incombustible gas. Nitrous oxide forms directly within the soil layer and does not migrate from a pool. A specially developed new mercury apparatus (circulating-type) divided the heavy fraction into incombustible and combustible components. But since there was a large amount of the incombustible gases (about 0.10000%) and very little of the heavy hydrocarbons (usually about 0.00100%), the separation of gases in the apparatus was not sufficiently sharp.

Stationary mercury devices were replaced by field apparatus. The most widely used apparatus was type TG-3, which determined total combustible gases with an accuracy of $10^{-5}\%$. Methane and heavy hydrocarbons were assumed to be included in the total combustible gases taken from a depth of 3 m. Nitrous oxide was successfully eliminated. The first broad investigations with the TG-3 apparatus proved that the combustible matter contains not only hydrocarbon gases, but other gases, also. Moreover, methane may originate in the depths as well as at the surface.

It was necessary to develop apparatus for the separate determination of heavy hydrocarbons and methane. The new apparatus TG-4 divided combustible gases into methane and heavier volatile hydrocarbons. It was improved (TG-5A) and in 1947 was in widespread use.

Investigations with the TG-5A apparatus showed that the methane fraction contains, besides methane, carbon monoxide and volatile organic substances of complex composition. This was proved by showing that methane-oxidizing bacteria, which are very sensitive indicator, did not develop in gases taken from soil near Moscow (non-oil-bearing territory). Soil gases gradually vanished with increase in depth below the surface. They were formed directly in the soil. The heavy hydrocarbon fraction also consists of certain complex volatile organic substances which are absorbed by activated charcoal. Volatile organic compounds contained in the soil may be evolved by plants and in the bacterial decomposition of the remains of organic matter.

N. G. Kholodnyi (23) ascertained that various organs of plants liberate complex volatile organic compounds into the atmosphere and that these (phytogenic) substances are a constant component of the atmosphere at the earth's surface wherever there is plant cover; the odors of flowers, barks, and leaves are due to phytogenic substances in the atmosphere. Further investigations by N. G. Kholodnyi led to the conclusion that gaseous organic substances contained in the soil air are formed in part under the influence of microorganisms in dead organic remains and in part in the tissues of living plants and animals for which the soil is the natural habitat. The author considers that the gaseous organic substances may consist of methane and volatile esters, alcohols, and acids (24).

According to the data of Professor G. F. Gauze (25) and Professor V. P. Tokin (26), onion and garlic liberate into the atmosphere volatile substances similar to volatile oils. The volatile organic substances consist partially of terpenes. Terpenes are hydrocarbons having the general formula C_nH_{2n-4} and are found in the sap and resin of coniferous plants and in many volatile oils. With the terpenes are found similar compounds containing oxygen. Therefore, the group of terpenes and their derivatives includes compounds belonging to various classes.

N. G. Kholodnyi (27) believes that, in the soil, volatile organic compounds of unknown composition are formed which may arbitrarily be expressed by the formula CH_xO_y. The above-ground organs of plants (flowers, leaves) liberate organic substances into the air including a significant amount of volatile oils. These substances may be represented by the formula $C_xH_mO_n$.

Special investigations conducted in 1946 - 1948 by M. I. Subbota showed that volatile organic substances are liberated not only by the soil, but also by plant roots. It is of interest to note that the liberation of volatile organic substances proceeds at different intensities in different seasons. The maximum quantity of emanation is observed during the period of vigorous growth of the plants and, after that, during the time of their flowering. The unique seasonal character of the liberation of organic substances is well known to specialists who study ester-bearing plants.

The number of plants which produce esters in large quantities exceeds 2,000 types (28). Of these, 200 types are used in industry. The amount of volatile oils in plants is usually 0.07 - 0.3%. These oils are released immediately after they are produced. Observations showed that one thousand mature specimens of juniper release into the air almost 30 kg. of volatile oil per day. It has been noted that young leaves produce more esters than old ones. It may be suggested on the one hand that the liberation by plants of volatile organic substances is a defensive reaction against several injurious bacteria. On the other hand, these emanations are required by other bacteria which do not injure the plant.

Volatile organic substances are registered by the TG-5A apparatus. They pass freely through bubblers containing caustic alkali, are burned with formation of CO_2, and are recorded as hydrocarbons, irrespective of their composition. In this case part of the volatile organic substances is absorbed in the apparatus by activated charcoal together with heavy hydrocarbons, while the remainder passes freely through the charcoal together with methane.

Experiments have shown that, if roses are covered with a funnel and air is drawn through the latter, the TG-5A apparatus registers concentrations over 0.00100%, consisting of methane and heavy hydrocarbons. Up to 0.1% of combustible gases may be evolved in vacuo.

It is evident from this that soil gas contains a great variety of combustible gases formed within the soil layer itself: methane, volatile organic substances, carbon monoxide, and others. In order to avoid these soil gases, it is necessary to go to greater depths below the soil or to construct apparatus that will determine hydrocarbon gases not by the products of combustion, but directly. For correct interpretation of the results of gas surveying, it is necessary to employ heavy hydrocarbons and methane for the most part.

VARIOUS TYPES OF GAS SURVEYS

The various forms of the gas survey differ chiefly in the method of taking samples and in the manner in which soil gases of contemporary origin affect the results.

In the ordinary gas survey, samples of gas are taken from shallow bore holes 1.5 - 3 m. in depth with the aid of a special capping device. This form of the gas survey is most commonly used and was originally developed by V. A. Sokolov. For the purpose of obtaining stable gas-survey indices at a point, G. A. Mogilevskii employed the delayed gas survey in 1935. This differed from the ordinary gas survey in that samples were taken not directly after drilling the bore hole but after a period estimated to be 12 to 24 hours (the hole was hermetically sealed directly after drilling).

Somewhat later V. A. Sokolov (29) suggested the gas-flow survey. In this variation of the method experiments were conducted to determine the rate of gas diffusion. In 1943 an attempt was made to conduct a survey by taking samples from the soil layer without drilling holes (gas-soil survey). In a number of cases good results were obtained by using a mercury apparatus to analyze for nitrous oxide since the latter originates in the soil; but the gas-soil survey was not successful in looking for hydrocarbon gases.

In 1945, according to the suggestion of Academician P. A. Rebinder and V. A. Sokolov, a gas-survey was conducted with sorbents for the purpose of increasing the concentrations of hydrocarbon gas and obtaining more stable results. The first experiments were entirely satisfactory; however, further development has been delayed.

In 1947 the method of the deep gas survey was developed, which consists in taking several samples along the section of the bore hole at depths from 6 to 20 m. The interpretation of data takes into consideration not only the absolute concentrations but also their variation with depth. The soil layer and its gases of contemporary origin may be avoided with this method.

METHODS OF FIELD WORK

Arrangement of Sampling Points

The success of the gas survey depends to a considerable extent on a properly chosen sampling density. In prospecting for petroleum, samples of gas are taken from shallow wells, which are arranged along profiles transverse to the supposed trend of the structure.

Profiles are located 0.5 - 2 km. apart, while sampling points are separated by 100 - 300 m. In planning the work only the approximate positions of profiles and points are given; these are fixed more precisely in the course of field work. This is done because the conditions of the region cannot be foreseen beforehand, and the geologist must be given the opportunity for creative direction of the prospecting work. The distance between profiles and points is chosen depending on the geological structure of the region. If the structures in the region are large and flat, the distance chosen may be greater. If the gas survey is conducted in regions of salt domes or lithological deposits, the distance between points is decreased.

The uniform system of profiles, in which the profiles extend parallel to each other and are equal in length, is the one most commonly used. In the non-uniform or staggered system, short profiles alternate with long ones. The staggered system of profiles is used in cases where the approximate limits of the structure are known, and fewer wells can be drilled beyond the boundaries of the structure than over it. The differentiated system differs from the staggered in that the distance between profiles over an anticlinal structure is made greater than that over a syncline.

In surveying sections characterized by an oil field of small areal extent (reef massifa, some salt domes, etc.), a uniform triangular grid is used in which the distance between profiles and points is maintained constant and does not exceed 200 - 250 m.

Sometimes, in evaluating the relative promise of a number of well-studied areas, the so-called "group" method of arrangement of sample points is used. In this method several groups of bore holes are drilled within the limits of the areas in order to determine the average concentrations of hydrocarbons in any given area, while other groups of holes are drilled within the bounds of the supposed background sections. The coefficient of contrast (see below), calculated for each area, makes it possible to determine the most likely area for deep drilling.

In the process of surveying, all sections with higher microconcentrations of hydrocarbon gas are immediately verified by drilling control wells. If the high concentrations of gas are confirmed, the dimensions and form of the anomaly are redetermined with greater precision. For this purpose additional short profiles are made up, and sampling points are concentrated within the supposed field of the anomaly. These investigations are conducted until the authenticity of the gas anomaly is proved, its dimensions accurately known, its origin is established, and its relation to the geological structure is established.

Drilling Bore Holes

The bore holes are usually drilled with a manually-operated assembly consisting of light tubes 33 mm. in diameter and a seismic or worm drill 50 -

104 mm. in diameter. In order to protect the hole from soil which might fall into it, a shallow pit 0.4 - 0.5 m. deep is dug beforehand.

In 1952 G. G. Grigor'ev constructed and used a vibro-drill for drilling shallow wells. Use of the vibro-drill sharply increased productivity and replaced the arduous manual labor by mechanized work. It must be noted, however, that the mechanization of drilling work has so far been carried out very feebly.

Taking Gas Samples

In all of the gas survey variations the sample of subsoil air is taken in such a manner that it cannot be diluted by atmospheric air. For this purpose there are several sampling systems and special water pumps.

We shall consider the method of gas sampling used in each variety of the gas survey separately.

1. In the ordinary gas survey, samples of subsoil air are taken from shallow bore holes 3 - 4 m. in depth with the aid of the tube sampler constructed by V. A. Sokolov or the pneumatic gas sampler constructed by S. P. Boravskii. The tube sampler is a brass tube 10 - 12 mm. in diameter and 3 - 4 m. in length (depending on the depth of the hole), to the lower part of which is attached, at a distance of 20 cm. from the end, a rubber disc corresponding to the diameter of the bore hole. The rubber disc is fastened to the tube with the aid of metal discs and a bolt of smaller diameter. In the brass tube there are not less than 10 perforations below the disc for the withdrawal of gas (Fig. 14).

Before the work is begun, the tube sampler is cleaned to remove all traces of hydrocarbons. For withdrawal of gas, the sampler is lowered to the bottom of the well, a small amount of the rock from the drilled hole is poured over the rubber disc, and the bore hole is filled with a thick clay suspension to a height not less than 50 cm. from the disc of the sampler.

The clay suspension, as a rule, is made from clay drilled out of the bore hole. If there is no clay near at hand, material that has been previously certified to be free of absorbed hydrocarbon gas is brought from another place. Water for the preparation of the clay suspension must not contain any trace of dissolved hydrocarbon gases.

The pneumatic sampler (Fig. 14) consists of an exhaust tube, a pneumatic seal, a delivery tube, and a Schinz pump with manometer. The sampler is lowered into the drilled hole, after which air is delivered by means of the Schinz pump to the rubber sealing chamber; the latter, when inflated, is pressed tightly against the walls of the well. The chamber is checked for leaks by means of the manometer. A pressure drop indicates a leak in the chamber or delivery tubes that must be eliminated.

This is followed by the taking of samples through the second (exhaust) tube, which reaches to the bottom. In contrast to the tube sampler, the pneumatic sampler obviates the need of a clay suspension to seal the well and greatly eases the work. The pneumatic sampler provides better security of the sealed-off part of the well against the penetration of atmospheric air.

The water pump of S. P. Boravskii, used since 1945, serves for the withdrawal of gas samples. It consists of the following main components (Fig. 15): a glass gas-collecting tube, a metal leveling bottle, a three-way stopcock, and a Boravskii vessel for stoppering filled sample bottles under

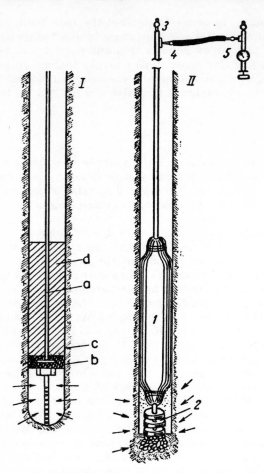

Fig. 14. Sampler for shallow bore holes.
I—tube sampler: a—brass tube, perforated
at the lower end; b—rubber disc; c—rock
face; d—clay suspension. II—pneumatic
sampler: 1—carcass of rubber balloon;
2—aperture for withdrawal of gas; 3—tube
for removal of gas from bore hole; 4—tube
for delivery of air into rubber chamber;
5—Schinz pump with manometer.

water. The gas-collecting tube and the metal leveling bottle are connected
by a rubber tube.

In order to take a sample, a bottle containing boiled water is placed
neck downwards on the outlet pipe of the Boravskii vessel, which is filled
with water. After the sample has flowed from the bore hole into the inner
gas-collecting tube of the pump, it is transferred to the bottle. For this
purpose the leveling bottle is raised, and the inner gas-collecting tube is
connected through the three-way stopcock to the Boravskii vessel. As a
result of this operation, gas from the collecting tube is driven into the
bottle by the water. The gas-collecting tube of the pump is filled with
boiled water. To minimize solution of gas, the use of salt water is

recommended. The stopcocks of the water pump are lubricated with vacuum grease or pure glycerine. The apparatus must be airtight.

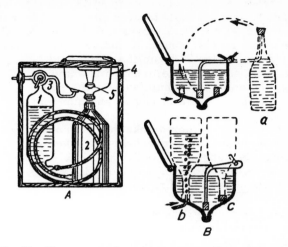

Fig. 15. Water pump for taking gas samples. A—water pump: 1—gas-collecting tube; 2—leveling bottle; 3— three-way stopcock; 4—arrangement for corking gas samples under water; 5—tap for discharge of water flowing out of the bottle. B—scheme of filling and cork- ing gas samples under water: a, b, c—successive posi- tions of the bottle.

Subsoil air is withdrawn in the following manner. The water pump is connected by means of a rubber tube to the sampler. The air is displaced from the inner gas-collecting tube by water and the stopcock is opened for withdrawal of gas from the well. In order to accelerate the withdrawal of gas, a slight partial vacuum is produced by lowering the leveling bottle to the bottom of the shallow pit in which the well was drilled.

At first, when a sample is being drawn into the gas-collecting tube, the air contained in the rubber hose and sampler tube is also drawn in, so that a mixture of atmospheric air and subsoil air is trapped in the sealed-off space at the bottom of the well. This volume is arbitrarily called the volume of "dead" space.

It has been shown, by way of special studies conducted by Z. M. Tabasaranskii and a number of other geologists, that for qualitative sam- pling it is sufficient to discard beforehand a volume of the air-sample mix- ture equal to the volume of the so-called "dead" space. The volume of this preliminary discard must be determined accurately and depends on the diameter and depth of the well bore, and the type and peculiarities of the sampler.

Sampling work in areas characterized by the prevalence of dense and viscous clays or any rocks with high moisture content presents considerable difficulty. In order to withdraw the gas sample, it is necessary to establish a considerable degree of vacuum. This is done with the aid of a Schinz pump connected to the leveling bottle. Use of the Schinz pump is, in gen- eral, undesirable, because the standard conditions of sampling are altered. Use of the Schinz pump leads to withdrawal of gases sorbed by the rock and dissolved in the water, which results in an increase in the concentration of hydrocarbons.

Samples of subsoil gas are taken in specially treated bottles of 0.5 1. capacity which are filled with boiled water and closed by rubber stoppers. In the bottle a water seal 5 - 6 cm. above the stopper remains. To each bottle are attached two labels: primary and secondary. On the secondary label are indicated the region of sampling, name and number of party, number of profile, point, and sample, date of sampling, and name of technician. On the primary label are written the name of region and number of profile, point, and sample.

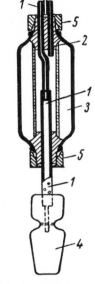

In field investigations, hitherto unknown outcrops of natural gas are often found. It is necessary to take samples of all such discharges of gas for analysis. The method of sampling is described in the Geologist's Handbook under natural gas and therefore will not be given here.

2. In the deep gas survey, the same Boravskii water pump and a special depth sampler are used. The depth sampler (Figure 16) consists of a gas-collecting section and a sealing section. The gas-collecting part is made massive in order to decrease the volume of air remaining in the sealed-off part of the well and to insure vertical descent of the sampler in a "deep" hole.

The pneumatic seal is constructed according to the principles used in the Boravskii sampler; however, the rubber is connected to the body of the seal by another, more convenient method which makes possible the quick replacement of a worn-out chamber by a new one. The depth sampler is lowered into the well on a thin steel cable to which the gas-withdrawal and pressure tubes are attached by means of a special clamp. This arrangement makes it possible to draw gas samples from wells at any depth up to 20 - 25 m.

Fig. 16. Diagram of depth sampler. 1—gas-withdrawal tube; 2—pressure tube; 3—rubber sealing chamber; 4—guide weight; 5—ring for securing rubber chamber.

The deep gas survey is used for detailed investigations and is usually conducted in the following manner. Wells are drilled according to the differentiated system with concentration in the central part of the structure. In comparison with the ordinary survey, the distance between wells in some cases may be greater, because the data for each well are more reliable than the data of the ordinary gas survey.

A deep bore hole is drilled initially to a depth of 3 - 4 m. and the first sample is taken. After this, the well is deepened to 5 - 6 m. and the second sample is taken. The third sample is taken from a depth of 6 - 8 m. In a 10-m. well, four samples are taken; in a 20-m. well, up to six samples are taken, in both cases from specific depths. Gas survey charts are compiled for each depth separately, as is the average for all depths. The boundaries of the various accumulations discovered by such testing are recorded separately.

3. The gas-soil survey is not carried out at the present time. However, in the period from 1944 to 1947, several areas were investigated with positive results (with gas analysis by means of the mercury apparatus).

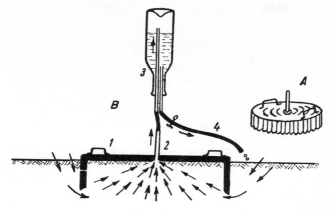

Fig. 17. Surface sampler (cap) with aspirator. A—general
view of cap; B—diagram of gas withdrawal: 1—metal cap
with serrated edges; 2—brass outlet tube; 3—bottle for gas
and aspirator; 4—rubber tube for discharge of water. Arrows
indicate path of gas.

In the gas-soil survey, gas-sampling is done by means of a special
sampler or cap (Fig. 17). The gas sampler consists of a steel cap 0.4 m.
in diameter and 0.08 m. high. In the center of the cap, there is a hole with
a brass outlet tube for withdrawal of gas. The lower edge of the cap is
toothed; the teeth are pointed. Two handles are attached to the upper surface of the cap, near the rim. At the place where the cap is placed, vegetation is sheared off. The cap, on being rotated by means of the handles,
cuts into the soil and is driven home with a light sledge hammer. The top
of the cap must be in contact with the soil. For some distance around the
cap, the soil is tamped and coated with clay. Gas sampling is done with the
aid of a common aspirator, as shown in (Fig. 17), or a Boravskii water
pump.

4. The delayed gas survey is seldom used. It is conducted in the following manner. A gas sampler is lowered into the bore hole and clay suspension is poured in, up to the level of the pit. Then, by means of the
Boravskii pump, a volume of subsoil gas equal to twice the internal volume
of the sealed-off part of the hole is withdrawn. After this the outlet tube of
the sampler is closed by a plug or a clamp, and the arrangement is allowed
to stand for a period up to a day or more before the gas sample is taken in
the usual manner. This delay makes it possible to obtain a more consistent
sample of the subsoil air; however, it is inconvenient because of the low
output, which requires that each sample point be visited twice.

5. The gas-flow survey is not adequately developed and should be
used only for experimental purposes. It consists in the following. In a
soil with continuous structure a cap is sunk to a slight depth leaving a gap
of up to 5 cm. between the cap and the soil. The cap differs from that
used in the gas-soil survey in that several holes are made along the
periphery of the top for free entrance of air. Some time after the cap is
sunk, air is withdrawn. It is assumed that during this interval a certain
amount of hydrocarbon gas diffuses through the soil into the atmosphere
and that this gas will be entrained by the air flowing into the cap and carried into the bottle. It is expected that samples will be obtainable without

a complete vacuum. Knowing the time of sampling of the gas and the concentration, it is possible to calculate its "output" per unit time.

6. The gas survey with sorbents, or the adsorption method of accumulation of hydrocarbons, is conducted in the following manner. Subsoil air
from shallow wells is drawn through a tube containing silica gel. The
latter absorbs hydrocarbon gas present in the subsoil air; the absorbed
gas consists mainly of heavy hydrocarbons (methane is essentially not
retained by the kinds of silica gel employed). For a marked increase in
concentrations 10 1. of gas is passed through the silica gel at a rate of
500 cm.^{3}/min.

After this the tube containing the silica gel goes to the laboratory,
where the gas is extracted. V. A. Sokolov and N. M. Turkel'taub (29) arrived at the conclusion that this method makes it possible to increase the
concentration of hydrocarbons in the subsoil air being analyzed by a factor
of ten. The latter is of enormous importance in the gas surveying of platform formations, where the concentrations of heavy hydrocarbons are very
low and interpretation of the results of the ordinary gas survey is difficult.
In practical use this method has encountered a number of difficulties of a
procedural character and has not as yet been used as extensively as it
deserves.

Seasonal Fluctuations of Gas Content

During the period of development of the method, it was noticed that when
gas surveys were repeated in a given area in different seasons (in different
years or even in different months of the same year), the gas anomalies obtained often did not correspond to each other in configuration nor even in
the average concentrations of subsoil gases.

Special investigations of this question by means of gas analysis using
the mercury apparatus showed that in all regions a sharp fluctuation is
observed in the average concentrations of the heavy fraction (nitrous oxide
and a trace of heavy hydrocarbons) in samples taken in different months.
The concentrations are highest in June, July, and August, lower in May and
September, and so low in the remaining months that they are at the limit of
sensitivity of the apparatus (Fig. 18).

Seasonal fluctuations chiefly affect the incombustible part of the heavy
fraction. In winter the heavy fraction consists mainly of combustible gases;
the incombustible components vanish. Consequently, the seasonal character of the gas-survey indices is expressed almost exclusively by the appearance in the soil and subsoil of the incombustible part of the heavy
fraction (30). During those periods in which the concentrations of incombustible components in the subsoil are highest, they are disseminated not
only in the area directly over the oil pool but throughout the entire surrounding area as well. As a result, anomalies of the heavy fraction run
together become less clear and are more difficult to interpret.
During those periods in which no incombustible gases can be detected in
the samples using the mercury apparatus, anomalous regions are generally
not observed. This is due to the fact that the concentration of the heavy
fraction decreases in autumn 8 - 10-fold on the average and as much as
100-fold in some regions.

In the great majority of regions, incombustible components constitute
the predominant part of the heavy fraction. For example, in districts of

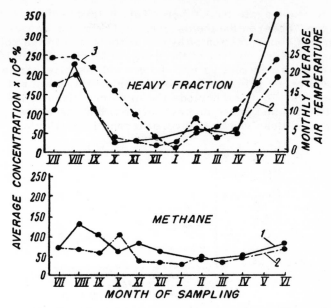

Fig. 18. Variation of average gas concentrations with month of sampling. 1—absorbed gas; 2—free gas; 3—monthly average air temperature.

Tataria they reach 97%; in Bashkiria, 60 - 90%; in the Saratov region, 93%; in the Apsheron peninsula, not less than 70%.

The maximum content of incombustible components of the heavy fraction in the subsoil air coincides with the maximum activity of the subsoil bacteria. Under the conditions of the dry Baku summer, in the total absence of rain, the cessation of bacterial activity occurs earlier (in August) than in more northerly regions. At this time the soil moisture at the surface falls to a minimum; as a result, the formation of incombustible gases in the soil ceases and the gases gradually disappear through gas-exchange with the atmosphere (31). Temperature has only an indirect effect on the seasonal change in the composition of the heavy fraction; this change affects the bacteria which form nitrous oxide during their periods of activity.

Combustible gases, including methane, undergo relatively mild seasonal fluctuations of concentration (Fig. 18). The transition to new methods of gas analysis and the rejection of the heavy fraction that includes nitrous oxide as a primary gas-survey index (1946) made it necessary to study the seasonal fluctuations of combustible gases as well. The results of these investigations (32) showed that the concentrations of combustible gases also exhibit seasonal fluctuations but that the character and magnitude of these fluctuations are entirely different. Maximum concentrations of hydrocarbon gases in the soil are recorded in the summer and occasionally in the winter.

In the spring and autumn during periods of heavy rainfall, concentrations of gas are minimal. In Figure 19 are shown the results of investigations conducted by V. S. Kotov for the Krasnodar region. From the graph it may be seen that concentrations reach a maximum between May and

August and increase again in October. This relationship was more clearly
observed in the Apsheron peninsula. One of the major causes of a seasonal
fluctuation in the concentration of hydrocarbon gases in the subsoil is the
change in the moisture content of the ground. During the autumn and spring
periods, the waters percolating into the ground dissolve part of the hydrocarbon gas and carry it in solution to deeper strata, down to the level of
the ground waters. In drier periods the moisture rises to the surface
through capillaries and pores and evaporates, leaving in the rock a residue
of the substances dissolved in it, hydrocarbons in particular.

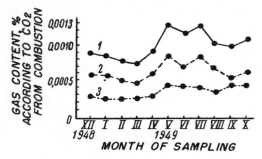

Fig. 19. Change of concentration of hydrocarbon gases depending on the month of
sampling. 1 —total combustible gas; 2 —
methane; 3 —heavy hydrocarbons.

However, the change in moisture content of the soil is not the only
cause of the seasonal character of gas-survey indices. Seasonal fluctuations in the concentration of hydrocarbon gases in the subsoil are jointly
influenced by several causes, including the following (32):
    1. Seasonal change in the moisture content and permeability to gases
of rocks lying above the level of the ground waters.
    2. Increase of aeration and gas-exchange of the soil during dry
periods.
    3. Generation of combustible gases in the spring by anaerobic
cellulose-destroying and other bacteria, and liberation of volatile substances by actively growing plants.
    4. Periodic oxidation of part of the hydrocarbon gases by hydrocarbon
bacteria.
    In Figure 20 is shown the variation in the concentration of combustible
gases with depth of sampling and time of year. In the diagram it may be
seen that at a depth of 1 m. seasonal fluctuations in concentration are considerably more sharply reflected than at a depth of 2 m., or especially 3 m.
This is due to the seasonal formation of combustible gases in the soil,
because the moisture content of the rock during the period of the survey
was nearly constant and did not increase until September - October.
    Increase of sampling depth makes it possible to eliminate the varia-
tions which are related to the seasonal formation of gases in the soil, but
it does not lessen the observed effects of the change in moisture content of
the rocks. In order to minimize these troublesome effects, it is necessary
to complete specific geological objectives in the shortest possible time. It
is also essential to take duplicate samples and repeat analyses along several profiles located in the area being investigated.

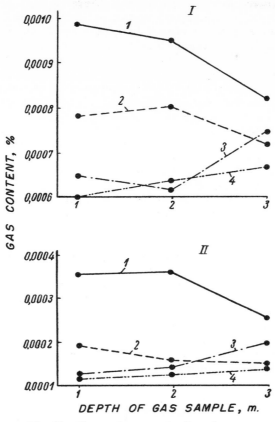

Fig. 20. Change in concentration of combustible gases depending on depth of sampling and time of year. I—total quantity
of combustible gases (as CO_2 after ignition);
II—heavy hydrocarbon (as CO_2); 1 —sampled in June; 2—sampled in July; 3—
sampled in August; 4—sampled in Septem-
ber-October.

Causes of Variations in Gas Concentrations

Seasonal fluctuations in soil gases are noted only by prolonged observation
of the changes in gas concentration. Furthermore, non-seasonal fluctuations in the concentration of hydrocarbon gases in a bore hole also occur.
    One of the main causes of the variation in the concentrations of hydro-
carbon gas in the subsoil is gas-exchange between soil and atmosphere,
especially diurnal gas-exchange (31). Since diurnal temperature changes
do not extend to depths greater than 1 - 1.5 m., it may be assumed that at
a depth of 3 m. they will have no effect on the composition of the subsoil
gas. Besides gas-exchange, the method of sampling and, especially, the
volume of preliminary evacuation and the method of sealing the hole affect
the fluctuations in gas concentrations. Obviously, a certain amount of
atmospheric air remains at the bottom of the hole after it is sealed, and

it is necessary to discard this air before sampling.

In gas surveying, a standard quantity of air is always discarded. However, the same amount of air cannot be discarded from sand and clay, for example, because clay contains much less free gas (i.e., free to enter the bottom of the sample hole) than sand or other coarsely porous rock. This leads to different sampling conditions in bore holes located side by side. To this should be added the fact that the properties of the rock have a substantial effect on the degree of aeration of the subsoil and the ability of the clay to retain a greater quantity of hydrocarbons.

If the hole is poorly sealed, samples taken at the bottom will be contaminated with atmospheric air drawn in from that part of the shaft situated above the clay suspension. This occurs especially often when the rock has dried out and cracked to a great extent or has great porosity. The latter promotes both absorption of the clay suspension and penetration of air through the cracks in a path which by-passes the sealed part of the well. Prolonged storage of samples leads to solution of part of the gas in the water-seal of the sample-bottle, and sometimes to bacterial oxidation of a certain amount of hydrocarbons as well.

In (Fig. 21) are shown characteristic gas analyses consecutively carried out at the same sampling point. In these analyses sampling and storage errors are absent, and the only operative factors are the diurnal gas-exchange of the subsoil and the nonuniform concentration of hydrocarbon gases in the rocks. Extremely good reproducibility is noted. Unfortunately, the great inconvenience of conducting gas analyses directly at the sampling point, due to the difficulties of manipulating vessels and accumulators under such conditions, made it necessary to resort to gas analysis in the field laboratory.

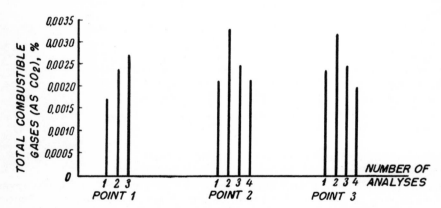

Fig. 21. Example of the reproducibility in hydrocarbon gas analyses made at the same sampling point.

There are analytical errors of another type which depend on the method of analysis. There have been cases where the analysts failed to take into account the high CO_2 content in some samples, so that the CO_2 passed into the field apparatus and was recorded as hydrocarbon gases. When the methane content of the samples is high, the field apparatus cannot accurately determine heavy hydrocarbons since part of the methane cannot be desorbed from the charcoal.

To all this should be added the fact that poorly cleaned gas bottles, dirty drills, dirty samplers, etc., may serve as a source of errors. Thus, in the gas survey, high concentrations are sometimes reported when the actual concentration is as low as 0.00050%.

GAS ANALYSIS

Natural soil gases are usually complex mixtures consisting of the most varied components. The most widespread components are nitrogen, methane, carbon dioxide, and oxygen, which comprise the bulk of the sample; the remaining gases are present in trace quantities. However, these traces are sometimes the most important constituents since they simplify elucidation of the origin of the gas.

Analysis of any natural gas begins with a total gas analysis. By total analysis is meant quantitative determination of the chief components of the gaseous mixture: carbon dioxide, total hydrocarbon gases, oxygen, carbon monoxide, hydrogen, and nitrogen, together with inert gases. Total gas analysis is usually conducted in a VTI apparatus. Besides the total gas analysis, it is necessary for the purposes of geochemical prospecting to resolve the hydrocarbon gases into methane and heavy hydrocarbons.

If an analysis is performed on a gas sample taken from a natural outlet or from a deep well and containing several percent of hydrocarbon gases, the separation of the hydrocarbons is carried out in the so-called fractional distillation apparatus of V. A. Sokolov. In this apparatus methane, ethane, propane, butane, and the vapors of heavier hydrocarbons are isolated.

Gas samples obtained in the course of a gas survey usually contain less than 1% hydrocarbons. At such low concentrations, separation of hydrocarbons in the Sokolov distillation apparatus is impossible. For this purpose it is necessary to use either the Sokolov stationary mercury apparatus or the titrimetric gas analyzer constructed by N. M. Turkel'taub. At the present time, the most important apparatus for the gas survey is the titrimetric analyzer TG-5A, while that for the analysis of gas from natural outlets is either the VTI or the Sokolov. Let us turn to a very brief description of the construction and principles of operation of these devices.

Total Analysis of Natural Gas in the VTI Apparatus

The VTI (All-Union Thermotechnical Institute) apparatus for total gas analysis (33) consists of the following main parts (Fig. 22): a two-column measuring buret with fork and leveling bottle, 1; seven absorption vessels with stopcocks, 2 - 8; a vessel for ignition of gas over an incandescent spiral, 9; an ignition loop with cupric oxide, 10; and a manifold, 11. Within the absorption vessels are located glass tubes for the purpose of increasing the contact surface of the reagent with the gas.

The absorption vessel 2 serves for the determination of carbon dioxide and is filled with a 40% solution of caustic potash (KOH). Vessel 3 is intended for absorption of oxygen. It is filled with an alkaline solution of pyrogallol. Vessel 4 is filled with an ammoniacal solution of cuprous chloride and serves for the determination of carbon monoxide. Vessel 5 absorbs ammonia vapors. Vessel 7 is filled with water acidified with sulfuric acid. This vessel serves to hold the main mass of the gas being

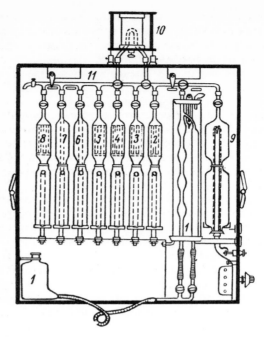

Fig. 22. VTI apparatus for total gas analysis.

analyzed for the duration of the analysis. The remaining vessel is for
storage. Before the start of the analysis the apparatus (manifold, ignition
tube with cupric oxide, etc.) is filled with nitrogen. The nitrogen is usually
prepared in the apparatus itself by absorption of the carbon dioxide and
oxygen.

The gas being investigated is introduced into the buret and its volume
is measured. After this the gas is transferred to absorption vessel 2 (containing KOH) for determination of carbon dioxide; from 2 it goes once
more to the buret for measurement of volume. The gas is transferred
back and forth between the absorption vessel and the buret until its volume
no longer decreases: this indicates that all the carbon dioxide has been
absorbed by the alkali.

The content of carbon dioxide in the gas mixture is determined from
the volume of gas absorbed. Then the gas is transferred to absorption
vessel 3 (containing pyrogallol) and oxygen is determined. After this hydrogen is determined by ignition. For this purpose the gas is passed
through a loop containing cupric oxide and heated to 300°. This heating is
accomplished by means of a special electric mantle; the temperature is
observed with the aid of a thermocouple. The volume of hydrogen is determined from the decrease in volume of the gas mixture after combustion of
the hydrogen. Then total hydrocarbon gases are determined. The hydrocarbon gases are ignited in a mixture with air over an incandescent platinum spiral at a temperature of $850 - 900^{\circ}$. The resulting carbon dioxide
is absorbed by alkali and the quantity of hydrocarbons is determined from
the volume change.

Hydrocarbons may be determined by ignition of the gas, not only over
a special platinum spiral, but also in a tube containing cupric oxide. Since

hydrocarbons ignite at a temperature of 850 - 900°, the tube containing cupric oxide is made of silica; around it is wound nichrome wire, through which current flows.

The accuracy of determination in the VTI apparatus reaches $\pm$ 0.2% (by volume). Nitrogen, together with the inert gases (helium, argon, neon, krypton, xenon), is determined from the difference between the volume of gas taken for analysis and that of the residual gas which was not absorbed by the reagents and not burned in the tube. As a result, the determination of the nitorgen volume is not sufficiently accurate.

The determination of hydrogen in the VTI apparatus is not always accurate either, because: the presence of heavy hydrocarbons which can burn at a lower temperature than methane makes the analysis unreliable, especially when the hydrogen concentration is low.

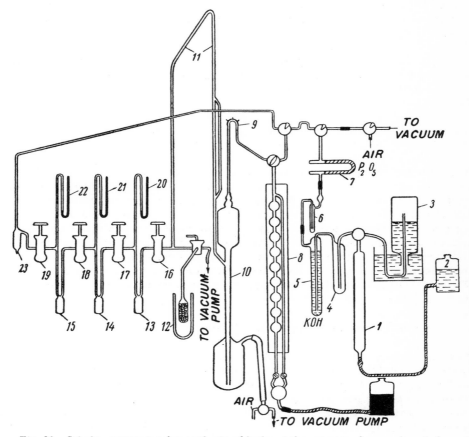

Fig. 23. Sokolov apparatus for analysis of hydrocarbon gases. 1—gas buret; 2—leveling bottle; 3—sample bottle; 4—water trap; 5—bubbler with 40% KOH; 6—trap for KOH; 7—tube with P_2O_5; 8—gas-measuring buret; 9—measuring arc; 10—mercury pump; 11—connecting tube; 12—bulb containing activated charcoal, submerged in a Dewar vessel containing liquid air; 13-15—condensation bulbs; 16-19—two-way vacuum stopcocks; 20-22—vacuum gauges; 23—mercury trap.

Analysis of Hydrocarbon Gases in the Sokolov Apparatus

The analysis of hydrocarbon gases in the apparatus of V. A. Sokolov consists in the fractional distillation of the hydrocarbons at low temperatures
and low pressures (16). The apparatus is first evacuated with the aid of
an oil pump (Fig. 23) and a charcoal-filled tube cooled in a Dewar flask
with liquid air. The hydrocarbon gas, after it has been freed of other
gases by means of a VTI device, is admitted to the apparatus and cooled by
the liquid air to a temperature of -180° or lower. At this temperature all
hydrocarbons except methane condense. The methane is separated from
the heavy hydrocarbons by evacuation.
     Then the temperature is raised between -155 and -140° and the ethane
is distilled off, whereupon its volume is measured in the buret. Then the
propane is distilled off at a temperature between -135 and -120°. Butane
comes off at a temperature between -120 and -100°. The residue usually
consists of pentane and higher hydrocarbons and is reported in the sum
total. The accuracy of determination in the Sokolov apparatus is equal to
0.01%.
     The purity of the distilled gases may be tested by ignition. This is
necessary in many cases because the gas sometimes contains nitrous oxide,
which condenses in the apparatus together with the heavy hydrocarbons and
falls in the ethane fraction.

     Analysis of Microcentrations of Hydrocarbon Gases in Stationary
     Mercury Apparatus

A stationary mercury apparatus intended for the analysis of gas-survey
samples was constructed by V. A. Sokolov (29). There are many models
of this apparatus, of which the stationary mercury apparatus, Model No. 3,
and the circulative mercury apparatus are used at the present time for
special analyses. These are high-vacuum glass assemblies fitted with
mercury valves which serve for admission of the gas and its circulation in
the apparatus during the analysis. Glass stopcocks are not suitable in
high-vacuum assemblies; therefore, mercury valves are used instead.
With this apparatus microanalyses of hydrocarbon gas may be performed
with an accuracy of $10^{-5}\%$.

     Stationary Mercury Apparatus, Model No. 3

This apparatus consists (Fig. 24) of a mercury pump and special mercury
valves connected to an oil pump through a vacuum line. On the right side
of the apparatus there is a buret with a leveling vessel, which serves for
admission of the gas to be analysed into the apparatus. Special absorption
bulbs contain KOH and phosphoric anhydride. In the center of the apparatus
there are two coils for the condensation of hydrocarbons and a tube for
ignition by means of a platinum filament. On the left side of the apparatus
are placed a bulb containing activated coconut charcoal and a graduated
capillary for measurement of the volume of hydrocarbons in the sample.
     The apparatus is completely evacuated before the analysis. This is
done with the pump and the charcoal-filled bulb; the latter is submerged in
liquid air in a Dewar vessel. At low temperatures the activated charcoal
acquires the ability to absorb all gases present in the apparatus. After

this the three-way stopcock is closed and the charcoal is isolated from the apparatus.

The bottle containing the gas to be analysed is placed in a water bath. Before the gas is admitted to the apparatus, it is washed in bubblers containing KOH solution. After this, 100 cm.^{3} of gas is transferred from the bottle to the buret for analysis. The gas is freed from CO_2 in the bubblers containing KOH, and from moisture in the tubes containing phosphoric anhydride.

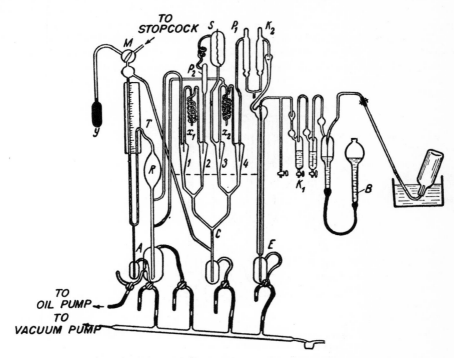

Fig. 24. Stationary mercury apparatus, Model No. 3. R —mercury pump; A — mercury trap; C —multiple mercury trap with bulbs 1, 2, 3, 4; E —inlet trap; B —buret with leveling vessel; K_1 and K_2 —absorption bulbs containing solid and liquid KOH; P_1 and P_2 —tubes containing phosphoric anhydride; x_1 and x_2 —coils; S —combustion tube; y —bulb containing coconut charcoal; M —three-way stopcock; T —graduated capillary.

By lowering and raising the mercury in the inlet valve, small portions of gas are admitted to the apparatus. The condensing coils are immersed in Dewar vessels containing liquid air. In the first coil all heavy hydrocarbons and nitrous oxide are condensed, while methane passes into the tube containing the platinum spiral heated to redness and burns with the formation of CO_2. The products of combustion of the methane are condensed in the second coil, which is also immersed in liquid air. The residual gas (nitrogen, oxygen, and inert gases) then passes into the bulb of the mercury pump R and is pumped out by the oil pump and removed from the apparatus. For more thorough elimination of air, a charcoal-filled tube is used.

After a high vacuum is established in the apparatus, the Dewar vessel is removed from the second coil and the volume of carbon dioxide is measured in the graduated capillary. The volume of carbon dioxide formed in the combustion of methane will be equal to the volume of the methane. After removal of the carbon dioxide from the apparatus, the Dewar vessel is withdrawn from the first coil and the total volume of heavy hydrocarbons together with nitrous oxide (heavy fraction) is measured.

Stationary Circulative Mercury Apparatus

The circulative apparatus is constructed according to the same principles as the mercury apparatus, Model No. 3. A diagram of this apparatus is shown in (Fig. 25). It differs from Model No. 3 in that the gas being analyzed is passed through the coils and combustion bulb several times.

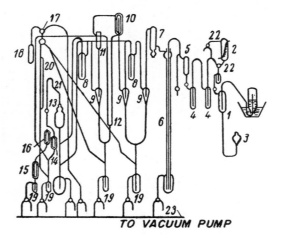

TO VACUUM PUMP

Fig. 25. Circulative mercury apparatus for the microanalysis of hydrocarbons. 1—measuring pipet; 2—bulb for preliminary combustion; 3—leveling vessel; 4—bubblers containing KOH solution; 5—tube containing solid KOH; 6—inlet trap; 7—tube for P_2O_5; 8—condensation vessel; 9—mercury valves; 10—combustion bulb; 11—small tube for P_2O_5; 12—fork-valve; 13—mercury pump; 14—absorption bulb containing fused P_2O_5; 15—absorption bulb containing fused KOH; 16—trap-valve; 17 and 22—three-way vacuum stopcocks; 18—bulb for charcoal; 19—traps; 20—measuring tube; 21—measuring arc; 23—manifold.

This makes possible a more detailed study of the heavy fraction. In order to determine the composition of the heavy fraction, the latter is burned in the combustion bulb and the products of combustion are absorbed in KOH. From the result of this operation it is possible to determine the total volume of the heavy fraction, the volume of incombustible components, and the volume of carbon dioxide formed in the combustion of the heavy hydrocarbons. From these data the carbon number is determined. By the carbon number is meant the ratio of the volume of carbon dioxide formed in the combustion of the heavy hydrocarbons to the volume of the heavy hydro-carbons.

The general shortcoming of stationary apparatus is the need for pro-longed storage of samples before analysis and the impossibility of taking the results of analysis into account in the direction of field surveys.

Analysis of Microconcentrations of Hydrocarbon Gases in the TG-5A Apparatus and the Chromatographic Apparatus

The TG-5A apparatus, constructed by N. M Turkel'taub, makes possible the determination of microconcentrations of methane and of individual vola-tile, heavy hydrocarbons, beginning with ethane. The great advantage of the apparatus consists in the fact that it is easily transported and makes analysis possible in the field laboratory or even right in the field.

The TG-5A apparatus determines the total quantity of hydrocarbons and the quantity of methane separately. The quantity of volatile, heavy hydrocarbons is calculated by taking the difference between total hydro-carbons and methane. The total quantity of hydrocarbons is determined through the catalytic combustion of all hydrocarbons to CO_2 over a plati-num wire, absorption by a 0.005 N solution of $Ba(OH)_2$, titration of the un-reacted excess of the reagent with a 0.005 N solution of hydrochloric acid. The course of the analysis may be expressed by the following equations:

$$CH_4 + 2O_2 = CO_2 + 2H_2O$$
$$C_3H_8 + 5O_2 = 3CO_2 + 4H_2O$$
$$CO_2 + Ba(OH)_2 = BaCO_3 + H_2O$$
$$Ba(OH)_2 + 2HCl = BaCl_2 + H_2O$$
$$\text{(excess)}$$

Titration with hydrochloric acid of the $Ba(OH)_2$ remaining after re-action with carbon dioxide is done in the presence of phenolphthalein, which imparts a rosy tint to the solution. The end point of the titration is indi-cated by the decolorization of the solution. The total quantity of CO_2 formed by combustion of all the hydrocarbons is determined by calculation.

For the determination of methane, the gas being studied is passed through dry activated charcoal of a special type which sorbs heavy hydro-carbons but passes methane. The methane is then burned to CO_2 and determined in the same way as total hydrocarbons.

The purifying system of the apparatus (Fig. 26) consists of a prelimi-nary air combustion bulb, two helical bubblers containing a 40% solution of caustic potash (KOH), and a tube containing solid alkali. The air combus-tion tube is intended to free the air entering the apparatus from accidental traces of combustible gases. The helical bubbler with 40% KOH is intended to free the gas being analyzed and the air from traces of acidic substances, particularly CO_2, while the tube with solid alkali is intended to free the gas and air from moisture. Atmospheric air contains about 0.028 - 0.032% CO_2, while soil air contains as much as 0.1 - 1.0% and sometimes more. In gas extracted from a core, the quantity of CO_2 may reach 10% or more. Even a trace of CO_2 entering the apparatus will cause the results of the analysis to be incorrect; therefore, the proper choice of reagents in the

purifying system is very important. The helical bubblers are so constructed as to acheive maximum contact between the gas passing through
and the alkali (34). With higher concentrations of CO_2 a second, additional
bubbler containing alkali is used.

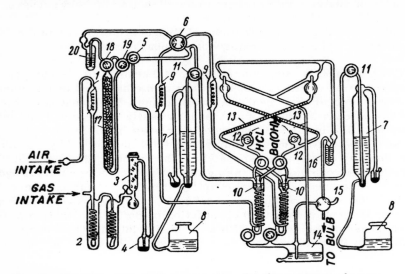

Fig. 26. Diagram of titrimetric analyzer. <u>Purifying system</u>: 1—preliminary combustion bulb containing platinum spiral; 2—helical bubblers
containing KOH solution; 3—vessel containing solid alkali (in the TG-5A)
or glass wool (in the chromatographic gas analyzer); 4—mercury trap.
<u>Distributing system</u>: 5—three-way stopcock for directing the gas into
two channels; 6—four-way stopcock; 7—aspirators for holding gas which
has passed through the apparatus; 8—leveling bottles for production of
vacuum in the apparatus and circulation of gas. <u>Analytical part</u>: 9—
bulbs for combustion of gas; 10—vessels for absorption of combustion
products (CO_2); 11—stopcocks for regulating rate of gas flow; 12—
three-way stopcocks for admission of $Ba(OH)_2$ to the absorption vessels
and titration of excess with hydrochloric acid; 13—microburets for
measurement of the volumes of $Ba(OH)_2$ and hydrochloric acid solutions
used; 14—overflow bottle for spent liquids; 15-16—four-way stopcock
and trap for protection against entrance of CO_2 from the air; 17—tube
containing activated charcoal for separation of gases by adsorption;
18-19—regulating stopcocks; 20—trap.

The combustion bulb is a glass vessel with a sealed-in platinum wire.
The bulbs are supplied with power from a storage battery and the temperature of the wire is maintained between 800° and 900°. One three-cell
storage battery of the ZIS type has the capacity for 10 - 12 hours of operation on the TG-5A apparatus. The apparatus must be absolutely airtight.
In order to check the cleanliness and lack of air in the apparatus, an
analysis of air is periodically conducted; the result of this must be negative.
When the total volume of gas passing through the combustion bulb is
100 cm.^{3}, the sensitivity of the apparatus is 0.00026%. In an eight-hour
working day, 7 or 8 analyses may be performed with this apparatus, although if the gas concentration is as high as 0.1%, only 3 or 4 analyses are
possible. This is explained by the fact that, after the analysis of samples
with a high hydrocarbon content, prolonged cleaning of the apparatus is

required in order to remove all traces of hydrocarbons.

When the hydrocarbon concentration in the mixture is over 0.1% (0.5 - 10% or more), it is necessary to dilute the sample several-fold with pure air; the extract degree of dilution is noted (the volume is measured with a buret). The dilution is taken into account in the analytical calculations. The hydrocarbon content is determined in percent with an accuracy of 1×10^{-5}.

A party conducting a gas survey or gas-core survey must have at least four TG-5A outfits operated by the same number of analysts. The number of outfits depends on the number of drilling crews in the party and the method of drilling. Each analyst keeps an analytical journal in which all necessary data on the sample and the course of analysis are recorded and analytical calculations are performed. Besides the analytical journals, a laboratory record of the analytical results is also kept.

In gas analysis with the TG-5A apparatus, it must be kept in mind that the apparatus infallibly separates hydrocarbons contained in pure air. If the gas sample contains, besides hydrocarbons, carbon monoxide and various volatile organic substances formed in the soil, the sharpness of separation is diminished. In an analysis carbon monoxide will pass through the charcoal, burn to CO_2, and fall in the methane fraction. Volatile organic substances may fall either in the methane or in the heavy hydrocarbon fraction, depending on their physical properties. Accurate analysis of hydrocarbons is hindered by the presence in some gases of hydrogen sulfide and ammonia, as well as a high percentage of carbon dioxide.

Carbon monoxide may be eliminated by passing the gas through a special type of hopcalite (gas-mask type filter) before combustion. Not all kinds of hopcalite are suitable for elimination of carbon monoxide from gases, as it is known that hopcalite oxidizes not only carbon monoxide, but also heavy hydrocarbons beginning with butane. The special kinds of hopcalite recommended by N. M. Turkel'taub for use in the TG-5A apparatus absorb only 14% of pentane, 25% of hexane, and up to 50% of octane; butane passes completely through hopcalite. Consequently, these kinds of hopcalite pass gaseous hydrocarbons completely and partially oxidize the vapors of liquid hydrocarbons..

It is almost impossible to eliminate volatile organic substances from soil air in an analysis because their composition is unknown and their properties have not been studied. A better method of eliminating these soil gases consists in sampling the gas at depths to which these gases do not penetrate. At the same time it is necessary to study all the combustible gases of the soil layer in order to make a new, more nearly perfect apparatus.

The titrimetric gas analyzer with chromatographic separation makes possible the separate determination of methane, ethane, and the sum of the heavier hydrocarbons when these are present in low concentrations in the gas mixture. The chromatographic apparatus is nearly identical in construction to the TG-5A. Gas analysis with this apparatus is performed in the following manner. The gas sample is freed from CO_2 and then divided in the apparatus into two equal streams. In one stream, as in the TG-5A apparatus, the total hydrocarbon content is determined. The other stream is directed into a tube filled with charcoal which adsorbs all the hydrocarbons. In the apparatus the charcoal is kept at a constant, fixed moisture content in order to maintain the definite properties necessary for separation of the hydrocarbons.

The chromatogram is developed by flushing the charcoal with air which is passed through the absorbent in portions of such volume that the individual components are separately eluted. The content of the latter in the gas sample is determined in a manner analogous to that in which the total hydrocarbon content was determined. The first portion of air elutes the methane while the second portion elutes the ethane. The heavier hydrocarbons are retained by the charcoal and are not separated. One analysis with this apparatus lasts about 4 hours.

The titrimetric gas analyzer with chromatographic separation is used for the resolution of heavy hydrocarbons when the content of the latter in the sample is high enough (over 0.00100%). Analytical data obtained with the chromatographic apparatus are used to detail gas anomalies and to determine the composition of gases migrating from pools.

Recently, N. M. Turkel'taub together with V. A. Sokolov and Professor A. A. Zhukhovitskii have suggested a new apparatus for the analysis of hydrocarbon gases, the chromathermograph (35). In this apparatus, the development of the chromatogram is combined with gradual heating of the adsorbent.

INTERPRETATION OF GAS SURVEY RESULTS

The interpretation of the results of the gas survey, or in general, any other geochemical method of oil prospecting, is made with consideration of all existing information on the geological structure of the region, its gas- or oil-bearing character and its geological history. Only by such a carefully integrated analysis of all data is it possible to reach a correct conclusion from the results of the gas survey. Sometimes the assertion may be heard that, because the gas survey is a direct method of prospecting for oil, it is sufficient to obtain a gas anomaly in any given area in order to have positive proof of an oil pool. From gas-survey practice, several cases are known in which a gas anomaly proved on examination to have no connection with any oil pool but was due to other factors.

Presentation of Survey Results

The results of analyses of gas survey samples are recorded on a map at each point in the form of segments of a straight line, all drawn to the same scale. Separate maps are usually compiled for heavy hydrocarbons, methane, and total hydrocarbon gases. Sometimes they may be combined into one map by first indicating the heavy fraction by solid lines at the sampling point, and then showing the methane by superimposed dotted lines. It is more convenient in these cases to use colors: heavy hydrocarbons are indicated by red ink while methane is shown with blue or green.

In (Fig. 27) is shown an example of a portion of a gas-survey map bearing the results of analyses. There are, also, other methods of indicating the results of analysis (for example, in the form of a "peak", columns, small circles, triangles), but they are less convenient and are less often used. The scale of the gas-survey map is chosen according to the detail of the work. In reconnaissance surveys the scale of the chart is usually equal to 1:100,000 and 1:200,000, while in detailed surveys it is 1:50,000 - 1:25,000, rarely 1:10,000.

How detailed a survey shall be made is determined by the extent to

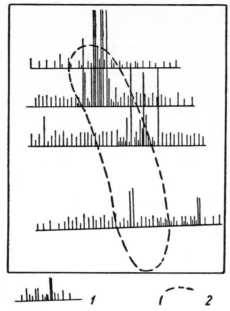

Fig. 27. Presentation of the results of gas
analysis on a map. 1 —concentration of
heavy fraction; 2 —structure contour.

which the geology of the region has been studied. In a well studied region
detailed investigations are always carried out, but in an inadequately
studied region only reconnaissance surveys are conducted. It is expedient
for the scale of the geochemical map to agree with that of the geological
or structural map. This simplified comparison of the results of work done
by different methods and is convenient for utilization of geological data in
the interpretation of geochemical data.

By gas anomaly is meant a group of points of increased gas concentrations distributed throughout a definite area and visibly distinct from the
background of lower gas concentrations. An anomalous zone is a separate
portion of a gas anomaly in the case where the areal distribution is not
continuous. Gas background refers to the widely distributed, low concentrations of gas, that are characteristic of non-oil-bearing areas.

The chief causes of gaseous hydrocarbon background are regionally
scattered organic matter and hydrocarbon gases genetically related to
rocks. Organic matter and combustible gases are encountered in greater
or lesser amounts in almost all rocks. They are formed simultaneously
(syngenetically) with rock and are, therefore, arbitrarily called syngenetic.
An especially large amount of organic matter and bitumen is contained in
oil-shales.

In continental deposits, from which gas-survey samples are usually
taken, organic matter was formed as a result of the death of vegetation and
animals on the surface. A large amount of organic matter accumulates in
the soil layer, and is partially carried thence into rivers, where it settles
in the form of alluvial deposits, together with diluvium and eluvium. During their life, a number of plants accumulate bituminous matter in their

bodies, particularly in their roots; on the death of the plant this matter
passes into the soil in "finished" form. To this matter are related vegetable waxes, tars, rubber, etc. During the further conversion of organic
matter combustible gases are evolved as by-products.

The gas background is due not only to syngenetic gas, but also to contemporary gas formation occurring in the subsoil layer. As a result of the
transformation of dying organic matter, methane, carbon monoxide, and
various volatile organic substances are formed along with nitrogen, carbon
dioxide, and other gases. These combustible gases may diffuse down from
the soil by one path or another, establishing an unusual background.

The magnitude of the syngenetic background is not constant for all
geological provinces. But even within the limits of a single geological
province, areas with backgrounds of various magnitudes may be observed.
Thus, the gas background is the result of complex transormations of
organic matter, taking place in rocks and soils.

Compilation of Maps

Two kinds of maps are compiled. On the first, a detailed map of the factual
material of the gas survey, are recorded the results of analyses. On this
map there are no geological data. Only such topographical peculiarities of
the area are shown as are necessary for general orientation and determination of the reliability of results from the point of view of surface con-
taminations associated with populated points, machine-tractor stations,
swamps, etc. Correlation zones are outlined on the map (which, therefore,
is sometimes called a correlation map). For this purpose sections characterized by relatively higher concentrations of hydrocarbon gases are
first marked off on each profile. The magnitude of increased gas concentrations may be different on different profiles since it depends on the time
of sampling (season) as well as the magnitude of the background. This is
especially important when Quaternary deposits are thin and various units
of the bed rock of the area are of different age and are not gas-saturated
to the same degree.

After the zones of increased concentrations have been outlined on all
profiles, they are correlated with corresponding sections on adjacent profiles, and, as a result, the anomalous areas (or gas anomalies) are distinguished. Within the boundaries of a correlation zone or anomaly, there
may be points of high concentrations as well as low, but the former predominate over the latter.

The map of detailed results, or correlation map, is compiled at the
time of work in the field and there verified and detailed. Anomalies that
have been correctly distinguished and verified are recorded on the second
map, the final map of gas survey results. On this map must be recorded
geological data and geophysical survey data in order to compare the results of the gas survey with the geological structure of the area, evaluate
these results, and reach a conclusion as to the likelihood of finding oil in
the area.

The clearness and reliability of anomalies are determined by their
contrast. By the coefficient of contrast is meant the ratio of average gas
concentrations at points lying within the limits of a distinguished anomaly
to the average concentrations at points lying beyond those limits, i.e., to
the background. In calculating contrast, all points within the limits of an

anomaly are taken into account regardless of the concentration of gas—
high or low—recorded for them. The more points there are, within the
limits of the anomaly, with high concentrations in comparison with the low
ones, the more contrast the anomaly will have.

Anomalies having coefficients of contrast equal to 1.2 - 1.5 are considered to be weak. Anomalies having coefficients of contrast equal to
1.6 - 2 are quite reliable, while anomalies with a contrast from 2 to 10 are
rarely encountered. Anomalies of high contrast are usually due to the
penetration of gas through disjunctive dislocations.

The most reliable anomalies are those related to heavy hydrocarbons
since the latter are not formed in the surface layers (under conditions
where the sampling point is far enough removed from the soil; the latter
may contain volatile organic substances which may be erroneously determined as heavy hydrocarbons). Methane anomalies are usually less reliable. When heavy hydrocarbons are present in high concentrations, they
are separated into ethane and heavier hydrocarbons in order to determine
more precisely the composition of the gas within the limits of the anomaly.

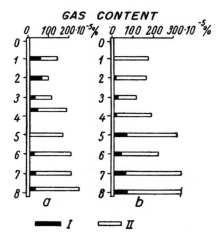

Fig. 28. Examples of increase in content of combustible gas in the Mashtagin area. a—beyond the
limits of the oil pool; b—in the region of the oil
pool. I—heavy hydrocarbons according to CO_2
from combustion; II—light hydrocarbons.

In order to obtain more contrasting anomalies and reliable results
from the gas survey, the deep gas survey is used in some regions. Higher
gas concentrations can be obtained within the limits of anomaly if the depth
of sampling is increased. As an example of increase in content of combustible gas the results of observations in the Mashtagin area are given
(36): the first diagram characterizes background values while the second
characterizes anomalous ones (Fig. 28).

Even better results are obtained in districts of the Northern Caucasus
(Fig. 29). In the first graph is shown the increase in concentrations of
hydrocarbon gases in the zone of the gas anomaly along the section of a
bore hole drilled into Quaternary sandy soils. In the second graph is shown

the same phenomenon for a hole cutting rocks of various ages: Quaternary soils, as well as Maikop and Pontian clays (37). It should be noted especially in interpreting the results of a deep gas survey that the age of the rocks and the scattered syngenetic organic matter contained therein must be taken into account. V. S. Kotov notes that wells from 6 to 10 m. deep often penetrate layers of bedrock. Quaternary deposits may be characterized by the absence of hydrocarbons, while the underlying bedrock is permeated with gas in relatively high concentrations. An example of this is shown in Figure 29, where the well was drilled through Maikop layers which were characterized throughout the entire territory under investigation by a high concentration of syngenetic gas, regardless of the oil-bearing character of the region.

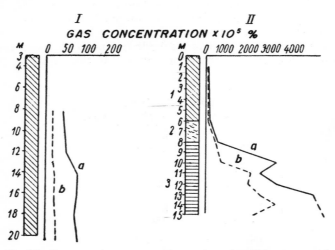

Fig. 29. Increase in concentrations of combustible gases with depth. I—region of gas anomaly; section of Quaternary layers; II—example of high concentrations of syngenetic gas in bedrock; 1—Quaternary sandy soil; 2—Pontian clays; 3—Maikop clays; a—total content of hydrocarbon gases (as CO_2); b— heavy hydrocarbons (as CO_2).

In compiling maps of a deep gas survey it is necessary to compile separate maps for different depths as well as a general composite map. In Figure 30 are shown maps of one area for depths of 1, 3, 4, 6, 8, and 10 m. It may be seen that the results obtained with samples taken at depths of 1, 3, and 4 m. are much less clear. At these depths three anomalous areas are noted: the indistinct central portion, the diffuse northern part, and the very limited southern portion. At depths of 6, 8, and 10 m., the central anomaly expands as it indicates an oil pool, the northern one contracts in volume (apparently, it is associated with gas formation at the surface), and the southern one expands; the latter is explained by outcrops of bedrock having high concentrations of syngenetic gases and bitumens. The compilation of maps of averaged data for this area makes it possible to eliminate accidental high concentrations of gas in the northern anomalous portion and to define sharper boundaries for the central portion.

Gas anomalies may be of different origin. Most frequently they are associated with migrations of natural gas from oil and gas pools. Anomalies

of other origin are generally called "false". "False" anomalies are
formed in the following ways.

1. As a result of the migration of methane from coal beds.

2. As a result of outcrops of bedrock characterized by a higher content of primary gas or syngenetic organic substances which produce hydrocarbon gas.

3. As a result of contemporary gas formation in regions of greater
accumulation of dead vegetable remains.

The limits of all gas anomalies, migrational and "false", are marked
on the initial gas survey map of detailed results. To this map are attached
a list of all anomalies and a brief description thereof giving their average
gas concentrations and coefficients of contrast. On the final interpretation
map, which is compiled from calculations based on the geological structure
of the region, "false" anomalies may not be shown. This is noted in the
text with a statement of the reasons.

TAKEN FROM A DEPTH OF:

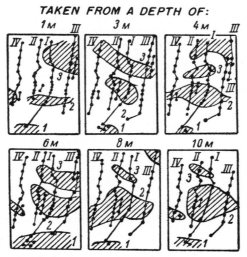

Fig. 30. Gas survey results for different
depths of sampling. I, II, III, IV —number
of profile; 1 —southern anomalous portion;
2 —central anomalous zone; 3 —northern
anomalous portion.

Forms of Gas Anomalies

Gas anomalies may have various forms, namely: (1) a large, continuous
patch, (2) a ring, (3) a group of patches concentrated in a limited area,
which are difficult to combine into one continuous anomaly, or (4) a local,
elongated patch of high contrast.

The shape of the anomaly, being unrelated to the geological structure
of the region, cannot have any great significance in the interpretation of
gas-survey results. It acquires meaning only upon comparison with the
tectonic peculiarities of the region to which it is chiefly related. Therefore, in determining the shape of a gas anomaly, the distribution of the
latter with respect to the tectonic structure is taken into account.

Depending on the position of the gas anomaly in the structure, direct and displaced anomalies are distinguished. By <u>direct</u> anomaly is meant an anomaly which is located either directly over a structural high at its most elevated part (continuous) or around the structure in the form of a ring (annular). By <u>displaced</u> anomaly is meant one which is not located over the entire area of the structure, but on one side, or with a small portion on any side. The name of the anomaly indicates its shape and correspondence to definite structural elements or the character of its distribution over stratigraphic or lithologic pools.

The direct anomaly may have various shapes: (1) It may be continuous, i.e., have the shape of a large, circular patch. (2) It may be spotty and consist of a whole group of separate patches around the central part of an uplift. (3) It may be local, i.e., extremely limited in area with high contrast and either be predominantly linear or appear as isolated points.

A direct anomaly may also be annular in shape, forming a continuous ring, or zonal-annular. In the latter case the ring is discontinuous and consists of separate anomalous zones distributed along the periphery of the structure in the form of a discontinuous ring. A displaced anomaly, located on the side of a geological structure, may be continuous, spotty, and local (Table 15).

TABLE 15. Types of Anomalies

Type of anomaly		General characteristics
Relation to structure	Shape	
Direct	Continuous	Anomaly is superposed on an anticlinal high
	Spotty	Same; anomaly is in the form of a group of spots
	Local	Anomaly corresponds to local portions of tectonic faults. High, but variable contrast is characteristic
	Annular and zonal-annular	Anomaly in the form of a ring or separate spots surrounding the structure with a gap within the ring
Displaced	Continuous	Anomaly in the form of a large patch corresponds to the side of a structure, a highly fissured area, or a "zonal" oil pool
	Spotty	Anomaly in the form of spots corresponds to the side of a structure or a "zonal" oil pool
	Local	Anomaly associated with migrations of gas along a dislocation corresponds to the side of a structure

The origin of the direct or spotty anomaly is quite clear and needs no explanation. As an example of a direct anomaly, the results of a gas survey completed in 1945 on one of the oil formations of the Apsheron peninsula, in which silica gel was used for accumulation of gas, are given (Fig. 31). The central part of the gas anomaly corresponds to the top of a geological structure and coincides with an oil pool. In Fig. 32 is shown a direct gas anomaly which does not correspond to the tectonic structure, but is linked to a stratigraphic oil pool in Karagan and Chokrak strata.

The spotty gas anomaly is essentially a variety of the continuous anomaly and is formed when the concentrations of gas at separate points is sufficiently high. Fig. 33 shows a spotty gas anomaly of one of the regions of southern Bashkiria that was discovered in the course of the work in 1942. The separate attenuated spots cannot be united because of the considerable distance between them.

The annular anomaly was first distinguished by V. A. Sokolov in 1934 during a gas survey in Ishimbai. Since then, annular anomalies have been observed in many regions and have been explained in various ways.

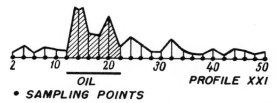

Fig. 31. Profile of a direct gas anomaly. Scale of peaks: 1 cm. = 0.0020% heavy fraction.

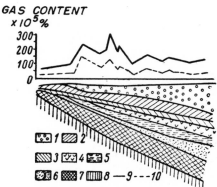

Fig. 32. Schematic geological-gas-survey profile of a direct gas anomaly. 1—strata overlying a pool and Quaternary deposits; 2—Pontian; 3—Maotis; 4—Sarmatian; 5—Karagan; 6—Chokrak and the boundary of oil-bearing formation; 7—Maikop; 8—foraminiferous strata; 9—total hydrocarbon gases (by combustion to CO_2); 10—heavy hydrocarbons (by combustion to CO_2).

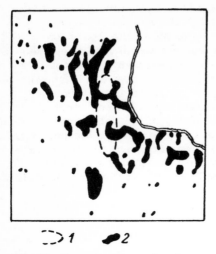

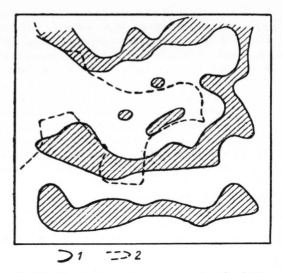

Fig. 33. Spotty gas anomaly. 1—
outline of anticlinal structure; 2—
areas of higher concentrations of
the heavy fraction.

Fig. 34. Typical annular gas anomaly. 1—higher
concentrations of the heavy fraction; 2—outline
of oil-productive reef.

In Figure 34 is shown a typical annular anomaly established by a surface (soil gas) survey of the heavy fraction in Ishimbai in 1943. A ring of
high concentrations of the heavy fraction surrounds an oil pool, while the
concentrations over the pool itself are low. In Figure 35 is shown a semiannular anomaly established by a heavy-fraction survey in the Saratov
region. The left side, which was recorded in summer, is clearly shown,
while the right side, which was recorded in autumn during a lull in the
activity of nitrous oxide-producing, denitrifying bacteria, is indistinct.

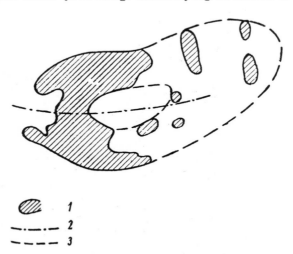

Fig. 35. Semiannular gas anomaly. 1—areas of
high concentrations of the heavy fraction; 2—axis
of the structure; 3—hypothetical contours of the
anomaly, if the entire area had been surveyed in
the summer.

It is of interest to note that annular anomalies are most often formed by the heavy fraction. Sometimes annular anomalies acquire an abnormal shape. Thus, for example, several annular anomalies of the Kuibyshev Transvolga region are characterized by the fact that over the oil-bearing area, gases are absent, while beyond the limits of the pool (background) they have very high concentrations (Fig. 36). Here the meaning of anomaly and background is reversed.

Sometimes multi-annular gas anomalies are observed with up to five or six rings extending around the structure. As E. M. Geller states, it is possible to distinguish a multi-annular anomaly only with the aid of a structure map, but this method of detection of anomalies is faulty and the form of the anomaly is itself, doubtful. The contrast of such anomalies is low, not exceeding 1.2 - 1.4.

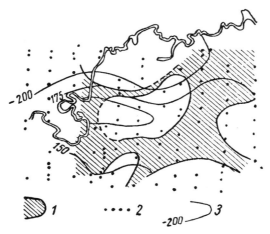

Fig. 36. Example of annular heavy-fraction gas anomaly. 1—zone of higher concentrations of the heavy fraction; 2—sampling point; 3—isolines of electrical resistivity.

Apparently, annular anomalies are mainly formed in those structures in which increased rock fissuring is observed at an abrupt fold in the strata, at a dip in the axis of the fold, and on either side of the fold. There are many other explanations for the appearance of a ring anomaly but the majority of them are ill-founded. We need only mention the widely accepted hypothesis for the formation of annular anomalies that was proposed by V. A. Sokolov (20). According to him, such anomalies are formed by an interrupted diffusion current flowing from an oil or gas pool where the stream of heavy hydrocarbons reaches the surface at the periphery but not in the central part of the area occupied by the gas cap.

The displaced gas anomaly is formed as a result of non-uniform migration of gas, corresponding to a zone of increased fissuring on any side of the structure. The displacement of the anomaly may also be due to the movement of ground waters, which deflects the stream of hydrocarbon gases.

All types of anomalies except local ones occupy an area either 1.5 to 2 fold greater than the area of oil-bearing character or equal to it. If the anomaly is detected by means of the heavy fraction, as determined in the mercury apparatus, its area may be 10 times greater than the oil-bearing area. Local anomalies, on the contrary, occupy a small area since they are formed as a result of migration of gas along zones of disjunctive dislocations.

Evaluation of the Survey Results

The authenticity of an anomaly and the likelihood of finding oil within the area of the anomaly may be ascertained only by strict correlation with the geological structure of the region. Numerous cases are known in which natural gas outcrops were associated with small pools having no industrial significance. A gas anomaly indicates the presence of a source of gas but does not specify its size. Sometimes a large oil formation is in no wise indicated by gas survey results. This has been known to occur with formations characterized by undisturbed tectonics and the virtual absence of faults. This is most often observed in the case of platform formations.

Overall geological data are helpful in determining the possibility of finding oil pools in areas where gas anomalies have been discerned. In the history of the gas survey, there was one example in which an extensive gas anomaly was found to correspond to a syncline. The geological structure of the region was such that no oil pool could be expected. However, the gas survey workers did not take geology into account and decided to proceed with drilling. In the end it was found that the anomaly was not formed by hydrocarbon gas and was not associated with any oil pool.

The gas survey has become firmly established in the general complex of oil prospecting work. In the majority of cases a gas survey is conducted after geological and geophysical surveys in order to evaluate the likelihood of finding oil under structures determined thereby.

The data of gas surveying are interpreted together with those of geology and geophysics in the planning of deep drilling. More rarely a geological survey is first conducted for reconnaissance in a territory, whose geological structure and oil possibilities have been studied very little or are entirely unknown. Then, after a gas survey, geophysical surveying and structural drilling are carried out in the most promising areas.

Gas survey results are not of equal value in all regions. The clearest, most reliable results are obtained in folded regions, such as the Caucasus. Less reliable results are obtained in the undisturbed, sloping structures of a platform, because gas migration here is less pronounced. In such regions a gas-survey method is used which includes preliminary accumulation of hydrocarbons in order to increase gas concentrations. In order to improve the effectiveness of the survey, various geochemical investigations are conducted. Coincidence of anomalies obtained by different methods makes the survey results more valuable and their interpretation more certain.

The use of the gas survey is not limited to prospecting for oil and gas formations. Attempts, sometimes quite successful, have been made to use the gas survey in prospecting for coal formations (38), for the survey of ozokerite deposits (39), in prospecting for helium formations (40), and in searching for leaks in gas mains.

In conclusion it should be noted that the gas survey can be perfected much further and is in need of serious investigations of a theoretical character.

BIBLIOGRAPHY

1. V.A. Sokolov. The gas survey as a method of prospecting for oil and gas formations. Inform., sb. NGRI. ONTI, 1933.
2. V.A. Sokolov. The gas survey. Az. neft. khoz., No. 9, 1933.
3. V.A. Sokolov. New method of surveying oil and gas formations. Tekhnika nefti, No. 16 (163), 1933.
4. V.A. Sokolov. The gas survey. ONTI, 1936.
5. N.D. Elin. Use of the gas survey has increased oil reserves. Tekhnika nefti, No. 53 (137), 1934.
6. A.N. Kozhushko. The future of the Malgobek region lies in the Akhlov area. Groznen. neftyanik, Nos. 2-3, 1934.
7. V.A. Sokolov. Main results of gas-survey work, Sb. rabot po gazovoi s'emke. Tr. VKGR. ONTI, 1939.
8. G.A. Mogilevskii. Effect of meteorological and soil conditions on the composition of soil air. Byull. neft. geofiziki, No. 6, 1936.
9. G.A. Mogilevskii. New field method of gas surveying. Neft. khoz., Nos. 4-5, 1937.
10. P.L. Antonov. Toward the theory of the gas survey. Neft. khoz., No. 5, 1934.
11. P.L. Antonov. The problem of mapping oil formations according to gas survey data. Neft. khoz., No. 10, 1935.
12. L.A. Kuznetsov, E.E. Maidyuk, M.I. Peisik, M.I. Subbota, Z.M. Tabasaranskii, and I.A. Shmelev. Present state and prospects of development of the method of the gas survey. Neft. khoz., No. 7, 1947.
13. Ya. Eventov. Method of the gas survey in Germany. Groznen. neftyanik, Nos. 6-7, 1934.
14. G.A. Mogilevskii. The gas survey in America. Razvedka nedr, No. 7, 1939.
15. I.K. Kupalov-Yaropolk. Gas prospecting in the USA. Byuro tekhn. ekon. inform. TsIMTnefti, M., 1947.
16. A.G. Mileshina. On the study of fissuring in carbonate-type rocks. Sb. ''Geokhim. metody poiskov nefti i gaza'', No. I. Gostoptekhizdat, 1953.
17. E.E. London. Role of tectonic dislocations and fissuring of rocks in the formation of gas anomalies. Sb. ''Geokhim. metody poiskov nefti'', No. 1. Gostoptekhizdat, 1950.
18. V.P. Miroshnichenko. Phenomena of mud volcanism in the Ashkahabad earthquate of August, 1948. Izv. Akad. Nauk SSSR, ser. geol., No. 5, 1951.
19. V.A. Sokolov. Essays on the origin of petroleum. Gostoptekhizdat, 1948.
20. V.A. Sokolov. Direct geochemical methods of prospecting for petroleum. Gostoptekhizdat, 1947.
21. V.A. Sokolov. On the theory and method of the gas survey. Sb. ''Geokhim. metody poiskov nefti'', No. 1. Gostoptekhizdat, 1950.
22. P.L. Antonov. On the measurement of the diffusion parameters of several rocks. Sb. ''Geokhim. metody poiskov nefti i gaza'', No. I, Gostoptekhizdat, 1953. On the diffusion permeability of several clay rocks. Sb. ''Geokhim metody poiskov nefti i gaza'', No. II. Gostoptekhizdat, 1954.

23. N.G. Kholodnyi. The atmosphere as a possible source of vitamins. Doklady Akad. Nauk SSSR 18, No. 6, 1944.

24. N.G. Kholodnyi, V.S. Rozhdestvenskii, A.A. Kil'chevskaya. Assimilation of volatile organic substances by soil bacteria. Pochvovedenie, No. 7, 1945.

25. G.F. Gauze. Medicinal substances in microbes. Izd. Akad. Nauk. SSSR, M.-L., 1946.

26. V.P. Tokin. Bactericides of vegetable origin (phytocides). Medgiz, M., 1942.

27. N.G. Kholodnyi. Soil gases and their biological significance. Priroda, No. 3, 1953.

28. S. L'vov. Works of the jubilee scientific session of the LSU, pp. 223-243, 1946.

29. V.A. Sokolov and N.M. Turkel'taub. Geochemical surveying by the method of accumulation of hydrocarbons on adsorbents. Geokhim. metody poiskov nefti i gaza, No. I. Gostoptekhizdat, 1953.

30. M.I. Subbota. Complex study of the causes of the seasonal character of gas survey indices. Nefti. khoz., No. 7, 1947.

31. A.G. Doyarenko. Elements of the aerial regime of the soil. Nauchnoagronom. zhurn., No. 3, GONTI, 1925.

32. M.I. Subbota. Seasonal fluctuations of gas survey indices and methods of allowing for them. Geokhim metody poiskov nefti i gaza, No. I. Gostoptekhizdat, 1953.

33. A.A. Cherepennikov. Direction of the sampling and analysis of natural gases. Gosgeolizdat, 1951.

34. N.M. Turkel'taub. Chromatographic apparatus for the analysis of hydrocarbon gases. Zav. laboratoriya, No. 5, 1949.

35. N.M. Turkel'taub. Chromatographic methods of resolution of hydrocarbon mixtures. Geokhim. metody poiskov nefti i gaza, No. I. Gostoptekhizdat, 1953.

36. M.I. Subbota and V.S. Klyucharev. Method and experience in application of the gas survey in depth. Sb. "Geokhim metody poiskov nefti", No. 1, Gostoptekhizdat, 1950.

37. V.S. Kotov. Experience in the application of the deep gas survey. Polevaya i promyslovaya geokhimiya, No. 1. Gostoptekhizdat, 1953.

38. G.S. Chikryzov. Experiment in the use of the gas survey for the detection of deep-lying coal deposits. Razvedka nedr, No. 12, 1938.

39. N.A. Khramov. Prospecting for ozokerite formations and the surveying thereof. Gostoptekhizdat, 1952.

40. E.K. Gerling. Attempt to detect the earth's helium respiration. Sb. "Akad. V.I. Vednarskomu k pyatidesyatiletiyu nauchn. i pedag. deyatel'nosti", Vol. I. Izd. Akad. Nauk SSSR, 1936.

CHAPTER FIVE

Core-Gas Surveys

INTRODUCTION

The core-gas survey is one of the geochemical methods of prospecting for oil and gas formations that uses hydrocarbon gases. This method differs from the gas survey in that gases absorbed by rocks[1] are studied, i.e., bound gases, while the gas survey studies free gases contained in the top-most layer of the zone of aeration.

Problems of the Method

The core-gas survey is a prospecting method and is used both for detailed and reconnaissance investigations. Detailed investigations are conducted mainly in areas where geological data indicate the possible presence of petroleum. It is only necessary to decide which of the areas under consideration is most favorable and holds first priority for exploratory drilling.

A detailed survey may be conducted by taking ground samples at the usual depth for geochemical methods (3 m.) or at greater depths (6 - 20 m.); in the latter case it is called the deep core-gas survey. The problems of the deeper survey are the same, but more reliable results are obtained. Detailed surveys on a small scale (1:100,000 - 1:200,000) are conducted even in geologically little-studied areas where no individual structures have yet been found.

The detailed core-gas survey is often conducted in conjunction with a gas survey in order to shed more light on the gaseous regime of subsoil layers, i.e., both free and bound gas are studied. In conjunction with these studies, bitumen investigations are conducted by the luminescence method.

The core-gas reconnaissance survey is conducted for the purpose of evaluating the general prospects of large areas. Sometimes the problem of determining the gas content of rocks of different ages (in well exposed regions) and that of evaluating their reservoir properties may be solved by this method. This survey is carried out in conjunction with geological studies. The core-gas survey may also be used to study the gas saturation of cores from exploratory wells.

Core-gas surveying has several advantages over gas surveying. It can be conducted in moist areas where ordinary gas surveying does not work. Gas extracted from rocks by using a vacuum extractor or by heating the rock always contains more hydrocarbons than does free gas. For this reason the accuracy of analytical results for gas extracted from a core increases and the anomalies found are more positive. Core-gas surveying

---

[1] "Porod" is used in Russian for "rock" in the most general sense and in this chapter as well as others refers to consolidated and unconsolidated forms. Ed.

may be used at any time of the year, even in the winter, when ordinary gas surveying is not usually feasible.

Core-gas surveys give good results in areas where the rocks are fractured and fissured. For this reason, regions where folding has taken place are most favorable for using the method.

Origin and Development of the Method

Core-gas surveying grew out of the gas survey method developed by V. A. Sokolov. In 1934-1935 the geologist G. A. Mogilevskii constructed a special apparatus which he used to study the gas saturation of rocks (1, 2, 3). The use of core-gas surveying to supplement gas survey data in moist areas was begun in 1941-1942. E. M. Geller played an important role in this work. M. I. Subbota was the first to apply core-gas surveying to a whole formation in 1943 in the Ishimbay region. Questions on the length of time a core may be kept before degassing, the seasonal variations in concentration of sorbed gases, the depth of sampling, etc., were answered.

In 1944-1945 research on this method was accelerated. The study of cores from "krelius" bore holes was begun (N. A. Koprova, B. A. Lobov). In 1947 an improved field degasifier (PDP) was built. M. I. Subbota proposed a new type of degasifier in 1948. Subbota's apparatus, a thermal degasifier, has been further improved. Starting in 1948 the core-gas survey became one of the standard methods used in petroleum prospecting.

In the USA the core-gas survey, under the name of the soil-analytical survey, began its development only in 1937 after publication in an American journal of a reference to an article by G. A. Mogilevskii.

THEORETICAL BASIS OF THE CORE-GAS SURVEY

In the process of the migration of gases within the earth's crust, absorption (sorption) of a definite part of the gas by rocks[2] occurs. Absorption[3] (sorption) of gases and vapors occurs both at the surface of a solid body (adsorption) and throughout its mass (internal absorption). Adsorption is the condensation of gas on the surface of the body and takes place relatively quickly. Internal absorption takes place extremely slowly, since the penetration of gas molecules into non-porous bodies proceeds by diffusion. Other forms of sorption are capillary condensation, which is characteristic in the narrow capillaries of a sorbent and is due to decrease of vapor pressure, and chemisorption, in which gases and vapors react chemically with the solid body.

In gas absorption it is very difficult to consider adsorption, internal absorption, capillary condensation, and chemisorption in pure form.

---

[2]Many rocks (especially clays) contain small amounts of sorbed hydrocarbon gas which was formed directly in the rock itself during its accumulation (syngenetic gas), consolidation, and transformation (diagenetic gas). These hydrocarbon gases have no connection with the migration of gas from the depths.

[3]"Pogloshchenie" has been translated as "absorption" and, as the authors indicate, is used in the same general sense as "sorption", whereas, "absorbtsiya" has been translated as "internal absorption" and is used in a more restricted sense. Ed.

Therefore, it is usual for analysis to be limited to the determination of total absorption capacity, i.e., sorption. This depends on the sorptive capacity of the rocks, the properties and pressure of the gas, and the temperature and moisture content of the rocks. The process of sorption is always exothermic and, therefore, the degree of sorption sharply increases with a decrease in temperature. On the contrary, increase of temperature decreases sorption; this effect is used for recovery of the absorbed gas. For a given gas and sorbent, the quantity of gas sorbed upon establishment of equilibrium is determined by the following equation:

$$a = f(pT),$$

where, a is the quantity of gas sorbed by 1 g. of rock; p is the equilibrium pressure; T is the absolute temperature.

In the study of adsorption equilibria, the relationship between the quantity of adsorbed substance and the partial pressure at constant temperature is investigated. The adsorption isotherm makes it possible to determine experimentally the capacity of the adsorbent (sorption capacity).

The theory of adsorption may be regarded as a theory of adsorption equilibrium. However, the adsorption isotherm does not give accurate information as to the rate of adsorption. The theory of adsorption assumes that the forces causing adsorption are chemical forces, the action of which extends to a very short distance. Therefore, Langmuir holds that adsorption is always unimolecular.

On the basis of the premises stated above, Langmuir derives the equation

$$a = \frac{V_m bp}{1 + bp}$$

where a is the quantity of adsorbed substance; V_m is the volume of adsorbed gas needed to form a complete unimolecular layer; p is the equilibrium pressure; b is a function of temperature (V_m and b are constants).

The Langmuir equation applies to experimental data in the entire range of pressures from zero to saturation. At low temperatures or low degrees of adsorption, the equation is used in the following form:

$$a = V_m bp.$$

This equation was obtained by neglecting the quantity bp in the denominator, because it is negligible in comparison with unity. Since V_m and b are constants, the product $V_m b$ will be represented by H (the Henry coefficient), after which the equation will have the following form:

$$A = Hp,$$

whence,

$$H = \frac{A}{p}.$$

The adsorption coefficient H is the ratio of the quantity of substance in the adsorbed phase per unit volume to that in the gas phase. It characterizes the adsorption capacity of the given adsorbent. The adsorption coefficient is a logarithmic function of temperature, namely:

$$H = Ae^{Q/RT},$$

where, Q is the heat of adsorption; A and R are constants.

The adsorption of gases and vapors by solid bodies depends on the effective surface of the adsorbent. Adsorbents, such as activated charcoal, have a specific surface of the order of 1500 m.^{2} per g. and possess the greatest adsorption capacity of all known sorbents. Silica gels have a specific surface of the order of 500 m.^{2} per g. and are good sorbents, while clays, having a specific surface of about 1 m.^{2} per g., are relatively weak ones. Sands have the least adsorption capacity.

In laboratory investigations the degree of sorption, a, is usually expressed in milliliters (cubic centimeters) of gas sorbed by 1 g. of sorbent (a, in cm.^{3}/g.) under standard conditions (760 mm. pressure and 0° C). Since the core-gas survey is concerned with very low concentrations of sorbed hydrocarbon gas, it is inconvenient to give results in cm.^{3}/g.; small values, difficult to represent, are obtained. Therefore, results are usually given in cm.^{3} of gas per 1 kg. of rock.

The study of the sorption of gas by rocks was begun relatively recently, mainly in connection with the problem of safety in mining. According to the data of G. D. Lidin (4) the sorption capacity of Donbas coals is expressed by the following figures (Table 16).

TABLE 16. Sorption Capacity of Donets Coals (according to G. D. Lidin)

Gas	Anthracite coal, ml./g.	Bituminous coal, ml./g.
Carbon dioxide . .	25.20–34.50	24.30
Methane.	5.50–7.00	4.90
Oxygen	1.10–1.52	1.10
Nitrogen	1.09–1.67	1.16

The sorption capacity of rocks characteristic of oil formations was first studied in Baku in 1938 (V. M. Fokeev). In 1944 the work was continued on Saratov gas and oil formations. As a result of the investigation, V. M. Fokeev ascertained that propane and hexane are adsorbed much more than methane. The sorption capacity of various rocks is given in Table 17. The sorption capacity of these rocks for hexane is slightly less than for propane.

TABLE 17. Sorption Capacity of Sedimentary Rocks (according to V. M. Fokeev)

Rock	Gas	
	methane, ml./g.	propane, ml./g.
Silty clay	0.276	0.743
Clay containing a little sand . . .	0.135	0.221
Limestone containing biomorphic detritus	0.130	0.233
The same, recrystallized	0.100	0.126

In 1945 V. E. Vasserbern studied the sorption capacity of rocks for other gas- and oil-bearing areas of the Saratov region (5). According to the data of V. E. Vasserbert the sorption capacity, even of different portions of one and the same rock, fluctuates strongly. The range of values for the sorption capacity of rocks for methane is given in the following data.

Clays . . . . 0.074 - 0.220 ml./g.
Casting sand . . . . 0.110 ml./g.
Sands and sandstones. . . . . . 0.060 - 0.074 ml./g.
Limestones and dolomites . . . Zero - 0.071 (rarely to 0.104) ml./g.

The variations in the sorption capacity is apparently the result of changes in the petrographic and physical properties of the rocks.

Determination of the sorption capacity was carried out under static conditions by the volumetric method. The test gas was brough into contact with the rock in a vacuum after preliminary removal of absorbed gas and water vapor from the rock. The rock intended for this purpose was reduced to a fine powder and dried in a vacuum at 100° C for 1.5 - 2 hours. The powder so prepared became saturated by the gas in the course of several hours. In Figure 37 is shown a typical isotherm of the sorption of methane by yellow-brown clay, sandy clay, and calcareous clay. The accuracy and reproducibility are indicated by the white and black circles corresponding to two different experiments. This graph and the figures given earlier demonstrate the low sorption capacity of all rocks studied.

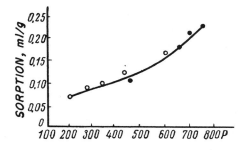

Fig. 37. Sorption isotherm for methane on clay.

The study of the sorption of gas by rock, undertaken by V. M. Fokeev and V. E. Vasserberg was conducted with samples specially prepared for the experiment, and 100% pure gas was used for saturation. In 1951 a study of sorption was completed by N. D. Tyuryaev and M. I. Subbota with rock samples that had not undergone any preliminary treatment. In this study the time of contact with gas was increased to 43 - 51 days. The methane concentration was reduced to 1.5288 - 0.7950 %, i.e., nearly 100 times. Thus, an attempt was made to approximate the experimental conditions of the natural environment.

The gas was recovered in the following manner. A piece of rock saturated by gas was quickly transferred from the saturating apparatus to a small flask containing boiled water and closed by a stopper with an outlet. In the process of boiling, the rock disintegrated into fine particles and gave off all the gas, which was drawn off with the aid of a mercury pump. The gas was analyzed by means of a TG-5A apparatus with an accuracy of $10^{-4}\%$.

In these experiments the total absorption capacity of the rock was determined, i.e., sorbed gas contained in the pores and dissolved in the moisture in the rock was recovered. In the core-gas survey all the gas, regardless of the manner in which it is bound to the rock (except for chemically bound gas), is pumped out of the rock, and therefore, the data of these experiments may be compared with field results. Table 18 gives some typical experimental results.

TABLE 18. Experimental Determinations of the Total Absorption Capacity of Rocks

Name of rock	Concentration of methane in air at saturation, %	Total moisture content of rock, %	Total absorption capacity, ml./g.
Yellow-brown clay, very sandy, stratified, of Quaternary age.	1.263	22.7	0.00021
White clay, very calcareous, of Quaternary age. .	0.9280	20.4	0.00024
Dark-gray clay, carbonaceous, from the coal measures.	0.7950	26.5	0.00070
Clay-sand soil, dark brown, swamp-soil, with plant roots	0.9478	25.0	0.00971

From the table, it may be seen that yellow-brown clay has a negligibly small absorption capacity which characterizes not sorption but porosity of this rock for the most part. Dark-gray carbonaceous clay containing traces of organic matter has three times more absorption capacity. Without doubt, part of the measured gas is sorbed by the rock, whose sorption capacity has been further increased owing to organic inclusions. Soil, rich in organic matter, absorbs nearly 50 times as much methane as clay that has no trace of organic matter.

If the figures obtained are converted to ml. per kg., it may be expected that when the concentration of methane in the subsoil air is about 0.01%, yellow-brown clay will contain 0.0021 ml./kg., dark-gray carbonaceous clay will contain 0.0070 ml./kg., and soil will contain 0.0971 ml./kg.

In a number of cases, these values approach the results obtained in the core-gas survey, but generally, they are lower. How may this be explained? Apparently by the fact that the experimental saturation of rock by hydrocarbon gas does not exactly reproduce natural conditions. In the natural environment, the rock is in contact with the gas for many thousands and millions of years. During this time the gas is able to penetrate into those parts of the rock (and into the crystal lattice of minerals), which it cannot reach in the short periods of these experiments.

It is known that helium has a very high diffusion coefficient and passes through glass to an appreciable extent. However, some minerals in which helium is generated partially retain it. V. V. Belousov (6) holds that helium escapes from a mineral as a result of diffusion through the crystal lattice and that the mineral retains, on the average, about 35% of the helium formed within it.

In Table 19 are given selected data on the content of helium recovered from various minerals and rocks, taken from the work by V. V. Belousov (6).

TABLE 19. Content of Helium in Various Minerals (according to V. V. Belousov)

Name of mineral	Helium content, cm.^{3}/g.	Author
Cleveite (Uraninite)	0.0000072	Ramsay
Monazite	0.00000241	Strutt
Zircon	0.000123	,,
Orthite	0.002200	,,
Gadolinite	0.010500	,,
Hematite	0.000073	,,
Calcite	0.00000058	,,
Garnet	0.000029	,,
Basalt	0.0000019	,,
Limonite	0.000150	,,

The relatively high content of helium in minerals is difficult to explain from the point of view of the theory of sorption, since solid bodies possess practically no sorption capacity for helium. V. V. Belousov (6) holds that we have here a case of solution of a gaseous substance in a solid body, combined with filling of separate, very small cavities. Interesting data for interpreting the relation between rock and absorbed gas are given by A. A. Cherepennikov (7) with regard to gases from the salts of the Solikamsk mine.

As the data given by V. V. Belousov (6) and A. A. Cherepennikov (7) indicate, the absorbed gas recoverable from rock is contained in the pore spaces between the mineral grains, in cavities within the minerals themselves, and sorbed on the grain surfaces. Thus, the gas permeates the entire mass of the rock. For this reason experimental data on the gas saturation of various rocks are lower than results obtained in the recovery of gas which has been impregnating the rock in its natural environment for millions of years.

This is confirmed by experiments on the recovery of helium from minerals (6). The fact that helium is practically not sorbed is utilized in the determination of the internal free volume of the rock before its saturation with the test gas (5). However, helium is sometimes recovered from minerals and rocks in quite appreciable amounts.

The same effect is observed in the saturation of rocks by methane. The sorption capacity of most rocks for methane is insignificant, however, an appreciable amount of methane may be recovered from certain rocks in nature. Thus, in the core-gas survey, hydrocarbon gases that have been associated with rocks in a great variety of ways are studied. Therefore, it is more correct to say that the method is based on an investigation of the total absorption properties of a rock and not merely its sorption capacity.

METHODS OF FIELD WORK

The method of field work in the core-gas survey differs little from that of the gas survey, described in Chapter IV. Here we shall dwell only on some of its specific peculiarities. The distribution of profiles and points in reconnaissance and detailed surveying is done according to the uniform, staggered, and differentiated systems. Small-scale reconnaissance investigations are conducted, independently or in conjunction with a geological survey, on natural outcrops. Rock samples intended for the study of absorbed gas are taken from freshly exposed rock surfaces.

Coring Operations

Sampling of rock from shallow wells 3 - 20 m. in depth is done either directly with a drill or with the aid of a special core-cutter. The core-cutter consists of a cylindrical body 60 - 80 mm. in diameter (depending on the diameter of the well) and 15 - 20 cm. long, into which a metal sleeve is inserted. The tip of the core-cutter has a sharp cutting edge and a threaded coupling for attaching it to the body of the device. The other end of the core-cutter is screwed on to a series of rods.

In operation, the core-cutter is lowered to the bottom of the well and driven into the ground with a sledge-hammer (for this purpose, a special anvil is screwed on the upper end of the rods). Then the core-cutter is lifted out of the well, the tip is removed, the sleeve is extracted with the rock, and the core is transferred to a clean bag (paper or cloth). All instruments, without exception, must be absolutely clean.

If the core-gas survey is conducted in conjunction with a gas survey, cores are taken at the beginning, the well is then sealed, and samples of free gas are taken. The deep core-gas survey may give much better results if the core is freed from drilling fluid immediately after removal and packed in paper or in a bag.

Taking rock in the form of a core is preferable to taking rock fragments from the drill (for example, a seismic or spiral drill). The advantage of this consists in the fact that in rock with continuous texture, the absorbed gas is better retained than in crumpled or shattered rock. For full retention of absorbed gas, it is necessary to transfer the rock samples immediately to special, hermetically sealed vessels whick simultaneously act as degasifier components. Practice, however, has shown that when the rock is stored in a package, a considerable amount of absorbed gas is retained by the rock.

Effect of Storage Time on Cores

Methods of rock sampling for degasification are closely connected with questions of the permissible storage times of cores from the time of sampling to the extraction of gas. The first investigations of the effects of storage time on gas content were conducted in 1943 in Ishimbai. Core samples were taken simultaneously from each well. One was put directly into a gas-extractor which was hermetically sealed immediately, and two were wrapped in paper packages. The core in one of the paper packages was stored for 2 - 3 days and was then subjected to degasification. The core in the other package was stored 20 - 30 days. As a result of this

investigation, it was found that the concentrations of gas in the core that
was sealed from air immediately were nearly the same as those obtained
from the core that was stored in air for 2 - 3 days. The general character
of the gas anomaly obtained was almost the same in both cases and indicated
an oil pool. After 20 - 30 days of storage, the concentrations of gas were
diminished and the configuration of the anomaly was changed. It must be
stated that in this first experiment the gas was analyzed in a stationary
mercury apparatus, and the hydrocarbons contained a considerable admixture of nitrous oxide. However, this is not of fundamental importance in
solving problems of methodology because the results were comparable in
all cases.

In 1949 more detailed investigations of this problem were conducted in
the Kirovabad region of Azerbaijan. Core samples weighing 1 kg. were
taken from each well and divided into two parts. From one part the gas
was recovered within a day after the samples were taken, while from the
other, the gas was recovered 3 - 4 months after sampling. The samples
were stored in paper packages in a compartment containing pure air. In
all cases, a decrease in the average concentrations of combustible gas
after 3 - 4 months of storage was observed. A second analysis showed
concentrations of 11 - 18% below the first. However, repeated analyses
did not all give decreases in gas concentration; because some samples
contained more hydrocarbon gases after storage. This is explained mainly
by a non-uniform gas impregnation of the rock.

L. N. Bykov (8) conducted similar investigations earlier with anthracite. From 100 g. of anthracite, taken from a mine of the Chistyakovskii
ore administration, about 613 cm.^{3} of methane was evolved on heating to
100°. After 13.3 months a second analysis was conducted, another portion
of this piece being used, and the methane content of the sample proved to
be equal to 120 cm.^{3} per 100 g. of coal. The author states that, notwith-
standing the quite prolonged time of storage of the sample in open air, the
coal retained about 20% of its original methane.

From the evidence given here, it is apparent that the absorbed gas is
retained for a relatively long time at high concentrations in extracted rock.
However, from the standpoint of the purposes of the core-gas survey, it is
necessary to strive to decrease gas losses. Therefore, the core is degassed not later than the next day after sampling.

Depth of Sampling

The depth of core sampling for the purpose of gas recovery is as important
as in the gas survey, if not more so. Soil gases, formed as a result of the
biochemical transformation of the soil and the decomposition of dead
organisms falling into it, penetrate downward along pores and cracks or in
dissolved form and are absorbed by the rock. We have already encountered
this phenomenon in considering the depth of sampling for free gas. This
question is complicated by the fact that core-gas survey results are already
affected by the organic inclusions themselves, such as plant roots penetrating the rock, soil carried down by moles, and also undecomposed
organic inclusions. The nearer to the surface the sample is taken, the
greater the probability that the rock will contain decomposing organic
matter.

Plant rootlets and other organic inclusions, heated to 100° in the degasification process, evolve volatile organic substances which pass into the gas sample along with the hydrocarbons and can easily be mistaken for hydrocarbons. For this reason rock samples must be taken from such depths that the possibility of contamination is minimized. The roots of many plants extend to a depth of 2 - 3 m., while those of others extend to 5 - 6 m. (9). From this, it would follow that the minimum depth of coring should be fixed, as a rule, at 3 m. Here it must be pointed out that the greater the depth from which the rock is taken, the more reliable the result will be, and therefore, it is always necessary to strive to increase the depth of sampling to the limit of technical possibilities and economic expediency.

For difficult regions the depth of coring must be established on the basis of preliminary investigations. If core holes are drilled to a depth of 6 - 10 m. or more, cores are taken not only at a single depth (the bottom), but along the entire length of the hole at 1 - 2 m. intervals.

In Figure 38 are shown the results of a survey made on a well drilled within the limits of a gas anomaly. It shows that a study of the gas-saturations of cores from several depths makes it possible to elucidate the changes in gas concentration not only for a given area but also with depth. If high gas concentrations remain constant or increase, it indicates the reliability of the anomaly and its connection with a deep source. On the other hand, if the concentration of gas decreases with depth, it indicates the presence of an anomaly due to surface-gas formation, i.e., a false gas anomaly. In the figure it is evident that high concentrations of gas in the

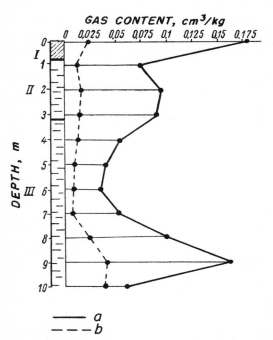

Fig. 38. Change in concentration of absorbed gas at different depths. I—soil of a marshy area; II—yellow-gray clay; III—dark-gray clay; a—methane; b—heavy hydrocarbons.

soil are the result of the formation of gas in the soil itself. Gases found in
the soil, which are absorbed by activated charcoal and therefore recorded
as "heavy hydrocarbons", are not petroleum hydrocarbons. They mainly
consist of various volatile organic substances originating at the surface.

The choice of depth for core-gas surveys in marshy areas is more
complicated. Marshy areas are characterized by accumulations of large
masses of plant remains undergoing slow decomposition with a limited access of oxygen. In such areas, even at a depth of several tens of centimeters, rocks of black, greyish blue, or dark blue color, characteristic of
a reducing environment, are encountered. Brown oxides of iron are
reduced here to ferrous oxide. The rock emits a sharp, marshy odor and
sometimes H_2S is observed. Gases recovered from cores contain much
CO_2, N_2, and CH_4.

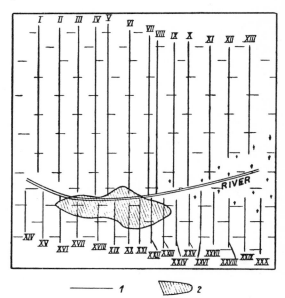

Fig. 39. Example of a core-gas survey in a marshy
area. 1—profile of wells with background concentrations of heavy hydrocarbons; 2—heavy-hydrocarbon anomaly.

Core-gas surveys in such areas necessarily have to go below the zone
of active formation of plants, i.e., to a depth at which hardly any unconvert-
ed organic matter is encountered. In peat bogs it is necessary to go below
the peat layer. Since much CO_2 and CH_4 are formed in marshes, the gas
must be freed from CO_2 by passing it through a solution of caustic alkali
before analysis in a TG-5A apparatus. Methane is not taken into account
in the interpretation. All correlations in such areas must be based on the
heavy hydrocarbons only.

In Figure 39 is shown a core-gas survey compiled for a marshy area.
From the map it is evident that the boundaries of the heavy-hydrocarbon
anomaly are adequately sharp and the coefficient of contrast of the anomaly
is as high as 2.2. By contrast, a map compiled for methane proved to be
indistinct, broad, and weak, and therefore unreliable.

Fluctuations in the Gas Content of Rock

The gas content of rock is defined as the total content of gases that are
sorbed, free (in the pores), and dissolved in water within the porous media.
In the core-gas survey, we are, of course, interested only in the methane
and heavy hydrocarbons that can be recovered. The gas content of rock is
not constant but fluctuates as a result of the following causes.

1. The lithological peculiarities of rock have a great effect on the non-
uniform impregnation by gas. Clay has a higher sorption capacity than
sand and therefore will hold more gas than sand under comparable conditions. Clay usually contains more organic matter than sand does, and this
in turn increases the sorption capacity of the clay. Clay is denser than
sand, and the gas contained in it escapes with greater difficulty to the atmosphere. Therefore, in the process of diurnal gas-exchange between the
topmost layer of the lithosphere and the atmosphere ("breathing of the
soil"), clay will retain more gas and undergo less aeration than sand. In
the storage of cores, clay will lose less gas (especially the gas held in the
pores) than sand.

2. Diurnal and seasonal fluctuations of gas content are closely connected with variations in atmospheric conditions: diurnal gas-exchange
(depending on the diurnal course of temperature and pressure), change of
moisture content, and seasonal change of temperature. These conditions
jointly affect the bacterial population that produces and absorbs hydrocarbon gases in the soil and subsoil. Seasonal variations in the concentrations
of absorbed gas are similar to the fluctuations observed in the free soil
gases (Fig. 40) and are due to the same causes that affect the free gases.

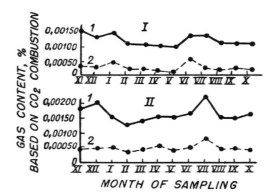

Fig. 40. Change in concentration of hydrocarbon
gases in the subsoil with respect to the month of
sampling. I—free gas from rock; II—gas absorbed by rock; 1 —methane; 2 —heavy hydrocarbons.

Fluctuations of absorbed gas cannot be explained by the condensation of
hydrocarbons with a decrease in temperature, since methane, ethane, and
propane have high vapor pressures at ordinary temperatures.

The sorption properties of rocks are also slightly changed within the
range of temperatures characteristic of the subsoil. B. E. Vasserberg

made a special study of this question (5). He ascertained that the seasonal fluctuations of gas-survey results observed by a number of authors cannot be explained by the assumption that the gas content of core samples taken in summer is higher simply because more sorbed hydrocarbons are freed. In the opinion of Vasserberg, it is more likely that seasonal fluctuations in the hydrocarbon content of the subsoil air depend on a change in the conditions of gas-exchange, due to closing of surface capillaries in the soil by water or ice. To this must be added the effect of the seasonal formation of gases of biochemical origin.

In order to reduce the seasonal errors in gas-survey results, it is recommended that specific areas be surveyed within brief periods not exceeding 1 - 2 months. It is also important to increase the depth of core sampling.

3. Fluctuations in the concentrations of absorbed hydrocarbons depend largely on the time and manner of storage of the cores and on the manner in which the rock is degassed. The longer the core is stored, the less gas it will contain. Therefore, the first analysis is nearly always higher than the second. However, the contrary also occurs. This is caused by the fact that rocks, particularly those of Quaternary age, have an inhomogeneous lithological composition. Although they may appear similar, samples taken from different parts of a inhomogeneous core may contain different amounts of absorbed gas.

4. One of the chief factors affecting the non-uniform impregnation of rocks by hydrocarbon gas is the existence of dissimilar conditions during the migration of hydrocarbons in different parts of the area. Migrating gas chooses the path of least resistance, and therefore, the gas concentrations will be higher in zones of tectonic disturbances and zones of increased fissuring and porosity. However, within the limits of the zone of aeration, the more porous and fissured rocks will contain less gas than dense sedimentary clays if, of course, the porous rocks are not covered at the top with a relatively impermeable cap.

5. The inhomogeneous impregnation of rock by gas is sometimes greatly affected by syngenetic hydrocarbon gas, which is closely related to the lithological peculiarities of the rock, having been generated at the moment of agglomeration and formation of the latter. Higher concentrations of absorbed syngenetic gas are usually observed in rocks characterized by a higher content of organic matter. Rocks of various ages have their characteristic background of syngenetic gas, which has no connection with the migration of hydrocarbons from the depths.

Practical core-gas survey work should be guided by the following principles.

a. Within the bounds of a gas anomaly there may be points with high concentrations of absorbed hydrocarbons, as well as points with low or even zero concentrations. These and other points may alternate throughout the area or be grouped in specific places. Repeated degasification of different pieces of a core from a single well will also, sometimes, give variable results owing to the non-uniformity of gas impregnation. However, increased concentrations of hydrocarbons are usually found in at least 40% of the analyses within the bounds of a gas anomaly.

b. Within the limits of the background, concentrations of absorbed gas are usually low and can be high only at random points. In the majority of cases these points are associated with contemporary gas formation.

c. A high gas background may be due either to syngenetic gas or to gas formation in marshy areas.

METHODS OF DEGASSING CORES

There are several methods of recovering gas from rocks: a. degassing with the aid of elevated temperatures; b. degassing with the aid of vacuum; e. degassing by pulverization of the rock; and d. degassing by displacement and washing. The methods enumerated are hardly ever used alone but are usually applied in various combinations.

Degassing at Elevated Temperatures

Heating of rock was used long ago for recovery of gas. However, the first important work was done in 1908 by R. Chamberlain, who heated igneous and metamorphic rocks to 850° in order to recover various gases from them. According to the data of R. Chamberlain (10), methane was obtained from gneisses, granites, and other rocks with the evolution beginning at a temperature of $+448^{\circ}C$ or higher. The high temperature at which the evolution of methane begins, indicates the complex nature of the bond between the methane and the rock. In all probability, methane is evolved as a result of chemical reactions occurring in heating of the crystalline rocks. Besides traces of methane, other gases such as hydrogen, carbon dioxide, carbon monoxide, and nitrogen were also evolved from the crystalline rocks.

Overheating of the rock during gas extraction leads to the formation of new gases, previously not present in the rock. Therefore, it was thought that heating above $+100^{\circ}$ in order to evolve sorbed hydrocarbon gases was undesirable. In 1927 L. N. Bykov (8), in order to study the gas content of coal, put samples into a copper flask with a capacity of 175 cm.^{3} and, after sealing, heated it in a water bath to 100°. In certain cases the temperature was raised to 200° in order to achieve complete desorption. The degasification of a single sample was continued for at least 3 hours in this method. However, even in a 30-hour period of degasification, not all the methane was evolved from coal. The results of analysis were given in cm.^{3} of methane recovered per 100 g. of coal. The error of analysis was found to be 1 cm.^{3}.

Degassing under Vacuum at Elevated Temperatures

G. A. Mogilevskii (1) was the first to carry out the desorption of hydrocarbon gas from rocks with the aid of vacuum and mild heating up to 70°. The core was put into a special vessel which was filled with water in order to displace atmospheric air. The vessel was connected through gas collectors to a vacuum pump. Mild heating of the vessel containing the rock (Fig. 41) in the presence of water did not make it possible to displace all the gas from the core.

In 1940 - 1941 a new desorption apparatus was constructed by the Neftegazos'emka bureau. Cores were degasified with the aid of a vacuum and heating to 70 - 100°. A diagram of the apparatus is shown in Figure 42. The apparatus consists of a water pump (gas collector plus leveling bottle), to which is connected a Kamovskii pump for production of vacuum. The

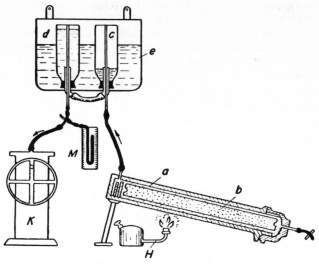

Fig. 41. Degasification apparatus of G. A. Mogilevskii.
a—vessel for core; b—core; c—bottle with aspirator
for collection of gas; d—leveling bottle; e—water bath;
K—Kamovskii vacuum pump; M—mercury vacuum
gauge; H—heater.

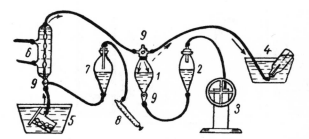

Fig. 42. Diagram of apparatus for degasification of
rock cores (1941). 1—central bulb for initial collection of gas; 2—leveling bulb; 3—Kamovskii
pump; 4—bottle for collection of gas; 5—glass gas-
extractor with core immersed in hot water; 6—condenser for water vapor; 7—bulb for preliminary
exhaustion of air from the condenser; 8—Schinz
pump; 9—glass stopcocks.

core is put into a glass gas-extractor which is then immersed in a water-
bath. Gas from the extractor first passes into the collecting bulb, and is
then transferred to the sample bottle. Evacuation is repeated until the
evolution of gas from the core has ceased. In this method of degasification
the gas sample became contaminated with the considerable amount of atmospheric air filling the free space in the gas-extractor that was not occupied by rock. In 1947 the construction of the apparatus was improved
and adapted to group work; however, the principal of operation remained
the same (Fig. 43).

The new field degasification apparatus consists of the following main parts: the apparatus proper, a Kamovskii pump, a glass gas-extractor, and a water bath with heater. A core taken from a well is put into the gas-extractor which is hermetically sealed and immersed in the water bath. With the aid of the Kamovskii pump and leveling bottle, a vacuum is established in the inner bulb, causing the gas and remaining air to pass from the extractor to the bulb. Degasification is done at a water-bath temperature of 100°. Water vapor is collected in a condenser lest it soften the grease in the central stopcock which must maintain a good vacuum.

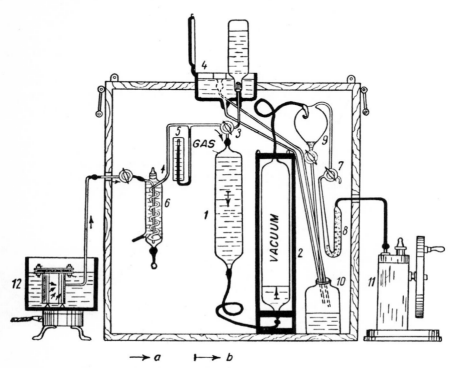

Fig. 43. Field desorption apparatus. 1—inner bulb; 2—leveling bottle; 3—central three-way stopcock; 4—Boravskii tank; 5—mercury vacuum gauge with scale; 6—trap for water vapor; 7—external three-way stopcock; 8—small tube for sorption of gas; 9—water trap; 10—overflow vessel; 11—Kamovskii pump; 12—glass gas-extractor with water bath; a—route of gas; b—route of water.

The first portion of gas pumped into the inner bulb is forced out by raising the leveling bottle and turning the stopcock to connect to the gas-collecting bottle, which is submerged in a Boravskii tank. After this the evacuation of gas from the extractor is repeated; this second operation achieves a considerably higher vacuum. The second gas volume is put into the same collecting bottle. The third and fourth evacuations usually suffice to recover all the gas that can be recovered by this method. The absolute pressure within the apparatus is ultimately reduced, usually, to 17 - 25 mm. Hg.

The vacuum is controlled with the aid of a mercury vacuum gauge. A water trap in the apparatus serves to protect the Kamovskii pump from

accidental intake of water, while the gas sorption tube serves to absorb any
gases that might be evolved from the oil in the Kamovskii pump.

The degasification of one piece of the core requires 25 - 35 min. The
weight of core material used amounts to 0.4 - 0.5 kg. and afterwards, the
core can still be used for further petrographic and micro-fossil study.
With the aid of the method described Neftegazos'emka conducted successful
investigations of the gas- and oil-bearing character of cores from various
areas. However, this procedure has several shortcomings which must be
taken into account in the interpretation of results. On of these is that, after
the gas-extractor is packed with the core, it still contains free space filled
with air. As a result, one can only investigate the gas content of a core
with regard to hydrocarbon and other gases not found in the atmosphere.

In an apparatus of this design it is impossible to attain complete degasification, and furthermore, samples may be contaminated by gases
evolved from the rubber gaskets, etc., or laboratory air passing into the
gas-extractor. In 1946-1947 E. M. Geller constructed a whole battery of
these devices, which operated under laboratory conditions. The vacuum
was produced by an oil pump driven by an electric motor (Fig. 44). This
apparatus had the same shortcomings as the preceding two.

Apparatus which works only with the aid of a vacuum does not give
reliable results in recovering gas from rocks and, therefore, is not used.
A major fault of devices of this kind is the excessively long time required
for more or less complete removal of gas from a rock sample. Furthermore, the gas is evolved more slowly from a whole core than from a
crushed one.

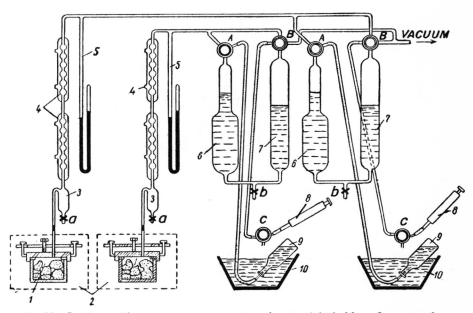

Fig. 44. Stationary thermovacuum apparatus. 1—gastight holder; 2—oven; 3—
water-vapor trap; 4—condenser for cooling of vapors; 5—mercury vacuum gauge;
6—initial collection bulb; 7—leveling bulb; 8—hand-operated pressure pump;
9—bottle for gas; 10—water bath; A, B, C—vacuum stopcocks; a, b—Hofmann
clamps.

Degassing by Disaggregation of the Rock under Vacuum

In order to accelerate the evolution of gas, the rock can be disaggregated under a vacuum. The rock is disintegrated either by mechanical or chemical means. One of the first devices, in which the rock was ground mechanically in a vacuum, was the mortar devised by K. A. Nenadkevich (11). The rock was ground in a mortar and the evolved gases were swept out by drawing pure air through the mortar.

In 1948 G. M. Agababov constructed a much improved vacuum mortar (Fig. 45). It consists of the following parts: (1) a steel body with a flange and drop screws; (2) a cover which is attached to the body by means of the drop screws; (3) drop screws (thumb-screws); (4) a rubber gasket between the cover and the body for better sealing; (5) a pestle with a handle, for grinding the rock; (6) a flexible tube; (7) an outlet for the removal of gas; (8) a water heater.

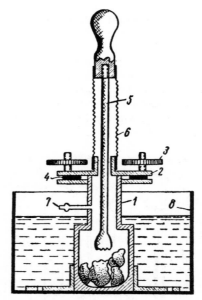

Fig. 45. Diagram of vacuum mortar for degassing cores. 1 —body; 2 —cover; 3 —thumbscrews; 4 —rubber gasket; 5 —pestle with handle; 6 —flexible tube; 7 —outlet for removal of gas; 8 —water heater.

The rock to be degassed is put into the mortar, hermetically enclosed, and ground for 20 - 40 min., depending on its strength. Before grinding, a small amount of air is drawn out of the mortar. Then, as the rock is converted to a powder, gas is pumped out of the mortar with the aid of a vacuum produced by leveling vessels filled with mercury (mercury pump). For complete recovery of gas, the mortar may be set in a hot water bath. The mortar is not suitable for the degasification of soft rocks.

The vacuum ball mill constructed by M. M. Elinson (12) is based on the principle of grinding rock in a vacuum. In Figure 46 is given the plan

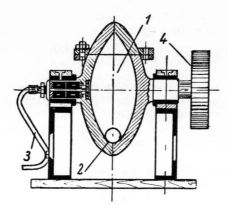

Fig. 46. Vacuum ball mill. 1—chamber
for rock; 2—steel balls for grinding of
rock; 3—tube for exhaustion of gas;
4—pulley for electric motor drive.

of construction of the mill. The vacuum mill consists of a body (frame), a
rotating chamber for rock, which contains steel balls (of the ball-bearing
type), and a tube for exhaustion of gas. The mill is turned by an electric
motor. The rock is placed in the chamber along with the steel balls, a
slight vacuum is produced, and the motor is then turned on. When the
chamber rotates, the steel balls crush the rock and grind it to a fine
powder. The gas evolved in this operation is collected for analysis. The
degasification of one sample requires 7 to 12 hours, so that the mill is inconvenient to use.

The vacuum mortar and the vacuum ball mill are intended for the degasification of dense rocks. These devices are invaluable for studying the
gas content of cores from "Krelius" bore holes drilled in limestones,
dolomites, marls, sandstones, etc. These methods of degasification are
not applicable to clays.

The recovery of gas from rock composed of limestone, dolomite, marl,
etc., is sometimes accomplished by dissolving the rock in appropriate
acids. E. M. Geller has constructed a degasification apparatus consisting
of a chamber for the rock and a set of burets containing reagents. The appropriate acid (hydrochloric acid for limestone, etc.) is admitted to the
chamber containing the rock, the latter is dissolved, and the liberated gas
is collected in a vessel and transferred to a bottle. In order to accelerate
the reaction, the chamber containing the rock may be heated by means of a
water bath. A shortcoming of this method is the formation of gases not
previously present in the rock, primarily a large quantity of carbon dioxide.

A. A. Cherepennikov (7) utilized the great solubility of salt in water
for the recovery of absorbed gas from samples of salt. Cherepennikov
states that better results were obtained by dissolving the salt sample in
degassed water and applying a vacuum without heating. By this method
carnallite yielded 10 - 12 ml. of gas per kg. of the potassium salt. From
90 to 170 ml. per kg. of salt was recovered from variegated sylvite and
about 210 ml. per kg. was recovered from milk-white sylvite.

Desorption by displacement and flushing with air or hot steam has not
as yet been used. These methods have found widespread application in

chromatographic apparatus for the purification of sorbents or recovery of a specific gas therefrom in a particular separation.

Degassing in Boiling Water

In 1948-1949 M. I. Subbota used a new method of desorbing gas from rock, namely, the degasification by steam of a core, first placed in boiling water. In this method the core disintegrates into its component particles and is converted to a clay suspension. From the latter, gas is recovered more quickly and more completely than from rock in degasifiers of earlier construction (3).

The thermal degasifier contains the following components (Fig. 47).

1. A vessel with a flange, to hold the cores. The capacity of the vessel is 2 liters. Six screws with wing nuts are fastened to the vessel around the periphery of the flange.

2. The lid of the vessel. The lid is clamped to the flange of the vessel by means of the wing nuts. Between them is a rubber gasket which must not make contact with the water in the vessel. To insure this, special grooves are cut in the lid.

3. A coil condenser. The coil is made from brass tubing 8 - 10 mm. in diameter and fitted into a galvanized iron tank. The capacity of the tank is 14 - 15 liters. The coiled tube in the lower part of the condenser is soldered to the body of the tank and brought outside. The upper end of the tube goes into a special pocket on the inner wall of the tank. The condenser is filled with cold well water, while the pocket is filled with boiled water. After degasification the coiled tube is rinsed with water with the aid of a rubber bulb.

4. A bottle for collecting the gas, which is slipped over the upper end of the coiled tube of the condenser.

5. Heating equipment — "primus" stove, "kerogas", electric heater, gas heater, etc., depending on local conditions. In forest regions remote from large populated places, it is most convenient to use a common wood-stove.

The thermal degasifier must be very thoroughly cleaned before the work is begun. The slightest trace of volatile hydrocarbons in the vessel may vitiate the results of a core-gas survey. The degasifier must be tested for cleanness before use. Pure boiled water is poured into the vessel, the lid is closed, the condenser is connected thereto, and the unit is placed on the heater. When the water boils, the air contained therein will pass into the bottle. If any traces of volatile hydrocarbons remain in the vessel or the condenser, they will be entrained by bubbles of air and steam and pass into the bottle. By analyzing the air obtained from the water with the TG-5A apparatus, the cleanness of the degasifier may be determined. If the concentration of combustilbe gas exceeds 0.0020 cm.^{3} per 1. of water (the zero reading of the apparatus), the cleaning of the degasifier must be repeated and its cleanness retested with the TG-5A apparatus.

After cleaning, 400 g. of rock are weighed on a technical scale and put into the vessel. Then the vessel is filled to the brim with boiled water and closed with the lid, which is clamped on by means of the wing nuts. Water is added to the vessel through the mouth of the outlet tube by means of a rubber bulb in order to insure that not a single air bubble remains. The vessel outlet is connected by rubber tubing to the lower end of the condenser

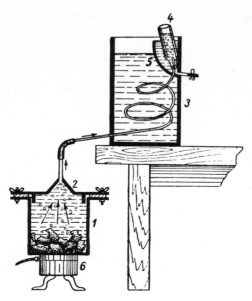

Fig. 47. Diagram of thermal degasifier for
cores of soft rocks. 1 —flanged vessel for
cores; 2 —lid of vessel; 3 —coiled condenser; 4 —bottle for gas; 5 —compartment
for collection of gas; 6 —heating equipment.

coil, which is filled with cold water beforehand. After this the heating of
the vessel containing the rock is begun.

In the process of heating the water and boiling it at a temperature
near 100°, the rock disintegrates into its component parts, and the steam
assists in removing the sorbed gas and transferring it to the bottle. The
boiling is continued until all the evolved gas has passed over to the bottle,
which is indicated by a constant gas level. Usually, the transfer of all the
evolved gas to the bottle requires 3 - 5 min. after the beginning of boiling,
rarely longer. The entire process of degasification takes 15 - 20 min.
over a gas burner, or 20 - 30 min. with a ''primus'' stove. Preparatory
operations take 10 - 15 min. and final steps take about 10 min. The
productivity of one thermal degasifier in an 8-hour working day amounts to
about 8 - 10 samples. After the core sample is evacuated, the collecting
bottle is sealed and labeled, and the gas volume is measured by comparison
with a standard graduated bottle.

The process of rock degasification with the aid of ''kerogas'' is shown
in Figure 48. It usually takes 12 - 18 min. to bring the water containing
the rock to a boil. During this period a volume of several cm.^{3} of gas is
evolved. The moment of first boiling coincides with the evolution of the
main mass of gas and the transfer of the latter to the collecting bottle.
Vigorous evolution continues for 2 - 4 min., depending on the density of the
rock and the power of the heating equipment. Further heating promotes the
evolution of residues of gas from isolated pores in the dense mass of the
rock, which is slowly disintegrating. In addition, boiling causes thermal
decomposition of bicarbonates with the formation of CO_2 and sometimes
also, H_2 as a result of corrosion of the metal.

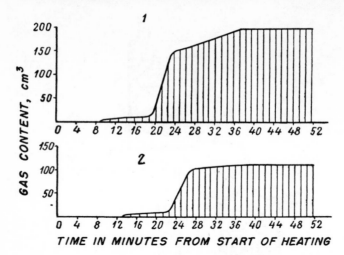

Fig. 48. Process of gas evolution from rock in a thermal degasifier. 1—evolution of gas from yellow-gray calcareous clay soil; 2—evolution of gas from ash-gray clay.

Among the hydrocarbon gases, methane is evolved first and then the heavy hydrocarbons. By boiling in the thermal degasifier, it is possible to recover 85 - 99.9% of the gas contained in the rock (this refers to all the gases: nitrogen, oxygen, carbon dioxide, hydrocarbon gases, etc.).

Usually, 80 - 95% of the hydrocarbon gases are recovered from friable rocks of Quaternary age, as has been demonstrated in special experiments. These tests were performed in the following manner. After recovery of the gas, the rock was not discarded but was cooled in the open air together with the water, and the degasification was repeated. The new gas volume was collected in a separate bottle. Then the rock was cooled again and degasified again, and a third sample was collected. This was repeated 8 times. Each sample of gas was analyzed separately.

As a result, it was found (Fig. 49) that, beginning with the third sample, the concentration of gas recovered from Quaternary deposits in oil-bearing areas was so small as to approach the zero reading of the apparatus. The total content of hydrocarbons in all eight samples was taken to be 100%. On this basis it was found that the first bottle contained 80 - 95% of the total original hydrocarbon content of the rock.

Gas is evolved slowly from dense shale of Maikop age. As is evident in Figure 49, the fifth "evacuation" is characterized by a new increase in the yield of hydrocarbon gas. This rise is explained by the fact that fine, very dense particles of shale begin to disintegrate and release the gas contained in them, which could not escape earlier. The first sample of gas from rock of this type contains from 45 to 65% of the hydrocarbon gas. Since the content of the latter in the rock is high, the incompleteness of recovery cannot affect the character of a gas anomaly.

Gas Analysis

The analysis of hydrocarbon gas recovered from a core is performed in TG-5A and chromatographic devices, which are described in Chapter IV.

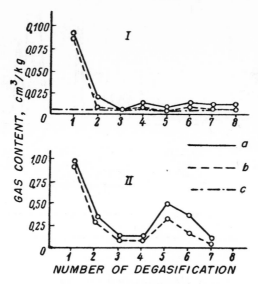

Fig. 49. Curves of gas evolution from rock in the thermal degasifier upon repeated heating. I— Quaternary clays, oil-bearing region; II—dense Maikop shales containing syngenetic bitumen and gas; a—total hydrocarbon gases (as CO_2); b— heavy hydrocarbons (as CO_2); c—zero reading of the apparatus.

The special feature of the analysis of gas recovered from a core consists in the fact that the sample often contains a large amount of CO_2 formed in the decomposition of bicarbonates. For this reason, it is necessary to add to the TG-5A devices bubblers filled with caustic alkali for the absorption of CO_2 or the preliminary elimination of CO_2. The analysis of hydrocarbon gas is done with an accuracy of 10^{-4}. The results of the analysis are calculated in cm.^{3} of hydrocarbons found in 1 kg. of rock (cm.^{3}/kg.), and therefore, all the gas obtained in the degasification of the rock is transferred to the apparatus. To determine the total characteristics of the gas, an analysis is performed with the VTI apparatus. Only a few samples are subjected to total gas analysis.

INTERPRETATION OF CORE-GAS SURVEY RESULTS

The results of the core-gas survey are recorded on a map and on a profile of the same type as that used in the gas survey. If there are areas on the chart which are characterized by increased concentrations of hydrocarbons, such areas represent gas anomalies or anomalous zones. This part of the work must be completed in the field, since it is then possible to verify gas anomalies in good time and to detail them if necessary. In the interpretation both heavy hydrocarbons and methane are considered. Heavy hydrocarbons are the chief indicator of oil-bearing character. In marshy areas methane cannot be used as an oil or gas indicator.

The gaseous background may be higher in a core-gas survey than in a gas survey owing to the more complete recovery of hydrocarbons, but

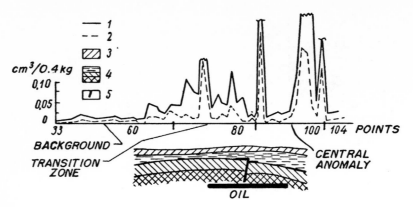

Fig. 50. Schematic core-gas survey profile over a formation. 1—total
content of combustible gas (as CO_2); 2—content of heavy hydrocarbons
(as CO_2); 3—Quaternary deposits; 4—various layers of the Maikop
group; 5—fault.

anomalies are more clearly distinguished for the same reason and often
have high contrast. In Figure 50 is shown a core-gas survey profile in
one of the oil bearing areas of southern Azerbaijan. The area is characterized by the presence of faults along which the migration of gas is
facilitated. The pool is located in strata of Maikop age, while migrating
gas was found in seams of Akchaghylian age. The coefficient of contrast
of the heavy hydrocarbon anomaly is 21.7, greater than the values usually
observed. In another part of this same region, the coefficient of contrast
of the total hydrocarbon gas anomaly is only 1.8, but even this is considerably higher than the contrast of gas survey indices (1.2 - 1.3) in the same
area.

In Figure 51 are shown the results of a core-gas reconnaissance survey conducted with cores from shallow wells in one of the offshore areas
of the Caspian Sea. Both profiles are transverse to the direction of the
fold. Wells 3 and 7 are located in the central part of the fold and have the
highest concentrations of hydrocarbons. The remaining wells are located
on the sides of the fold and contain little absorbed gas. The relatively low
methane content is noteworthy. This is explained by the fact that methane,
being a lighter gas, was lost during prolonged storage of the cores before
degasification (the cores were stored 4 - 6 months, packed in paper). Not-
withstanding this prolonged period of storage of the cores, good survey
results were obtained. Apparently, this is explained by the high original
content of heavy hydrocarbons in the samples, which made is possible to
retain part of the hydrocarbons until the moment of degasification.

Since the methods of interpretation of the core-gas survey and the gas
survey have much in common, we refer the reader to Chapter IV.

OTHER METHODS OF STUDYING THE GAS CONTENT OF CORES

The ''Thermobitumen'' Survey

In 1951 V. A. Lobov suggested heating the core to 200 - 250° in order to
recover hydrocarbon gas. In his opinion the core evolves gas much more

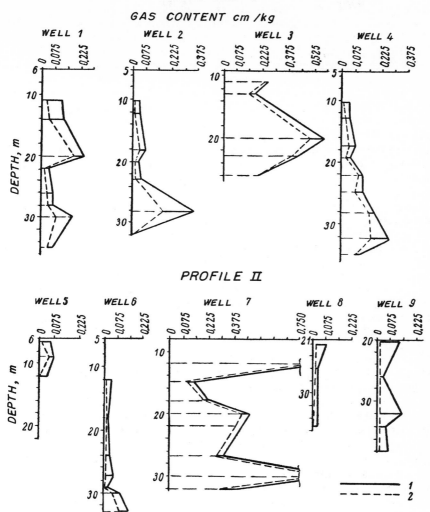

Fig. 51. Gas content of cores from shallow test wells in the Caspian Sea. 1—total hydrocarbons (as CO_2); 2—heavy hydrocarbons (as CO_2).

completely at a high temperature. Lobov called the field survey conducted by this method the "thermobitumen" survey. It was assumed that, besides gas, part of the oil bitumen was also recovered from the rock owing to volatilization at the elevated temperature.

The thermobitumen survey is a new, independent method. It is conducted in the field in the same manner as the gas survey. A sample of rock is taken from the bottom of a shallow well not over 3 m. in depth. The wells are distributed in the same pattern as in the gas survey, and the survey is often conducted in conjunction with a gas or core-gas survey. The sample is put into a flask and heated in a drying oven to 200 - 250° C. The evolved gas is recovered by flushing the flask with air.

Study of the evolved gas has shown that it consists mainly of CO_2 and CO, and contains slight traces of hydrocarbons. The quantity of CO sometimes reaches high percentages. Several investigators believe that the CO is formed by the incomplete oxidation of organic substances of contemporary vegetable origin with limited access of air. Others hold that the CO is the result of incomplete oxidation of non-volatile hydrocarbons derived from oil. This refers particularly to those cases in which the core is taken at great depth. This question is not yet decided.

Experimental surveys conducted in conjunction with the gas survey have shown that "thermobitumen" anomalies often coincide with gas anomalies and are located only within the bounds of likely structures. They have more contrast, and in regions where the gas survey gives indistinct results, the "thermobitumen" survey undoubtedly has prospects for development.

Change of Parameters of Monmorillonite as an Index of Hydrocarbon Migration

The name "montmorillonite" refers to an entire group of clay minerals of various compositions, which have similar physical properties. The physicochemical properties of clay minerals depend to a considerable extent on the crystal-lattice parameters of the minerals. The thorough study by S. I. Yusupova (13) of the properties of montmorillonite demonstrated the strongly developed character of its adsorption properties. Hydrocarbons adsorbed by montmorillonite cause expansion of individual sheets in the montmorillonite lattice.

Special experiments conducted by S. I. Yusupova with samples of montmorillonite clays from oil-bearing regions showed that when montmorillonite is saturated by oil, the C-axis spacing, which indicates the degree of expansion of the crystal lattice, is greater than when it is saturated by volatile hydrocarbons. Consequently, the magnitude of the C-axis spacing depends directly on the character of the oil fractions with which the montmorillonite has been saturated (14).

After these laboratory experiments, S. I. Yusupova in 1945-1946 conducted special field investigations in the region of Central Asia. Samples of clays rich in montmorillonitic minerals were taken directly from an oil stratum and from overlying layers. In the samples from the oil stratum, the largest C-axis spacing was observed. In samples taken from layers situated above the oil stratum, a decrease in this basic parameter was recorded.

The experimental field survey, carried out in conjunction with a gas survey, showed that samples of montmorillonite clays taken near an oil pool differ from clays taken on the sides of an oil-bearing fold. However, these same investigations have shown that the expansion of the montmorillonite lattice occurs not only under the influence of hydrocarbons, but also as a result of other causes, such as change in humidity, to name one. The new prospecting method is as yet insufficiently developed.

BIBLIOGRAPHY

1. G. A. Mogilevskii. Gasometry of wells. Byull. neft. geofiziki, no. IV. ONTI, 1937.

2. G.A. Mogilevskii. Description of a core drill for gasometry of wells. Soviet Patent No. 47654 (July 31, 1936).

3. M.I. Subbota. New method of core-gas surveying. Geochem. methods of prospecting for oil and gas, No. 1. Gostoptekhizdat, 1953.

4. G.D. Lidin. On the sorption capacity of the coals and anthracites of the Donbas. Izv. Akad. Nauk SSSR, Otdel. Tekh. Nauk, No. 3, 1941.

5. B.E. Vasserberg. Sorption of hydrocarbons by rocks and its effect on gas-survey indices. Sb. "Geokhim. metody poiskov nefti", No. 1. Gostoptekhizdat, 1950.

6. V.V. Belousov. Problems in the geology of helium. "Tr. geol.-razv. byuro gaz. mestorozhdenii", No. 6. ONTI, 1934.

7. A.A. Cherepennikov. Gas-bearing character of the salts of the Solikamsk potash mine. Sb. "Rudnichnaya aerologiya i bezopasnost' truda v shakhtakh" (K semidesyatiletyu akad. A.A. Skochinskogo). Ugletekhizdat, M., 1949.

8. L.N. Bykov. "Exogases" and the theory of the origin of sudden evolutions. ONTI—Gornoe izd-vo, 1932.

9. N.A. Kachinskii. Soil. Ogiz—Sel'khozgiz, 1946.

10. V.V. Belousov. Essays on the geochemistry of natural gases. ONTI, L., 1937.

11. K.A. Nenadkevich. On the content of H_2S in limestones and dolomites. Izv. Ross. Akad. nauk, pp. 1037-1040. Petrograd, 1917.

12. M.M. Elinson. Toward the question of the method of study of the gas content of rocks. Izv. Akad. Nauk SSSR, Otdel. Tekh. Nauk, No. 2, 1949.

13. S.I. Yusupova. Toward the characteristics of montmorillonite. Doklady Akad. Nauk SSSR 51, No. 8, 1946.

14. I.D. Sedletskii and S.I. Yusupova. Change of parameters of montmorillonite under the influence of oil. Doklady Akad. Nauk SSSR 46, No. 1, 1945.

CHAPTER SIX

Oil and Gas Logging

An increasing amount of exploratory drilling is being carried out in regions of the USSR where prospects of finding petroleum are good but where little work has been done. Consequently, new demands for investigating the stratigraphic sections in wells are arising because of the need for recognizing productive intervals of practical interest for testing.

Furthermore, in drilling wildcat, and especially supporting[1] wells, in regions of unknown structure, even very small amounts of hydrocarbons in the well bore are of considerable interest in recognizing strata favorable to oil or bitumen formation. These problems cannot always be adequately solved by existing geophysical methods. The most widely used method in practical petroleum geology is electrical well logging, which is based on the principle of measuring two parameters within the well bore: the resistance of the rocks to the flow of electric current and the effect of the spontaneous potential (SP). Although electric logging is an extremely reliable method for investigating well sections and discerning productive intervals, its use under certain specific geological conditions is restricted.

Thus, for example, in those geological provinces in which the drilling well penetrates carbonate rocks, the interpretation of electric logs presents a number of substantial complications, especially in selecting productive zones. Furthermore, recognizing the presence of thin, productive intervals on electric logs among a series of argillaceous sediments is, as yet, impossible. For these reasons, an unambiguous interpretation of electric logs is excluded in many cases.

Radioactive logging has several advantages over electric logging. A well can be investigated using this method whether the bore hole is full of drilling fluid or not, but in practice, it has not yet met with much success in locating productive intervals. However, the radioactive log distinguishes argillaceous strata distinctly and thus makes possible the correlation of well sections.

Sometimes, practical application is made of the so-called mechanical log, which is based on the rate of penetration. By taking into account a number of factors affecting the rate of drilling, this method makes possible the determination of the lighological composition of the rocks through which the well passes and, as a rule, porous reservoirs correspond to zones with the maximum rate of penetration. However, no conclusions can be drawn as to the productivity of the opened reservoirs on the basis of mechanical logging data. Hence, this type of log has no independent significance and can only be used in conjunction with other methods.

Recently, the first successful investigations were made by the so-

---

[1] "Supporting" wells are apparently shallow structure tests drilled to supplement surface geology data. Ed.

called caliper log, in which the diameter of the well is measured along its entire length. As a result of the mud circulation in the drilling process, different rocks undergo different amounts of erosion, and consequently, the diameter of the well varies along its length. Investigations have shown that maximum diameters correspond to clays and shales, and this makes it possible to correlate well sections accurately. This method is obviously incapable of giving any indication of the productivity of a section.

It is characteristic of all the methods enumerated above that productive intervals are ascertained in an indirect way, even though the direct determination of direct indices of oil- or gas-bearing character has an obvious advantage over these methods. At the present time, one widely used direct method in practical deep exploratory drilling is oil and gas logging which essentially consists in determining the petroleum content of rocks by the analysis of liquid and gaseous hydrocarbons recovered from drilling muds or cuttings.

The idea of the possibility of using gas logging on drilling muds first occurred to us in the Soviet Union in 1933 and belongs to the noted Soviet petroleum scientists, Professors M. V. Abramovich and V. A. Sokolov. Before long (in 1934) the first experimental work with drilling-mud suspensions and cores was also done in the USSR on the Achi-Su (Dagestan) formation by the geologist M. I. Bal'zamov, and on the Romny and Isachki by G. A. Mogilevskii.

Because of the lack of well-developed methods and apparatus and the sporadic nature of their application, no perceptible positive results could be obtained in the early stages of development. In 1937-1938 systematic and serious investigations were begun in this field for the purpose of improving both the method and the logging apparatus by G. A. Mogilevskii, N. S. Solov'eva, E. M. Geller, and others (1). These studies revealed considerable possibilities for the method (in particular, the continuous degasification of drilling mud was first used in the USSR by G. A. Mogilevskii).

In the USA the first reports on the application of gas logging appeared considerably later, in 1938. The Americans unsuccessfully try to appropriate the development and practical application of the method for themselves, ignoring the indisputable priority of Soviet investigators in this field. Borrowing our idea of the method, it is true that the Americans somewhat improve it technically, developing a special gas logging apparatus in which nearly all parameters (the content of combustible gases in the mud suspension, the separate sum of heavy hydrocarbons, the rate of penetration, the speed of the mud pump, the lag of the drilling fluid with respect to the bottom of the well, etc.) are automatically recorded on a special paper strip. However, in the use of these methods by us, as well as abroad, there are a number of substantial shortcomings. Semi-automatic gas logging apparatus now being manufactured by our domestic industry, although possessing a number of advantages over imported equipment, is in need of improvement and refinement.

The oil and gas logging equipment of today consists of a special type of field laboratory mounted in a truck and provided with the latest equipment. Thus, without leaving the vehicle, the geologist is able to make a great variety of determinations: the content of gaseous and liquid hydrocarbons in mud suspensions, drill cuttings and cores; the rate of drilling (in order to discern reservoirs in the section of the well being investigated);

the porosity and permeability of cores; the properties of the drilling mud (water loss and filter-cake thickness); the rate of the mud pump and the lag of the drilling fluid with respect to the bottom of the well, etc. (Fig. 52).[2] With these data, the geologist can direct the complex process of drilling deep wells with confidence.

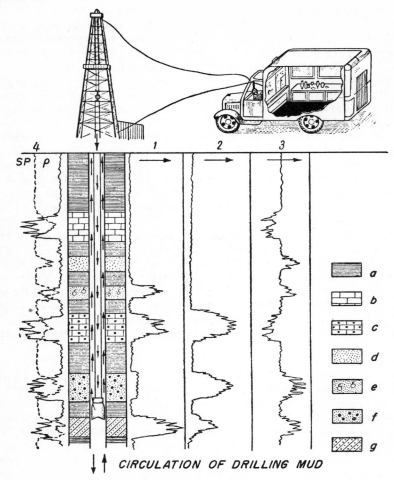

CIRCULATION OF DRILLING MUD

Fig. 52. Oil and gas logging arrangement. 1—oil and gas log; 2—luminescence log; 3—mechanical log (rate of penetration); 4—electric log; a—clay; b—limestone; c—oil-bearing limestone; d—water-bearing sand; e—gas-bearing sand; f—sand containing heavy oil; g—sand containing light oil.

[2]The word "glina" in this and a number of other figures in this chapter as well as at various points in the text has been translated as "clay", but apparently, it could also mean "shale" in many instances. Ed.

THEORETICAL BASIS OF OIL AND GAS LOGGING

The term, "gas logging," does not fully reflect the nature and capabilities of the method. Use of this term creates the impression that only gas pools can be discovered, while oil pools are detected by luminescence or bitumen logging. Such a separation of the functions of these methods is not correct because any oil pool (even one of heavy oil) contains a certain amount of dissolved gaseous hydrocarbons, depending on the conditions of its origin, the composition of the oil, and its preservation through geological time. V. A. Sokolov (2) hypothesized that even liquid hydrocarbons having a high vapor pressure dissolve in the drilling mud and are then recovered from it together with gas. Therefore, the method determines not only the gaseous components of the mud suspension, methane or ethane, but also all heavy hydrocarbons having appreciable vapor pressure and capable of being observed in the gas phase recovered from the drilling fluid. Thus, hydrocarbons that are liquid at ordinary temperatures, such as pentane, hexane, etc., may be determined in the gas phase (2). Therefore, instead of the old term, "gas logging," we use the new term, "oil and gas logging," which more correctly indicates the essence of the method.

In discussing the theoretical basis of oil and gas logging, the following varieties of the method must be distinguished: (a) mud logging; (b) drill cuttings analysis; (c) core analysis. Both the theoretical foundations and the possibilities of these variations are entirely different from one another. In the first case, the object of study is the mud suspension, this being the medium that transports liquid and gaseous hydrocarbons and other gases to the surface. In the second and third cases, the objects of investigation are drill cuttings and cores from the well, respectively. The most widely used method in practical petroleum geology is mud logging, because the sampling and analysis of cuttings, and especially cores, present considerable difficulties.

As experience in the use of the method shows, mud logging mainly registers macroconcentrations of hydrocarbons passing into the solution from disaggregated rock or from a productive level within the limits of the exposed part of the section. The author's investigations reveal that even fresh drilling muds sometimes contain hydrocarbons in macroquantities, depending on the geological age of the clay used in preparing the suspension (3). Owing to the presence of hydrocarbons in macroquantities in the composition of the original drilling mud, it is impossible by this method to register microconcentrations due to diffusion currents.[3] For this reason, it is necessary in mud logging to measure those concentrations of hydrocarbons that pass into the mud from productive levels within the open hole. As the well penetrates productive levels, oil, gas, and water pass into the drilling fluid and are transported by it to the surface. Thus, mud logging mainly determines macroconcentrations of hydrocarbons passing into the drilling fluid from productive levels. Mud logging fails to detect the regular increase in depth as a productive level is approached because it is incapable of detecting microconcentrations due to diffusion currents.[4]

---

[3]See Chapter IV on diffusion of gases.

[4]E. M. Geller came to an analogous conclusion earlier on the basis of other data.

Therefore, mud logging is helpful in locating productive levels of commercial and non-commercial significance in that part of the section that has been drilled, but it cannot predict the productivity of layers that have not been exposed. The prognosis of pools in the undrilled part of the section may be attempted of analyzing drill cuttings or cores. However, this point of view on the limitations of mud logging is not shared by one of the authors of the method. V. A. Sokolov (2) asserts that, "if a gaseous diffusion current permeates the entire thickness of rock over a pool, the results of all types of gas logging will depend on the intensity of this current," (my italics. Z. T.). According to Sokolov, oil and gas logging must reflect the diffusion current flowing from an accumulation of petroleum to the surface, and therefore, predictions of the productivity of layers in the unopened part of the section can be made on the basis of the data from mud logging. In view of the lack of special investigations in this direction, the possibilities of the various types of oil and gas logging have not as yet been elucidated.

When productive strata are exposed, liquid and gaseous hydrocarbons pass into the mud suspension and are transported to the surface in the following states: (1) dissolved in the drilling mud; (2) in the free state (gas in the form of bubbles and oil in the form of an emulsion); (3) sorbed by the rock chips (drill cuttings). When pressures are considerable and the amount of free gas in the productive reservoir is negligible, gaseous hydrocarbons are mainly transported in the dissolved state. If a large amount of free gas is present in the layer, gaseous hydrocarbons are partly transported to the surface in the free state in the form of separate bubbles. However, as the drilling mud approaches the top of the well, a certain amount of the hydrocarbons that were dissolved at high pressures will also appear as a free gas phase owing to the decrease in hydrostatic pressure. Furthermore, hydrocarbons that have been sorbed by rock throughout geologic time remain in the drill cuttings and reach the earth's surface in this state.

As has been mentioned, the analysis of drill cuttings and cores, in contrast to mud logging, can apparently record diffusion currents. Predictions of the productivity of strata in the undrilled part of the section can therefore be made from the data of these logging methods. Thus, their use can solve a wider range of problems than mud logging. Although the analysis of drill cuttings and cores is mainly oriented, not on free gas, but on gas sorbed by rocks, a certain amount of free gas may always be present, especially in large particles. A small amount of the sorbed gas may also pass into the clay suspension when the rock is crushed by the bit. On this account, gas logs obtained from drill chip studies cannot strictly reflect the distribution of gases sorbed by rock with respect to depth. In (Fig. 53) is given an example of the distribution of gas in a series of strata of various porosities after the diffusion of gas from an underlying pool has been established. If all misleading factors are excluded, and all other conditions are equal, gas logs based on drill cuttings must have roughly the same configuration as the theoretical curve given above (Fig. 53, I).

As shown by this curve, the content of free hydrocarbons and those sorbed by rock must increase steadily with depth, reaching a maximum at the productive level. Theoretically, the results of an analysis of drill cuttings must depend both on the pressure of the gas in the reservoir and on the sorption properties of the component rocks of each horizon. However, as has already been noted, when rock is disaggregated in drilling, part of the sorbed gas may pass into the clay suspension; at the same time, large particles of rock may retain free gas, as a result of which both the sorbed gas and, in part, the free gas will be recovered in the cuttings. Because of this circumstance and the influence of other factors which cannot be exactly calculated at the present time, experimental curves do not agree with theoretical ones.

Great discrepancies between experimental and theoretical curves are to be expected from analyses of drill cuttings when the rocks overlying the pool are substantially different in their sorption properties. However, even in this case, a series of peaks increasing successively with depth should be observed as a result of the increase of gas pressure; and sometimes such curves actually are observed.

Logging methods based on core analysis are used comparatively rarely, because cores are seldom taken continuously during the drilling of a well. Furthermore, it must be recognized that the percentage of core recovery is usually low; therefore, the amount of core logging at present is extremely small compared to cuttings analysis and mud logging.

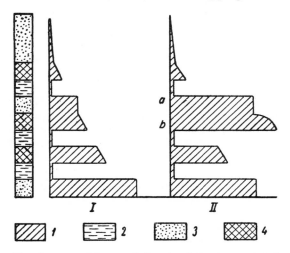

Fig. 53. Content of free and dissolved gas in a unit volume of rock (according to V. A. Sokolov). I—rocks with similar porosities; II—the porosities of a and b are three times greater than for the other strata; 1—gas pool; 2—water-bearing; 3—porous and sandy; 4—dense and porous with reduced permeability to gas.

Gas logs based on core analysis should agree more closely with theoretical curves, because hydrocarbons and other gases sorbed by rocks can be determined more accurately by the study of cores. However, the quantity of free gas determined in core analyses is very inaccurate, because this gas is easily dissipated during extraction. The number of oil and gas logs compiled from core analysis data taken mainly in test wells is small. Curves showing the distribution of gas concentrations with depth have about the same shape as those drawn from mud logging data.

Investigations have also shown that there is no regular increase of gas concentration with depth although all sorbed gas should be extracted in core analysis. The deviation of experimental curves from the theoretical may possibly be explained by the great variety in sorption properties of different rocks. For example, it wascertained from the data of Fokeev that argillaceous rocks have considerably greater coefficients of sorption than limestones or sandstones. Therefore, when these rocks predominate over an oil and gas pool, the content of sorbed hydrocarbons in these rocks will be highest even though they contain practically no free gases. At the same time, layers composed mainly of carbonates or sand overlying the pool will contain the smallest amount of sorbed gases when the content of free gas is greatest. Furthermore, it is evidently of substantial importance that in coring operations it is difficult to maintain standard conditions, and hence, the content of gas in the samples is considerably changed.

The type of changes in the curves of gas logs from core analyses (and also from drill cuttings) depends on many factors, the influence of which has not been adequately studied as yet. As a result, in a majority of cases experimental oil and gas logs obtained either from the analysis of cores or drill cuttings differ considerably from the theoretical, and practically no regular increase of concentration with depth is observed (i.e., as a productive level is approached).

Thus, both the theoretical foundations and the possibilities of logging with drilling muds, cuttings, and cores are quite varied. The influence of various factors, especially the drilling procedure, is most noticeable on the data of mud logging. Drilling procedures and other factors affect the results of drill cuttings and core analyses to a much lesser extent. The influence of these factors on logging results is not considered here, because this question is treated in a special section in which the effects of the drilling procedure and other factors are discussed in ample detail.

In the industrial application of mud logging, pools of very heavy oil, devoid of gaseous components, are not always detected. This shortcoming is easily overcome by bitumen logging, in which the presence of traces of heavy oil in the mud suspension can be ascertained without special effort. However, bitumen logging itself has another shortcoming. It is insensitive to the presence of purely gas-bearing strata because gaseous hydrocarbons are incapable of luminescence. If desired, the sensitivity of oil and gas logging could be increased by changing and improving both the method of degasification of the mud suspension and the analysis of the recovered gases. Strata containing heavy oils could then be detected.

The sensitivity of mud logging depends mainly on the method of degasification (the depth of degasification) of the drilling fluid and the sensitivity of the apparatus used for analysis of the recovered gases. However, the presence of hydrocarbons in the original clay suspension (3, 4) and also the use of petroleum products as lubricants in drilling (contamination of the suspension) limits the sensitivity of the method. Therefore, as the sensitivity of oil and gas logging of drilling muds is increased, the necessity arises of using special types of lubricants which cannot distort the data.

The distorting effects of various factors can be kept to a minimum if the mud suspension is examined after drilling has stopped and there has been no circulation in the well for several hours. Relatively recently in Saratov, E. M. Geller tried mud logging after the completion of a well, as in electric logging. This method is essentially based on the diffusion of gaseous and liquid hydrocarbons from productive layers into the mud column as a consequence of the considerable difference in the partial pressures between the formations and the well bore.

It was noted long ago that when the circulation of drilling fluid is stopped for a long time (for the raising and lowering of tools or in anticipation of electric logging work) the clay suspension in the shaft of the well opposite productive levels is enriched in hydrocarbons. This fact constitutes the basis of oil and gas logging after drilling. By lowering instruments into the well which record the gas content of the clay suspension, it is possible to reach definite conclusions as to the productivity of sedimentary layers in the exposed part of the section. The advantage of logging after drilling is the fact that the effect of the drilling procedure on the results is excluded and the cost is considerably·reduced.

The first experimental work in this direction, which was done in Saratov, gave encouraging results with respect to the possibility of conducting logging after drilling (the mud was degassed at the surface). At the present time suitable apparatus is being constructed on a large scale, and a method is being developed for conducting oil and gas logging directly in the well being drilled, which will greatly enhance the effectiveness of detecting oil and gas pools.

METHODS AND APPARATUS USED IN OIL AND GAS LOGGING

The methods and apparatus used in mud logging, on the one hand, and drill cutting analysis, on the other, are essentially different. In petroleum geology mud logging is the only widely used logging method, and therefore it will be discussed in detail. Questions regarding methods and apparatus for analyzing drill cuttings and cores will be mentioned very briefly and schematically.

Mud Logging

The advantage of mud logging over other methods is that the circulation of mud always accompanies drilling whereas, the sampling of cuttings, to say nothing of cores, is not always routine.

A drilling mud is used mainly to carry rock particles to the surface, to cool the bit, to produce a hydrostatic pressure on the strata, and also to form a filter cake on the wall of the bore hole in order to prevent crumbling of friable rocks.[5] Drilling mud, pumped through the drill pipe to the bottom of the well and in contact with oil and gas bearing strata, dissolves and sorbs a certain amount of liquid and gaseous hydrocarbons, which are transported to the surface as part of the suspension. It follows from this that, in order to obtain qualitative data during drilling, certain conditions must be maintained which entirely exclude the possibility of oil or extraneous oil products (with the exception of oil from an exposed stratum) from passing into the clay suspension.

Many difficulties that arise in mud logging are due to the use of oil and

---

[5]Recently, in regions with a predominantly carbonate section, water was used instead of a mud suspension. No basic changes in the existing methods of logging are needed for the study of wells being drilled with water.

oil products to improve the quality of the drilling fluid, to eliminate trouble in the well, and as a lubricant. However, as experience in the application of oil and gas logging has shown, not all oils and oil products distort the logging data. Thus, for example, it has been experimentally ascertained that when heavy oils (free of light components) are poured into the well bore, logging data are not affected at all if the degasification of the suspension is carried out without thermal treatment and at normal pressure (without vacuum). Therefore, the effect of additions of fluids on logging results may be minimized by using heavy, degasified oil in the drilling process.

Another necessary condition for qualitative mud logging is the absence of hydrocarbons or other combustible gases in appreciable quantities in the original clay. Examination of fresh mud suspensions reveals that, depending on the geological age of the clay used for the preparation of drilling fluids, they sometimes contain hydrocarbons in macroquantities. This, of course, will distort the logging data. Consequently, when drilling mud is prepared for use in wells being investigated by oil and gas logging, the content of combustible gases in the mud must be determined before it is pumped into the well.

The mud flowing out of the well, which has been enriched in combustible gases at the bottom is partially degassed at the surface and a mud channel system, but nearly all the dissolved hydrocarbons remain in the drilling fluid. The mud, flowing out of the well is further degassed by spraying it into a settling tank, and special structures are erected at the end of the mud channels for this purpose. However, such a system of degassing only eliminates the free gas and does not guarantee the complete removal of dissolved hydrocarbons. Therefore, when the original drilling fluid contains significant concentrations of hydrocarbons, the examination of the inflowing and outflowing drilling fluids is a much sounder method of degasification. This makes it possible to determine the increase in concentration of hydrocarbons as a result of enrichment due to productive strata.

In the final analysis, oil and gas mud logging consists essentially in determining the concentration of gaseous, vaporized hydrocarbons, and other gases in the drilling fluid flowing out of the well. The determination of hydrocarbons in the drilling fluid may be carried out intermittently or continuously (5).

Intermittent Degassing of Drilling Muds

In the first case, i.e., in the intermittent method of logging, samples of drilling mud are taken in a channel near the top of well at definite intervals (1 - 2 m. or sometimes oftener depending on the rate of penetration and purposes of logging). In this case, the sample of drilling fluid is collected by the operator in bottles or other containers. When the well is drilled through a thick, homogeneous layer, samples are taken infrequently, but when it is drilled through a heterogeneous series of sedimentary layers, especially reservoirs, the mud is sampled more often. The next operation consists in degassing the sample and analyzing the combustible gases recovered. Various analytical devices are used depending on the concentration of combustible gases (see the Chapter IV on gas analysis).

The first mud logging results were obtained in 1933 by M. I. Bal'zamov, but the method of degasification used was very primitive. During drilling operations, bottles were half filled with mud, collected from the channel, and shaken. As a result of shaking, free gas was evolved from the drilling fluid and mixed with the atmospheric air in the bottle over the fluid. The atmospheric air, enriched in hydrocarbon gases, was then analyzed. It is obvious that such a primitive method of degassing cannot give reliable or positive results in the absence of dependable analytical apparatus.

The intermittent method of sampling is used even now in a highly developed form, but degasification of the drilling mud is accomplished with the aid of heat and a slight vacuum. In this method of degassing, the free as well as the dissolved gases (and perhaps, part of the sorbed gases) are evolved. A considerable degree of degasification is obtained. In the intermittent method of mud logging the GKU-1 and thermovacuum degasifiers are widely used (Figs. 54, 55). The first of these is used only for supporting wells and the second, for exploratory wildcat wells.

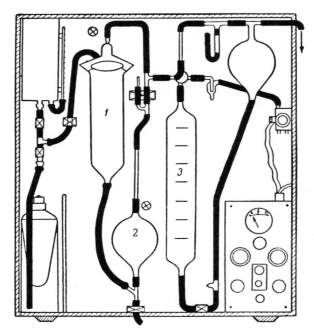

Fig. 54. Diagram of GKU-1 apparatus for oil and gas logging in supporting wells.

Degasifier of the GKU-1 apparatus (gas logging apparatus 1). The GKU-1 degasifier,[6] which is used for logging work in supporting wells, operates in the following manner. A stream of drilling fluid is drawn into the degasifying bulb 1 with the aid of a vacuum, is broken up by the deflector in the upper part of the bulb, and flows in a thin film along the walls of

---

[6]The GKU-1 degasifier was proposed and tested under laboratory and field conditions by the engineers, P. A. Levshunov, B. V. Vladimirov, and L. A. Galkin.

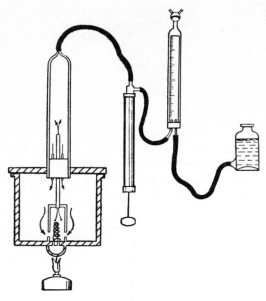

Fig. 55. PTVD-1 Degasifier.

the degasifier into the overflow vessel 2. Gases that are freed by applying a vacuum to the surface of the suspension (flow along the walls) enter the receiving bulb and then pass into the gas analyzer.

Thermo-vacuum degasifier. This apparatus used thermal treatment in a vacuum to degasify the drilling mud. Mud samples taken by the operator from the channel during a fixed interval of drilling are sent to the laboratory, where the dissolved gases and part of the sorbed ones are pumped out at 70 - 80° in a vacuum (absolute pressure, about 17 - 20 mm. Hg) (Fig. 55).

Comparison of this degasifier with other devices shows that the degree of degasification here is considerable. Predictions made in the Saratov Transvolga region, where the thermo-vacuum degasifier was mainly used, were confirmed in many cases in subsequent testing of the wells. However, this degasifier has two substantial shortcomings: the impossibility of continuous examination of muds and the bulkiness of the apparatus used for gas recovery.

The intermittent method of drilling mud examination used in the early stages of the development of oil and gas logging has a number of substantial shortcomings and, therefore, is seldom used at present. The more widely used method of continuous degasification of muds is absolutely preferable to the periodic procedure, because it sheds more light on the section in the well, reducing to a minimum the possibility of overlooking productive zones of small thickness. Oil and gas logging equipment that is now being manufactured by domestic industry is designed for continuous mud degasification.

Continuous Degassing of Drilling Muds

The following degasifiers are used at present in practical mud logging work for the continuous examination of drilling fluids: (1) box degasifiers; (2) floating degasifiers; (3) brush degasifiers; (4) DP-1 (breakup of mud stream), etc.

Box degasifier. The degasifier is placed in a channel as near as possible to the rotary table. A slight vacuum produced under the casing of the degasifier and the bubbling of atmospheric air through the clay suspension degasify the mud. In Figure 56 a simplified schematic diagram of the box degasifier (a) is shown and the movement of the clay suspension is indicated (b). The partitions shown in the drawing cause turbulent flow of the clay suspension; and in the opinion of the inventors of this degasifier (G. G. Grigor'ev and B. I. Anvaeer), this promotes an increase in the degree of degasification.

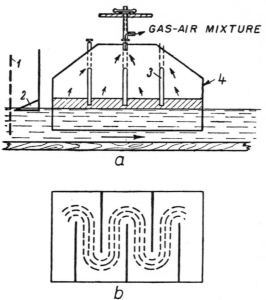

Fig. 56. Simplified diagram of box degasifier.
a—diagram; b—partitions causing turbulent flow
of the drilling mud (top view); 1—net; 2—deflector; 3—bubbling pipes; 4—shell.

The vacuum produced by a pump under the shell of the degasifier and the bubbling of atmospheric air through the pipes, together with the turbulent motion of the drilling mud, promote the evolution mainly of free gas, while dissolved and other gases remain in the mud. The recovered gaseous hydrocarbons and other combustible and incombustible gases (hydrogen, hydrogen sulfide, nitrogen, carbon dioxide, etc.), diluted by atmospheric air (gas-air mixture), are sent to the gas analyzer, where the concentrations of all combustible gases are determined, whether they are derived from petroleum or not.[7] The practical use of these degasifiers under different geological conditions reveals a number of shortcomings, the most substantial of which are the following:

---

[7] Besides petroleum hydrocarbons, the combustible gases recovered from the mud may contain other combustible gases not directly related to petroleum.

1. The degasifier mainly obtains the freely evolved gas, while hydro-carbons dissolved in the mud suspension remain unregistered. Consequently, in the investigation of well sections, strata containing heavy oils with very low solution gas are, as a rule, overlooked.

2. When the degasifier is mounted in the channel near the rotary table, the normal circulation of the drilling mud is altered as a result of the accumulation of cuttings. However, increasing the distance between rotary table and degasifier leads to substantial loss of free gas (Fig. 57).

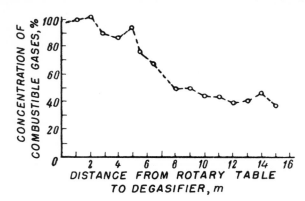

Fig. 57. Variation of concentration of freely evolved gas with distance between degasifier and rotary table.

3. The vacuum in the degasifier draws a small volume of drilling fluid into the shell. The topmost layer of this fluid does not flow properly and this hinders the degasification of the mud flowing underneath.

As a result of the shortcomings enumerated above, productive strata lacking in free gas have been overlooked in nearly all cases of mud logging with this type degasifier. Because box degasifiers reveal only those strata containing large amounts of free gas, their use is limited.

PG-1 degasifier (floating). In a floating degasifier the stream of drilling mud enters the device is dispersed into a spray when it strikes metal fins inside (Fig. 58). Increasing the surface area of mud in contact with air liberates both the free and the dissolved gas.

The hydrocarbon gases tend to rise upward into the gas collecting vessel, and the vacuum pump then sucks the air-gas mixture into the gas analyzer. The shape of the degasifier, which tapers toward the top, reduces the "dead" space. The apparatus is mounted on floats in the channel as near as possible to the top of the well, and to avoid flooding when the flow of drilling mud is rapid, a baffle-plate is set at an angle of 45° in the forward part of the degasifier.

The floating degasifier was suggested by engineers B. V. Vladimirov and L. A. Galkin. Tests of the device under the conditions of production revealed a number of advantages over existing degasifiers. At present it is widely used in a great variety of geological conditions and makes possible the detection of horizons containing light oil, as well as heavy oil.

DP-1 degasifier (breakup of mud current). In this degasifier a wire brush is used to break up the mud current. This increases the surface area available for degasification by spraying the drilling mud against inner walls of the degasifier (Fig. 59). Thus, the recovery of both free and dissolved gas is achieved.

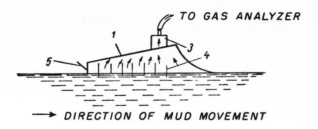

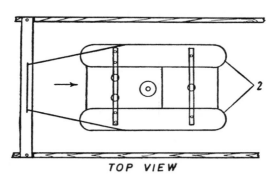

Fig. 58. Diagram of PG-1 degasifier in mud channel.
1 —shell of degasifier; 2 —floats; 3 —gas-collecting
vessel; 4 —metal fins; 5 —baffle-plate.

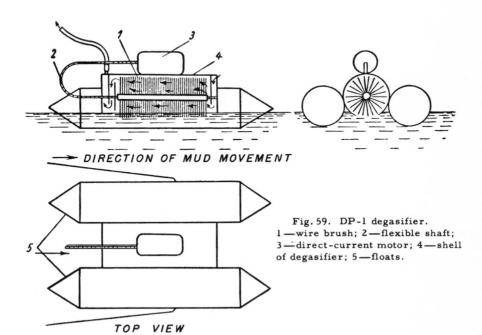

Fig. 59. DP-1 degasifier.
1 —wire brush; 2 —flexible shaft;
3 —direct-current motor; 4 —shell
of degasifier; 5 —floats.

A direct-current motor coupled by a flexible shaft to the axle of the wire brush provides different degrees of degasification by varying the rate of rotation, which is controlled by regulating the voltage. The floats supporting the degasifier at a definite level in the drilling mud eliminate a shortcoming of some other systems of degasifiers by maintaining a constant depth of brush immersion regardless of the mud level in the channel.

Aeration degasifier. Degasification of the drilling mud is accomplished by introducing atmospheric air into the mud at a pressure of 30 - 50 mm. of drilling fluid. This removes both free and dissolved gas (Fig. 60). Air pressure for the degasifier is produced in tank 3 by an automatic compressor controlled by the U-shaped water manometer. The gas-air mixture which collects in the upper chamber 2 of the degasifier is continuously admitted to the gas analyzer. Since the pressure in the degasifier is insufficient, the gas mixture cannot be transported to the portable truck laboratory. Therefore, the gas analyzer is mounted near the channel.

The difficulties in using this aeration degasifier are as follows:

1. It is difficult to maintain a stable supply of air to the degasifier.

2. A special pump must be used to provide pressure.

3. A vacuum is needed in order to draw the gas mixture to the analyzer, etc.

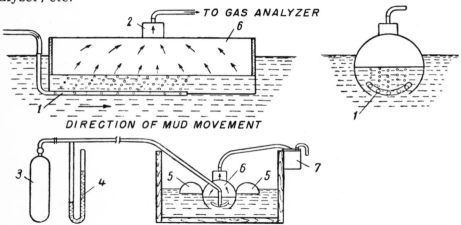

Fig. 60. Diagram of aeration degasifier. 1 —perforated pipes for supply of air; 2 —gas collecting vessel; 3 —air tank; 4 —U-shaped water manometer; 5 —floats; 6 —hull of degasifier; 7 —gas analyzer.

Air-lift degasifier. This degasifier consists of a vessel connected to pipes which are immersed in the channel containing the drilling mud (Fig. 61). First of all, a pump draws the drilling mud through a pipe into vessel a; then atmospheric air is supplied through pipe b. The air rises in the form of bubbles into vessel a, entraining the mud and creating continuous mud circulation in the degasifier system. Atmospheric air bubbling through the mud suspension is enriched by the evolved gases, and the enriched air separates from the mud in the degasifier-vessel and passes into the gas analyzer.

The following are disadvantages of this degasifier:

1. The supply of air to the degasifier depends on the physical properties of the drilling mud.

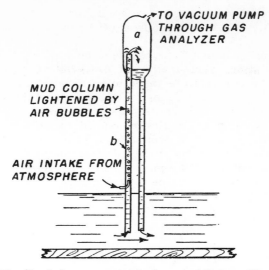

TO VACUUM PUMP
THROUGH GAS
ANALYZER

a

MUD COLUMN
LIGHTENED BY
AIR BUBBLES

b

AIR INTAKE FROM
ATMOSPHERE

Fig. 61. Laboratory model of an air-lift degasifier.

2. Frequent inspections of the atmospheric air intake are required to maintain normal operation. Otherwise, either the mud may stop flowing or an excess of mud may pass into the gas outlet tube which connects the degasifier to the analyzer.

3. The insignificant volume of drilling mud which undergoes degasification does not give a true picture of the content of combustible gases in the mud.

4. Furthermore, fluctuations of the mud level in the channel cause great difficulty in using the degasifier.

Analysis of Combustible Gases Recovered From Drilling Muds

In practical oil and gas logging work, gas analyzers constructed on different principles are used, depending on the method of examination of the drilling mud (intermittent or continuous). When the concentration of combustible gases in the mud is low, various analyzers designed for the determination of microconcentrations, such as the TG-5, etc. (see Chapter IV, section entitled, "Gas Analysis"), are usually employed (6). Portable field laboratories adapted to continuous degasification of drilling muds are provided with electric gas analyzers which record macroconcentrations of combustible gases.

These gas analyzers are based on the principle of the Wheatstone bridge (Fig. 62), where r_1 is the working (combustion) arm of the bridge, made of platinum wire; r_2 is the compensating arm of the bridge, also made of platinum; r_3 and r_4 are the ratio arms of the bridge, which are made of manganin wire; r is a balancing resistance; the resistance R_1 is used to make the voltage applied to the bridge equal to 1.1 v.; the resistance R_2 is used to make this voltage equal to 0.65 v.; the resistance R has a value equal to nine times the resistance of the microammeter and is used to increase its range; K_1 and K_2 are shunts used for the insertion and removal of R and R_2; V is a voltmeter used to establish working voltages on the bridge, equal to 1.1 and 0.65 v.; μA is a microammeter used to

determine the presence of current in the diagonal of the electrical bridge
while balancing it; and E is a source of direct current (after P. A.
Levshunov).

When a gas-air mixture flows through the working (combustion) arm,
which is maintained at a temperature of 700 - 800° C (with an applied
voltage of 1 v.), the combustible gases are burned and the additional heat
developed results in an increase in the resistance of the arm r_1. This increase causes the bridge to become unbalanced, as a result of which, current flows along the diagonal and is measured by the microammeter μ A.
The quantity of heat evolved is proportional to the total concentration of
combustible gases. Therefore, if the microammeter of the gas analyzer is
calibrated experimentally, the concentration of combustible gases in the
gas-air mixture may be determined.

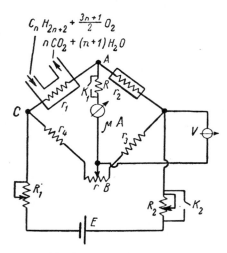

Fig. 62. Diagram of gas analyzer.

The operator using the apparatus records the microammeter reading
for every 25 cm. of hole drilled. This serves as a basis for the subsequent
plotting of an oil and gas log (with an automatic recorder these data are
recorded automatically on a paper strip).

When the combustible gases are ignited with a platinum spiral, it is
assumed that at a voltage of 1.1 v. (about 700 - 800° C) all combustible
gases are burned, while at 0.65 v. (about 500° C) only the heavy hydrocarbons (from ethane up), hydrogen, hydrogen sulfide are burned if they are
present in the natural gas. On the basis of this assumption, curves of
methane content are obtained from the mud log by taking the difference
between the reading at 1.1 v. and that of 0.6 v. A separate determination
of methane and heavy hydrocarbons is extremely important, because this
makes possible a preliminary determination whether a pool that has been
discovered contains gas or oil.

However, as experience shows, the isolation of methane from heavy
hydrocarbons, as well as the elimination of other combustible gases (hydrogen and hydrogen sulfide) in the existing method is quite a complex
problem. Special investigations in this direction, conducted by P. A.
Levshunov, led him to the following conclusions.

1. Gaseous hydrocarbons begin to burn at different temperatures and the higher hydrocarbons have lower ignition points. Because of this relationship, they may be distinguished by the voltage difference alone (Table 20).

TABLE 20. Minimum Voltage at the Ignition Point

Hydrocarbon	Gas-air mixture, %			
	4	2	1	0.5
CH_4	0.32	0.85	0.8	0.96
C_2H_6	0.7	0.78	0.72	0.8
C_3H_8	--	0.6	0.63	0.72
C_4H_{10}	--	0.4	0.6	0.65
1% CH_4 + 1% C_2H_6	--	0.15	--	--
1% CH_4 + 1% C_3H_8	--	0.70	--	--
1% CH_4 + 1% C_4H_{10}	--	0.65	--	--
0.5% CH_4 + 0.5% C_2H_6 + 0.5% C_3H_8 + 0.5% C_4H_{10} .	--	0.65	--	--

2. For any given gas the ignition voltage increases with a decrease in gas concentration.

3. As definite voltages are reached (different for different hydrocarbons), the current remains constant, then falls (Fig. 63).

4. For gas-air mixtures having the same concentration, the maximum values of current increase with increase of molecular weight of the hydrocarbon being burned (Fig. 64).

5. The value of current increases in proportion to the increase of concentration of combustible gases in the gas-air mixture (Table 21).

TABLE 21. Maximum Values of Current: Microamperes

Hydrocarbon	Gas-air mixture, %			
	4	2	1	0.5
CH_4	1,000	420	260	118
C_2H_6	1,480	980	440	200
C_3H_8	--	1,000	520	240
C_4H_{10}	--	1,220	640	340
1% CH_4 + 1% C_2H_6	--	700	--	--
1% CH_4 + 1% C_3H_8	--	750	--	--
1% CH_4 + 1% C_4H_{10}	--	920	--	--
0.5% CH_4 + 0.5% C_2H_6 + 0.5% C_3H_8 + 0.5% C_4H_{10} . .	--	940	--	--

In this method of gas analysis with a resistance bridge, the presence of hydrogen and hydrogen sulfide in natural gas leads to considerable

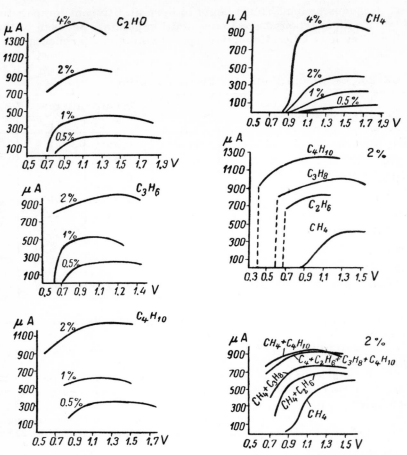

Fig. 63. Dependence of ignition
temperature of hydrocarbons on
concentration.

Fig. 64. Dependence of ignition
temperature of hydrocarbons on
molecular weight.

misrepresentation of the actual content of combustible gases derived from
petroleum. Obviously, if a natural gas contains hydrogen and hydrogen
sulfide in appreciable amounts, the ratio of light and heavy hydrocarbons
will be inaccurately determined. Therefore, predictions based on the continuous degasification of a drilling fluid and analysis of the recovered
gases are extremely arbitrary. Similarly, the determination of the nature
of an accumulation (i.e., whether oil or gas) on the basis of the ratio of
light and heavy hydrocarbons is also arbitrary.

Special investigations are now being conducted for the purpose of improving the resistance gas analyzer by increasing its sensitivity and
making it applicable to the determination of other combustible gases (e.g.,
hydrogen and hydrogen sulfide).

In the examination of drilling muds the determination of acid gases
(oxygen, carbon dioxide, nitrogen, and other gases) is also of interest.
These gases could be determined in the intermittent approach, but with
continuous analysis using resistance gas analyzers, they can no longer be
observed.

Oil and Gas Logs Based on Analyses of Cuttings and Cores

The methods and apparatus for analyzing drill cuttings and cores are much simpler than for mud logging. On drilling through a productive level a large part of the free gas contained in the rock particles passes into the drilling mud. However, a small amount of the free gas and nearly all the sorbed gas are retained by rock particles; these last are investigated by analyzing the drill cuttings.

In this method it is desirable to select rock fragments of definite size, since it will then be easier to relate the data obtained to the depth of the well (particles of different sizes move to the surface at different speeds). Usually, sieves with a definite mesh size are used for sampling the drill cuttings. The cuttings are then washed with water in order to free the rock fragments from mud, after which they are put into a hermetically sealed container and sent to the field or permanent laboratory for extraction and analysis (7, 8).

Metal vessels with hermetically sealed rims are used for collecting cuttings (Fig. 65). These vessels, although rather large, are convenient in that extraction of gas can be carried out in the laboratory without transferring the cuttings to another container. Sometimes, the cuttings are collected in glass jars with screw-on lids. The amount of cuttings collected varies from 200 to 400 g.

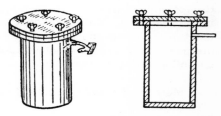

Fig. 65. Metal vessel for degasification of cores and drill cuttings.

The process of extracting gas from the cuttings is the same in principle as that used in degassing cores in the gas-core survey (see Chapter V). Extraction of gas is carried out at a temperature of 50 - 80° under a vacuum, which considerably accelerates the desorption of gas. Increase of temperature above this level accelerates the process of degasification, but is not safe. At a high temperature organic substances contained in the rock may decompose; this would cause substantial changes in the composition, as well as the amount of the hydrocarbons of interest. Extraction of gases can also be accelerated by acid treatment of the rock fragments.

Analysis of the recovered gas may be performed with the TI, Orsat, or other apparatus. At low concentrations of combustible gases the TG-3 or TG-5 apparatus may be used (titrimetric gas analyzer; for description of these devices see Chapter IV). It is expedient to determine not only combustible gases, but also the content of solid bitumens, chlorides, sulfates, carbonates, and other mineral compounds which characterize the geochemical situation in rocks surrounding an oil or gas pool. The results obtained are plotted on a log, the lag of the cuttings being taken into account.[8]

Such a thorough, complex study of the drill cuttings makes it possible

_____

[8]The time required for the cuttings to travel from the bottom of the well to the top is called lag (see section, ''Method of calculating lag of the drilling mud'').

to correlate well sections with confidence and also to reach better conclusions with regard to the productivity of any given strata. In the literature there are statements that even cuttings collected in cloth bags, in spite of the considerable time of storage, give fair results on analysis from the point of view of ascertaining the productivity of the intervals examined.

Oil and gas logs from core analyses are very seldom used in practice, because even the drilling of exploratory wells is not always accompanied by continuous coring. Furthermore, it must be recognized that the percentage core recovery under present-day conditions of drilling is low and, therefore, core analysis cannot be widely used. The oil and gas logs are based on the extraction of gaseous and liquid hydrocarbons from the core samples.

The first experiments in core analysis were conducted by G. A. Mogilevskii (5, 7). He also developed a method of degassing the cores, in which the core samples were placed in a metal holder, into which water was then introduced through a tube in order to displace the air. The gas was extracted from the rock by means of a partial vacuum produced by pumping water out of the holder and also by heating the cores to 70°.

Today this method of degasification has been greatly improved and is exactly the same in principle as that used in degassing cores in the core-gas survey (see chapter V). In order to increase the degree of degasification of sorbed gases, the core may be ground to finer particles in special metal "mills". The recovered gases are analyzed in the same apparatus used in the core-gas survey. In addition to the determination of combustible gases, the presence of solid and liquid bitumens, chlorides, sulfates, and other mineral compounds is also recommended (9).

Method of Luminescence Logging with Drilling Muds and Cuttings

The method of examining drilling muds and rocks for their content of solid and liquid bitumens is described in detail in chapter VIII entitled, "Bitumen-luminescence methods". Here we shall briefly dwell only on a method of preliminary examination of drilling muds and cuttings are used directly at the well under field conditions.

A rapid and qualitative determination of traces of oil in the field permits a more effective direction of the drilling operations. Where indications of oil or bitumens appear, a more frequent sampling of drilling mud and cuttings for detailed laboratory investigations can also be made.

The method of preliminary luminescence analysis of drilling muds consists in the following: during a definite interval of advance of the bit (depending on the purposes of the logging and also on the rate of penetration), the operator of the field laboratory takes a sample into a clean glass jar at the point where the mud flows out of the cased hole. Then the mud is sampled, lag being taken into account.

In order to reduce the viscosity of the mud suspension, pure non-luminescent water is added while it is being stirred with a glass rod. Oil floats on the surface of the mud and when the sample is put into the luminoscope, the operator reports the presence of traces of oil. Oil and other bituminous substances in drilling fluids may be present in the free state (in the form of a film on the surface of the mud) and as particles dispersed throughout the mass of the clay suspension. A small amount of oil and bituminous substances may also be present in the mud in the dissolved state (the solubility of oil in water is quite insignificant).

Regardless of the state in which the oil or bituminous substances exist in the drilling mud, reduction of the viscosity of the latter promotes accumulation of these substances on the surface of the mud. As a result, it is easy to observe them upon irradiation with ultraviolet rays. If desired, the oil and bituminous substances may be extracted from the mud and subjected to qualitative and quantitative analysis (see Chaper VII, "Bitumen Methods").

Substantial obstacles in the development of luminescence logging are the use of petroleum products in deep drilling for the practical improvement of the quality of the drilling fluids and the pouring of oil into the well when trouble occurs. Today, however, the experimental work of S. V. Boravskii has shown the possibility of applying luminescence logging even when oil is used as a lubricant. He suggested the introduction of luminescence preventatives (specifically, soot) into the oil used as a lubricant; these would make it possible to distinguish oil derived from a stratum, from the lubricating oil. From the viewpoint of luminescence logging, it is especially undesirable to use crude oil from the same formation or area where drilling is taking place.

If desired, the drilling crew can reduce the amount of lubricant passing into the drilling mud to a minimum by strictly observing certain technical precautions. At present, an appreciable amount of lubricant passes into the mud during drilling. Hence, in order to obtain a reliable interpretation of luminescence logging data, the operator must record the character of the lubricant used and its luminescence in the well record regularly and in sufficient detail.

For the sake of completeness, the examinations of the mud are supplemented by luminescence analysis of the drill cuttings, which are sampled exactly as in oil and gas logging. They are washed with water in order to be free from mud and are then studied in the luminoscope. If traces of oil or oil bitumens are present in the cuttings, the detection thereof with ultraviolet illumination presents no particular difficulty. However, the luminescence of mineral particles must be distinguished from that of bituminous substances.

In the examination of the cuttings a solvent such as chloroform, carbon tetrachloride, etc., is widely used, because its application to rock particle facilitates the detection of bituminous substances are found, samples of cuttings from the indicated intervals are put into a special container and sent to the laboratory for detailed qualitative and quantitative analysis [9] (see the chapter, "Bitumen Methods"). In sampling cuttings for luminescence analysis it must be kept in mind that rock particles of different sizes pass into the drilling mud at different rates. Hence it is necessary to select cuttings of uniform particle-size in order to relate the obtained results to depth. It is also necessary to beware of the possibility of contamination as a result of the petroleum products used in lubricating the drilling equipment or from other causes. However, if the precautions which were

---

[9]Sometimes the drill cuttings are dried out before being sent to the laboratory; this leads to a partial loss of the light components of the bitumen. Therefore, the best results are obtained by study of fresh samples, right at the well.

mentioned above in describing the analysis of drilling muds are observed, the deleterious effects of this factor may be avoided.

Cores from deep wells are subjected to similar examinations. The method of luminescence logging with cores boils down to the determination of traces of oil and bituminous substances in the core. Preliminary, purely qualitative determinations of oil and oil bitumens are performed at the well by the operator of the oil and gas logging apparatus. Core samples bearing indications of oil or bituminous substances are sent to the stationary or field laboratory, where they undergo detailed qualitative and quantitative analysis (see Chapter VII).

AUTOMATIC AND SEMIAUTOMATIC LOGGING EQUIPMENT

Methods of continuous degasification of drilling muds and continuous analysis of the recovered combustible gases have been described above.

The degasifier and gas analyzer are the most critical parts of oil and gas logging units. However, an apparatus that continuously records the depth of the well throughout the entire logging process is also needed in order to relate obtained anomalous values of the content of combustible gases in the mud to depth. For this purpose, the logging units are provided with depth-gauges which continuously record the change in the depth of the well (Fig. 66). A selsyn-controller, 3, mounted at the top of the derrick or below, is coubled to the swivel by cable 7. Thus the vertical motion of the drilling tools is transmitted through the cable to the selsyn-controller, which in turn sends electrical impulses to a receiver mounted on the logging unit. The receiver actuates the counter of the depth-gauge (panel III).

The depth-gauge is provided with two counters (Fig. 66); one of these, mounted on the left (a), registers only depth of the bit, while the counter on the right (b) registers the rise of the drill bit from the bottom of the hole. When the bit rises from the bottom, the left counter is automatically cut out and the right counter is cut in at the same instant. Later, when the bit is returned to the bottom, the right counter is automatically cut out and the left counter cut in, and the registration of bit penetration continues. After each 0.25 m. of penetration an electric bell is actuated, which reminds the operator attending the equipment of the need to take readings of the gas analyzer and other apparatus. The operator records two sets of gas analyzer readings in the journal: those obtained at 1.1 v. (total combustible gases) and those obtained at 0.65 v. (arbitrarily, heavy hydrocarbons).

If drilling is carried out very rapidly, the operator may record the readings of the instruments every 0.5 m., or even every meter. When the operator takes readings on the gas analyzer, he allows for the lag of the drilling fluid (see following section, ''Method of calculating lag of the drilling mud''). For this purpose the counters (panel II) which register the number of strokes of the mud pump are so arranged that the right counter lags behind the left one (Fig. 66, II) by the number of cycles needed to raise the drilling fluid from the bottom of the well to the top. On recording the depth with each 0.25 m. of penetration, the reading of the left counter is also recorded. However, the reading of the gas content of the clay suspension, as a given depth interval is drilled through, is taken at the moment when the reading of the right counter is equal to the previously-recorded reading of the left one, i.e., when that portion of drilling mud that flushed

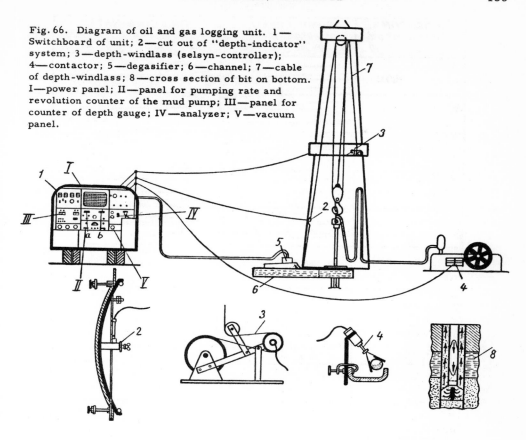

Fig. 66. Diagram of oil and gas logging unit. 1—
Switchboard of unit; 2—cut out of "depth-indicator"
system; 3—depth-windlass (selsyn-controller);
4—contactor; 5—degasifier; 6—channel; 7—cable
of depth-windlass; 8—cross section of bit on bottom.
I—power panel; II—panel for pumping rate and
revolution counter of the mud pump; III—panel for
counter of depth gauge; IV—analyzer; V—vacuum
panel.

the bottom in the given interval reaches the surface. Besides the readings
of the gas analyzer, the operator also records the reading of the instruments registering the depth of the well, the rate of penetration, the rate of
mud circulation, etc.

In automatic assemblies which include recorders, all the parameters
enumerated above are recorded both manually by the operator and on a
paper strip by an automatic recorder (10). An example of such an automatic record is illustrated in Fig. 67, where b is a sample of paper strip
before analysis by the geologist-interpreter and a is the same sample after
interpretation.

Recently a group of engineers (Yu. M. Yurovskii, B. V. Vladimirov,
and L. A. Galkin) has developed basic critical units of domestic automatic
oil and gas logging equipment, the testing of which revealed a number of
advantages over existing imported equipment. In Figs. 68, 69, and 70 are
illustrated curves of automatic recording (according to Yu. M. Yurovskii)
obtained in one of the oil formations of the Caucasus, where a production
test of particular units of domestic oil and gas logging equipment was conducted. The development of improved automatic logging equipment will
further increase the effectiveness of this method.

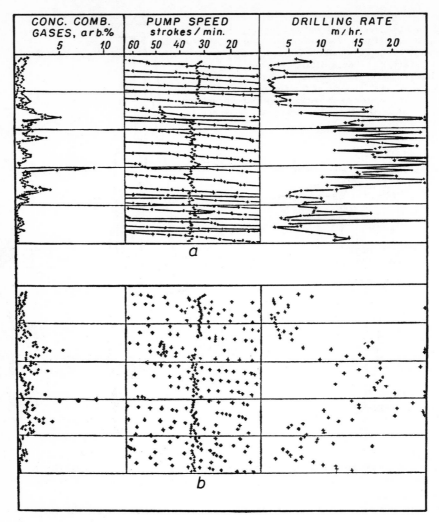

Fig. 67. Data of an automatic record (paper strip).
a —interpreted data; b —raw data.

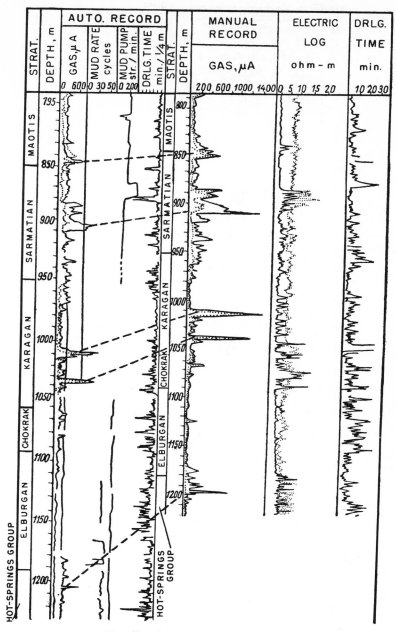

Fig. 68. Oil and gas log of Well A.

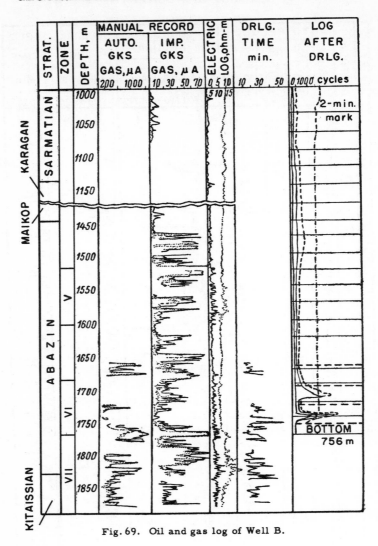

Fig. 69.   Oil and gas log of Well B.

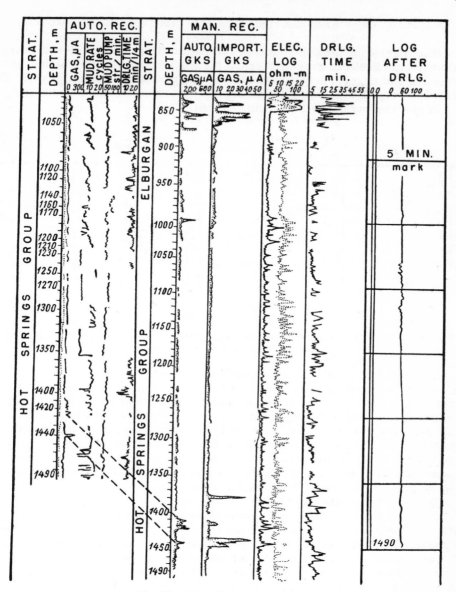

Fig. 70. Oil and gas log of Well C.

METHOD OF CALCULATING LAG OF THE DRILLING MUD

A certain period of time is required for the drilling mud, enriched at the
bottom in combustible gases, to reach the top of the well; this period is
called lag and is measured in minutes or in strokes of the mud pump. The
calculation of the mud lag is of exceedingly great importance in relating
oil and gas logging data to a definite depth.

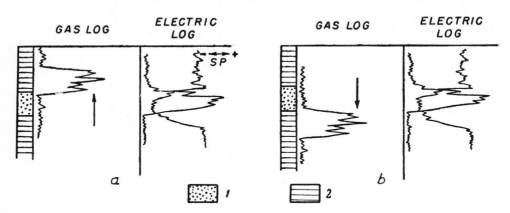

Fig. 71. Shift of gas anomalies depending on errors in the determination of the lag of
drilling mud. 1 —sand; 2 —clay.

Let it suffice to note that in conducting logging without calculation of
lag or with an insufficiently accurate determination of the mud lag, gas
anomalies (''peaks'') are shifted on the diagrams downward (Fig. 71, b) or
upward (Fig. 71, a) with respect to the productive layers to which these
anomalies are due (Fig. 71). The direction of shift of the anomaly with
respect to the productive layer (up or down) depends on the nature of the
error in the determination of the mud lag. The amplitude of the ''peak''
depends both on the accuracy of the method of lag determination and on the
drilling procedure, which involves the rate of penetration, the capacity and
quality of the mud pumps, the depth of the well, etc.

In order to correlate a gas anomaly with the correct section in the
well, it is necessary to determine the lag of the drilling mud as accurately
as possible. This is a practical rather than a theoretical problem, because
the well bore is not an ideal cylinder owing to the presence of many caverns
caused by erosion of the sides of the hole by drilling fluid or caving of
friable rock. Caliper measurements show that the diameter of the shaft of
the well is sometimes substantially increased opposite clays and shales.
Therefore, attempts to calculate the theoretical mud lag are subject to
error and can be used only in special cases where it is not possible to determine the lag directly. In the latter case, the use of the following indicators, which have already proved their worth in oil and gas logging work,
is recommended: (1) variously-colored cellophane strips; (2) oats or
barley; (3) gasoline (in rare cases in which no other indicator can be used).

In practice, the method of measuring the mud lag under field conditions
amounts, in a few words, to the following. Before screwing on the Kelly,
the operator drops an indicator into the drill pipe such as pieces of cellophane strip of a definite color, each 3 - 5 cm. in length (about 30 - 50

pieces in all). After the mud pumps are started, the operator records the number of strokes shown on the counter and awaits the appearance of the indicator in the mud channels, using special sieves. Sieves with 3 - 5 and 5 - 7 mm. openings are inserted into special grooves cut in the channels at a distance of 2 - 3 m. from one another (the sieve with larger openings is placed in front).

Taking the sieves alternately and wahing them with water, the operator looks for the appearance of the indicator in the mud and; as soon as the first signs of indicator are observed, records the reading of the mud pump counter. The difference between the last and first readings of the latter is equal to the total number of strokes (B_1) necessary for passage of the drilling mud from the top of the hole to the bottom and back. However, we are only interested in the number of strokes required to raise the mud from the bottom to the top of the well (R).

Therefore, knowing the depth of the well (H) and the inner diameter of the drill pipe, the mud volume in the latter (V_d) may be calculated. On the basis of the following specifications of the mud pump: the length of stroke (S), the diameter of the piston rod (d_r), the inner diameter of the cylinder (d_c), the number of cylinders in the mud pump (N), and the pump volumetric efficiency (P), we determine the volume of clay suspension (V_p) corresponding to one full stroke of the piston:

$$V_p = \left[\left(\frac{\pi d_c^2}{4}\right) S \cdot 2 - \left(\frac{\pi d_r^2}{4}\right) S \right] NP = \frac{3.14}{4}(2d_c^2 - d_r^2) NPS$$

$$V_p = 0.785 \, NPS \, (2d_c^2 - d_r^2).$$

By dividing the volume of mud in the drill pipe (V_d) by the volume corresponding to one full stroke of the piston (V_p), we determine the number of strokes needed to fill the drill pipe (R_2):

$$R_2 = V_d/V_p.$$

Thus, the number of strokes needed for the mud to go from the bottom to the top of the well (R) will be determined by difference: $R = R_1 - R_2$. The right counter lags behind the left one by this amount, which characterizes the lag of the drilling mud in strokes of the mud pump. It must be noted that this method of determining the mud lag is not absolutely accurate if the pump volumetric efficiency is taken from manufacturer's specifications. In this method a slight error is introduced, which is due to the fact that we are not in a position to determine the effective volumetric efficiency of the pump (P). Hence, it is far more accurate to make use of the weir suggested by GrozNII or AzNII (9) for determination of the output of the mud pump. Only then can the method described above attain the desired accuracy in calculating the mud lag.

Recently, a method that was proposed and developed by engineers B. V. Vladimirov and L. A. Galkin has come into wide use. This method is based on the use of a trapezoidal weir and permits accurate determination of the rate of mud circulation. Knowing the amount of mud flowing out of the well in the drilling process or, in other words, the rate of mud circulation is a necessary condition for correctly relating gas indications to

depth. Furthermore, quantitative evaluation of the gas content of an
interval of drilled hole is impossible without knowing the volume of mud
that circulates in the well during the time required to drill through the
given interval.

The device, which permits determining the volume of the effluent mud,
is called a discharge meter by the authors and consists of a trapezoidal
weir with adjustable sides. By means of the latter, the meter may be
mounted in channels of different widths (Fig. 72). The adjustable sides, as
well as the weir itself, are made of sheet iron. The device is fastened to
the sides of the channel with special clamps.

The controller of the discharge meter, which is attached with a special
clamp to one side of the channel ahead of the trapezoidal weir, consists of
a set of resistors connected to the segments of a commutator (each seg-
ment is connected to its neighbor through a resistor).

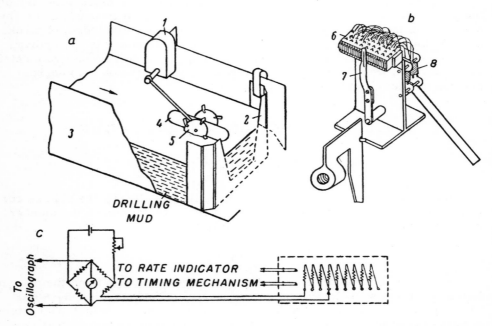

Fig. 72. Diagram of the arrangement of the discharge meter in mud channel. a —discharge
meter; b—controller of discharge meter with case removed; c —electrical diagram of discharge meter; 1 —controller of discharge meter; 2 —trapezoidal weir; 3 —side of channel;
4 —float; 5 —visual indicator; 6 —commutator; 7 —sliding contact; 8 —electrical resistor.

When the level of the drilling mud in the channel changes, the float
rises or falls, and a directly coupled sliding contact moves along the commutator, introducing more or less resistance into the arm of a Wheatstone
bridge. Thus, the height of the liquid surface ahead of the trapezoidal weir,
and therefore, the rate of mud flow, may be determined from the readings
of an electrical instrument in the diagonal of the bridge. The scale of the
instrument may be graduated in liters per second.

Regulation of the mud circulation rate during drilling is much improved and simplified by the use of the discharge meter. As stated above,
such regulation is exceedingly important in perfecting a method of relating

oil and gas logging data to depth. With the described apparatus, gas readings can be correlated with the well section automatically and more accurately. Tests under industrial conditions have shown that the trapezoidal weir has good operating characteristics. The system of remote control with the discharge meter has also proved well worth while.

In measuring the circulation rate by this method, errors may result from changes in the properties of the drilling fluid. In order to take this into account, equipment for measuring the effect of mud properties on rate of flow is used. This makes it possible to increase the accuracy of the measurement of mud rate and, therefore, the accuracy with which gas readings can be related to depth, (10, 11).

FACTORS AFFECTING RESULTS OF OIL AND GAS LOGGING

As the analysis of accumulated data shows, the results of oil and gas logging, i.e., the content of liquid and gaseous hydrocarbons in the drilling fluid, are affected by a number of factors that may be divided into two categories: procedural and geological.

To the procedural must be assigned those factors that are subject to change during the oil and gas logging operations. The most important of these are the following:

1. Method of mud degasification (completeness of degasification) and the volume of mud degassed per unit time.

2. Drilling procedure: (a) rate of penetration; (b) rate of mud circulation; (c) diameter of the bit.

3. Change in the physical properties of the drilling mud (specific gravity, viscosity).

4. Chemical treatment of the drilling mud.

5. Original clays used in preparation of drilling mud.

6. Pouring oil into the well bore.

7. Interruptions in the mud circulation.

8. Influence of higher productive zones on the penetration of lower ones.

By geological factors we mean those which are not subject to control and which the geologist must take into account in interpreting logs. The most important geological factors are the following:

1. Gas-oil ratio.

2. Physical properties of the crude oil (light or heavy oil).

3. Formation pressures.

4. Presence of dissolved hydrocarbons in aquifers.

5. Properties of the petroleum reservoirs, etc.

Gas-Oil Ratio and Crude Oil Composition

Among the factors belonging to the geological group, the most important is the gas-oil ratio, which varies from a few units in heavy crudes to 1000 m.^{3}/T in light oils. Therefore, in formations where gas-oil ratios vary over a wide range, their effect on oil and gas logging results is especially prominent. For example, in formations of the Caucasus, anomalies on oil and gas logs opposite oil pays having a gas-oil ratio over 50 m.^{3}/T are the most clear and contrasting. Less clear and less contrasting anomalies correspond to oil sands having ratios below 30 - 40 m.^{3}/T, and as a rule, those productive levels that are characterized by a negligible gas content (heavy oil) are the ones most often overlooked by oil and gas logging (Fig. 73). Analysis of accumulated data on platform formations also confirms the dominant importance of gas-oil ratios in oil and gas logging.

The magnitude of gas-oil ratios, as practical field operations have shown, depends on the composition of the crude oil and the formation pressures. Therefore, crude oil composition and formation pressures affect the log by their influence of the gas-oil ratio. The magnitude of the gas-oil ratio in a discovery well depends chiefly on the conditions of formation of this pool, i.e., on the original ratio of oil and gas in the productive stratum, the reservoir properties of the latter, and also on the preservation of the pool through geological time. Furthermore, the physical properties of crude oil as a solvent and the composition of the natural gas dissolved in it substantially affect the magnitude of the gas-oil ratio and, hence, the data of oil and gas logs.

The solubility of hydrocarbon gases in crude oil at constant temperature and pressure falls with an increase in the molecular weight of the solvent and rises with an increase in the molecular weight of the dissolved gases (12, 13, 14). Thus, methane, being the least soluble gas, is the first to evolve from the dissolved state, and, consequently, anomalies on logging diagrams are produced by methane.

Relatively lighter oils dissolve a correspondingly larger quantity of gaseous hydrocarbons than heavy ones, so that when the formation pressure increases, the volume of gas dissolved in the oil also increases, but with some deviation from Henry's Law (15). Therefore, it is obvious why heavy oils have negligible gas-oil ratios in comparison with light oils. It must be emphasized that heavy oils not only are poor solvents for hydrocarbon gases, but they also do not readily yield the small amounts of gas that are dissolved in them despite this fact.

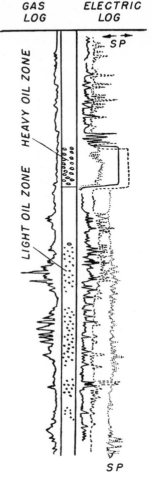

Fig. 73. Oil and gas log showing productive zones containing light and heavy oils.

Formation Pressures

Analysis of field data reveals that when under-saturated crude oils are encountered, the pressure in the reservoir is not important for oil and gas logging. This is confirmed by the fact that in some cases the magnitude of the formation pressures for both heavy oils and light oils may be the same, but the gas logs opposite these pays are essentially different owing to differences in the gas-oil ratios and composition of the oils. However, the formation pressure acquires a special significance when a gas pool is opened because of the compressibility of gas as opposed to oil, which may be considered practically incompressible.[10]

Influence of Water-Bearing Levels

In the geological interpretation of oil and gas logs, it is necessary to consider the possibility of errors in the data, due to the effect of oil formation waters and also that of aquifers that contain dissolved petroleum hydrocarbons. For example, in some cases after drilling through the principal oil zone, the concentrations of combustible gases in the mud do not fall to background values; instead, a very stable gas anomaly is observed resulting mainly from various waters that are saturated with hydrocarbons. Formation waters in contact with oil or gas pools dissolve a rather large quantity of hydrocarbon gases at high pressures, although the solubility of hydrocarbons in water (especially, salt water) under normal conditions is quite negligible.

The coefficients of solubility of the different hydrocarbons in water are quite similar to one another. The most water-soluble hydrocarbon of all is ethane, but even its coefficient of solubility is only slightly higher than that of other hydrocarbons (that of ethane is one and a half times greater than that of methane). In comparison with water, the solubility of hydrocarbon gases in oil is much greater. Thus, for example, the solubility of methane in oil is about ten times greater than in water (17).

The ratio of partial pressures to the solubility of hydrocarbons in the oil-water system at equilibrium must theoretically be the same for each phase, and therefore, bottom and formation (or capillary) waters under certain conditions may be regarded as a source of loss of gas, which to a considerable extent complicates the geological interpretation of diagrams, or even precludes, in some cases, an unambiguous answer to the question as to the presence or absence of productive levels. The idea of bottom waters as a source of loss of gas is also supported by the existence of the so-called "boiling waters".[11]

At present the influence of water zones on the data of oil and gas logging has not been adequately studied; hence, this factor must not be overlooked in log interpretations. In locating water zones, it is especially important to determine chloride ion, pH, and the concentration of salts in the mud filtrate, and also the specific gravity of the drilling mud.

Method of Mud Degasification

The method of degassing the drilling mud in oil and gas logging investigations is of substantial importance, first of all, because the degree ("depth") of degasification of the drilling fluid varies widely from one degasifier to

---

[10]Shchelkachev (16), discussing the regimes of oil formations, recognizes a so-called elastic regime in which movement of oil occurs as a result of the expansion of boundary water; however, in our case, the compressibility of water or oil can scarcely play any substantial role and is therefore insignificant in oil and gas logging.

[11]Waters saturated with soluble, gaseous hydrocarbons begin to evolve gases rapidly on pressure reduction in a manner reminiscent of the boiling of water.

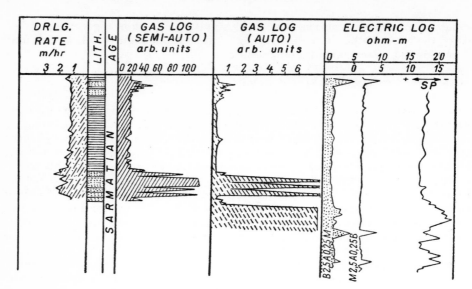

Fig. 74. Parallel testing of several degasifiers.

the next. It is sufficient to mention the box and thermo-vacuum degasifiers, the first of which reacts, as a rule, to the appearance of free gas in the suspension, while the second apparently registers both free and dissolved gases and, possibly, gas sorbed by the rock as well. It is obvious from the above that data obtained by the use of different degasifiers are not mutually comparable, either in the log correlations or in other operations.

Depending on the construction of the degasifier employed, the configuration of the gas anomalies opposite productive levels varies considerably, and in some cases (in the presence of heavy oil) they may even be overlooked altogether. For example, as a result of the use of several degasifiers in the Caucasus, as well as in other regions of the Soviet Union, it was impossible to obtain any sort of satisfactory results that were amenable to geological interpretation.

In degassing a drilling fluid under vacuum during thermal processing, argillaceous strata in most wells show a high gas content, obviously as a result of the evolution of absorbed gas. This does not appear irregular in the least if one considers that shales have greater sorption capacities than other rocks.

As another example demonstrating the importance of the method of degassing on the interpretation of gas logging diagrams, reference may be made to the results of the use of the box degasifier. In testing this equipment on drilling mud, it was determined that the optimum conditions for degasification are not attained. Not one heavy-oil zone was discovered with this degasifier, although the presence of indications of heavy oil was established through analyses of cores and cuttings.

In Fig. 74 are shown logging data obtained for the same interval in one well with several degasifiers used simultaneously. These data show that the type of degasifier employed has a very substantial effect on the final logging results.

Drilling Procedure

Rate of penetration. The effect of the drilling procedure, especially, the
rate of drilling, on the results of oil and gas logging is particularly important. However, if it is remembered that productive levels, as a rule, are
represented on a mechanical log by relative increases in the rate of penetration, this factor will only have an additive effect, because productive
levels must stand out more prominently on the gas log than they would in
the case of a uniform rate of penetration (Fig. 75) (18, 19).

The effect of this factor becomes negative in those very limited cases
in which the reservoirs consist of very dense rocks, such as hard limestones and dolomites, which have much lower rates of penetration. Here,
a unit volume of mud circulates past a smaller interval of drilled hole, and
the concentration of hydrocarbons in the drilling fluid is reduced. In such
cases, the introduction of corrections for the rate of penetration is very
desirable, but unfortunately, there is no generally applicable and adequately
proven method for introducing such corrections.

It may be assumed a priori that there is a direct or, perhaps, even
linear relation between the rate of penetration and the concentration of
combustible gases in the drilling muds. Therefore, it is quite possible
that, other conditions being equal, a twofold increase in the rate of penetration produces the same relative increase in the concentration of hydrocarbons, while on the other hand, a decrease in the rate of penetration
causes a proportional decrease in the concentration of hydrocarbons in the
drilling mud. In the American literature, there are statements that there
is a more complex relationship between these factors, namely, that the
concentrations of hydrocarbons in the mud suspension are proportional to
the square of the rate of penetration.

N. A. Karpova introduced corrections for the rate of penetration in
wells drilled in the Kuibyshev platform with good results. After the corrections were made, productive intervals could be distinguished on the un-
differentiated logs.

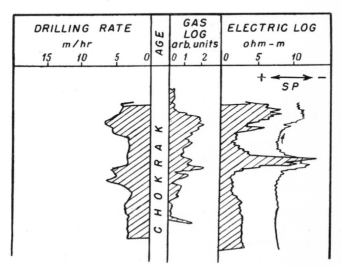

Fig. 75. Effect of drilling rate on oil and gas logging results.

Rate of mud circulation. In discussing the influence of the rate of penetration on the results of oil and gas logging, we assumed the rate of circulation of the drilling fluid to be constant. However, both the rate of penetration and the rate of mud circulation may change independently of one another in the drilling process, although in most cases, when the rate of penetration is increased, the rate of circulation must also be increased in order to insure the sufficiently rapid removal of drill cuttings.

Therefore, in some cases, these factors may cancel each other. For instance, if the mud pump rate increases in proportion to an increase in the rate of penetration, it is unnecessary to make corrections for either the rate of penetration or the rate of mud circulation. However, if the pumping rate increases as the rate of penetration decreases on the oil and gas log, which occurs very rarely, the interpretation of such a log cannot be considered of much value unless appropriate corrections are made.

Diameter of the bit. Besides the factors enumerated above, the diameter of the bit also affects the data of oil and gas logging. Naturally, other conditions being equal, the volume of space created by drilling a rock will increase with the diameter of the bit.

In this connection, Z. A. Tabasaranskii investigated the results of logging that was performed on a given interval when a well was first drilled and when the hole was later reamed. Data on the content of combustible gases in the drilling muds during the drilling and reaming operations are given in Table 22.

TABLE 22. Concentrations of Liquid and Gaseous Hydrocarbons in Drilling Mud, Arbitrary Units

Depth in meters	During drilling	During reaming
887	3.33	0.16
879	2.23	0.20
881	0.86	0.14
885	2.01	0.81
887	3.52	0.59
976	0.53	0.35
991	1.68	1.58
997	0.92	0.95

This illustrates quite well the effect of the volume of rock drilled per unit time on the logging results. The concentrations of combustible gases in the drilling fluid are considerably reduced by decreasing the amount of rock passing into the mud per unit time. It is important to note that the original drilling process was much slower than that of reaming the same interval. Therefore, if the drilling of the well had proceeded at the same rate as the reaming, there would have been an even greater contrast in the data of Table 22.

From this, it becomes clear that in coring operations, removal of the core will also affect the content of liquid and gaseous hydrocarbons in the drilling fluid. However, the core recovery percentage is low in most cases and, therefore, this circumstance can scarcely have any substantial influence on oil and gas logs in those intervals where cores were taken.

Clays Used in Preparing Drilling Mud

Investigations of fresh drilling muds reveal that the original clays used in the preparation of the suspensions contain combustible gases in appreciable concentrations in some cases (2). For example, in the examination of fresh muds prepared from Maikop clay, combustible gases were found in concentrations up to 0.3 - 0.4% (i.e., in macroquantities). In the preparation of drilling fluids from Apsheron clay, the content of combustible gases in the muds was only 0.1 - 0.2%.

Background values on gas logging diagrams are mainly due to those concentrations of combustible gases which are contained in the original clay used in the preparation of the drilling fluid. Therefore, it is desirable to determine the content of combustible gases in the original mud in order to distinguish background values for purposes of interpretation.

Addition of Crude Oil and Petroleum Products to Drilling Mud

Among the factors which introduce errors in oil and gas logging, additions of oil and oil products to the mud play a very important part. However, as investigations have shown, not all oils cause errors; e.g., the pouring of heavy oil, free of light fractions, into the drilling fluid does not lead to any error in the data of oil and gas logs provided the degasification of the mud is carried out under normal atmospheric pressure without thermal treatment. Despite the addition of heavy oil, the concentrations of combustible gases in the mud do not change at all until productive levels are uncovered.

If the degasification of the drilling fluid were conducted under vacuum, with thermal treatment, the addition even of heavy oil would cause substantial errors, in the oil and gas logs, to say nothing of cases where crude oil containing light components is used. On the platform (probably the Russian platform, Ed.), many cases have occurred in which crude with a content of light fractions was poured into wells, as a result of which further investigation of the wells became impossible under any conditions.

Therefore, accurate recording of the intervals of oil addition and the specific gravity and volume of the oil added is a necessary condition for the objective and sound interpretation of oil and gas logs. Any interpretation which ingores such facts cannot be considered flawless.

Effect of Higher Productive Zones on Penetration of Lower Intervals

In some cases the interpreter must reckon with the possibility of the influence exerted by higher productive zones on the penetration of lower ones. Observations reveal that stopping the circulation after drilling through a productive level leads to enrichment of the mud in the hole, in combustible gases as a result of the diffusion of hydrocarbons from the stratum into the drilling fluid.

Such manifestations of gas, resulting from higher productive levels, are sometimes so pronounced that they are not amenable to measurement with the gas analyzer, even on the high range. The longer the interruption in the mud circulation, the more pronounced the manifestation of gas, which of course, is quite natural. As a rule, such cases are observed when wells are left standing in anticipation of electric logging or when the circulation of mud is stopped while drill pipe is being pulled. Therefore, in carrying out logging where a sufficiently accurate calculation of the mud lag has not been made, such manifestations of gas due to higher levels may be erroneously ascribed to lower, non-productive levels. This has occurred in a number of cases.

Interesting data were obtained in one well where the intervals of pronounced gas manifestations coincide in most cases with the depth at which sharp decreases in the specific gravity of the mud were noted (Fig. 76). Because of these decreases, the higher productive level began to manifest itself. Here the effect due to the higher, purely gaseous level was superposed on that due to the lower ones. The effect of the higher level was noted only when a considerable drip in pressure occurred in drilling with an unweighted mud.

The coincidence of negative anomalies in the curve of mud gravity with positive anomalies in the curve of the content of combustible gases is explained by the above circumstance (Fig. 76). It follows from the data given that, in the interpretation of oil and gas logs and especially in the conduct of gas logging work, the influence of higher levels on the penetration of lower ones cannot be ignored without inviting errors. Thus, it is especially important to determine the mud lag, so that such gas manifestations due to higher productive levels may not be erroneously ascribed to lower, nonproductive intervals.

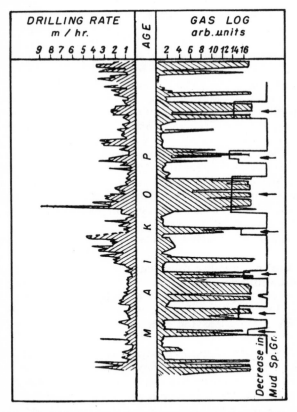

Fig. 76 Effect on gas log of decreases in the specific gravity of the drilling fluid.

Change in Physical Properties of Drilling Mud

Experience has shown that changes in the physical properties of the drilling fluid also affect the results of oil and gas logging. Of particular importance is the mud viscosity, which in deep drilling practice varies from 25 sec. to immobility. As the viscosity is increased, the volume of mud that is degassed per unit time is substantially decreased. This, in turn, leads to a decrease in the concentration of combustible gases, to say nothing of the fact that a viscous fluid has poor degasifying characteristics in itself. However, it should be noted that if the viscosity of the mud has a negative influence on its degasification, this factor, on the other hand, acquires a positive benefit when productive levels are encountered, because a viscous suspension localized the intervals of gas manifestations better.

The effect of the specific gravity of drilling mud on the results of gas logging has not been sufficiently studied. A few isolated observations indicate that a decrease in mud weight produces favorable conditions for a show of gas not only from the upper productive zones but also from the lower ones. Thus, the concentrations of hydrocarbons in the drilling fluid in such cases depends not only on the drilled-out rock entering the mud but also on the productive zone. This substantially complicates the interpretation of oil and gas logging data.

Obviously, the effect of the physical properties of drilling muds on the results of oil and gas logging is not limited to the situations discussed above. The mud is not a passive medium transporting hydrocarbons but reacts actively with the fluids in the well bore. Therefore, the effect of the mud properties (specific gravity, viscosity, etc.) is very complex. This problem cannot be satisfactorily resolved without special investigations in this field.

The effect of chemical treatment (addition of caustic soda, lignite, lime, etc.) on the content of combustible gases in the mud remains quite obscure. Special experimental work is required in order to elucidate this question.

The items discussed above are not all the factors that affect the results of oil and gas logging, but they are the main ones. Besides these factors, there are probably several others, the existence of which we do not even suspect today.

INTERPRETATION OF OIL AND GAS LOGS

Interpreting Manually Recorded Data

The purpose of the geological interpretation of oil and gas logs is to discern productive intervals of commercial interest in the section of the well being studied. The practice of interpreting these logs has shown that in some cases the geologist-interpreter can recognize gas anomalies having sharply increased concentrations above background without particular effort.

In those cases where the anomalous values are ten times greater than background, the task of the interpreter is reduced to distinguishing analogous intervals and comparing the latter with the data of mechanical and electrical logs. But, along with the easily differentiated oil and gas logs, there are also those whose interpretation is complicated by low concentrations that are close to the background values of other wells.

The original clay used in preparing the drilling fluid contains combustible gases, to which the background values are mainly due. Therefore, it becomes necessary to determine the content of combustible gases in the "pure mud". Investigations in the Caucasus have shown that when drilling fluids prepared with Maikop clays are used, the background is much higher than when those prepared with Apsheron clays are used (Table 23).

The intensity of the background, however, is not strictly constant because of the different rates of penetration of the various rock strata in the well. At high rates of penetration, a larger amount of drilled rock passes into the mud than at low rates. As a result, the concentrations of combustible gases in the drilling fluid change. However, these changes increase the intensity of the background to the same extent, except for those intervals in which an abrupt change in lithology and rate of penetration are observed.

Experience has also shown that, in general, the background intensity decreases when the drilling fluid is degasified under low-temperature conditions (in winter).

After distinguishing the background values, the log is divided into separate zone-intervals, within which are observed manifestations of oil and gas in excess of the background intensity. The geological section

TABLE 23. Background Intensities and Coefficient of Contrast of Gas Anomalies on Logging Diagrams

Formation	Background value, % abs.	Intensity of gas anomalies, % abs.	Coefficient of contrast
Krasnodar District			
B—Well 1.	0.5—0.6	5	10
A—Well 1.	0.3	1.8	6
A—Well 2.	0.3	2.2	7
B—Well 2.	0.2	1.9	9
A—Well 3.	0.2	1.3	6
A—Well 4.	1.8	11	6
A—Well 5.	0.2—0.3	2.5	8
A—Well 6.	0.2—0.3	5.5	18
A—Well 7.	0.1—0.2	4	20
B—Well 3.	0.2—0.6	11	18
Apsheron Peninsula			
B—Well 1.	0.3—0.4	4.5	11
A—Well 2.	0.1—0.2	6	30
Grozny Region			
A—Well 1.	0.1—0.2	1	5
B—Well 1.	0.1—0.2	1.1	5
Supporting well	0.2—0.6	1.2	2
B—Well 2.	0.3	1	3
A—Well 2.	0.5—0.6	7	11
etc.			

compiled on the basis of a study of drill cuttings, as well as the data of mechanical and electrical logging, makes possible both the elucidation of the character of gas anomalies found on the gas log and the selection of specific, likely objectives.

Interpreting Oil and Gas Logs of Single and Multilayer Formations

As has already been stated, the task of interpreting oil and gas logs is greatly simplified in wells containing only one productive zone or several at a considerable distance apart from each other. Such cases occur in platform formations where the number of productive intervals is relatively small. On the other hand, the interpretation of oil and gas logs in multi-layer formations of the type of the Apsheron peninsula, where there may be 40 or more oil-bearing layers, is a matter of substantial difficulty. This is mainly due to the small thickness of the separating argillaceous layers, and in this case, it is absolutely necessary to compare the gas log with mechanical and electrical logs.

In comparing oil and gas with electric logs, it is necessary first to delineate large stratigraphic units, within the boundaries of which there are several production objectives that may, in turn, be subdivided into individual layers (Fig. 77). An example of such large-scale division is the selection of the top and bottom of an oil pool in the Kirmakin formation in which there are several oil-bearing zones (Fig. 77, a). Another example may be taken from the interpretation of gas logs of the Krasnodar district, where the complex of heavy-oil zones in the Miocene is first segregated without being subdivided into Chokrak, Karagan, and Sarmatian (Fig. 77, b).

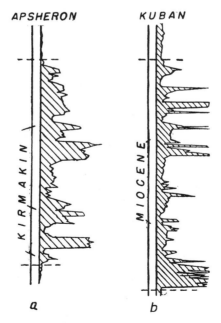

Fig. 77. Delineation of the upper and lower boundaries of large stratigraphic units.

Furthermore, within the limits of large geological formations that have already been delineated, individual strata or exploitation objectives must be sought if we are to be secure from gross errors such as are possible in comparing oil and gas logs with electric logs and other geological data.

It must not be assumed that the argillaceous rocks which separate productive levels are absolutely devoid of oil and gas. Whoever, has observed productive sands in outcrops cannot doubt that the shale sections separating the oil zones also contain thin productive seams of sand and sandstone. In some intervals the shale itself acquires an increased degree of sandiness and fissuring and contains oil, gas, or water. This explains the minor gas manifestations observed in the intervals between productive zones, which greatly complicate the interpretation of logs in multilayered formations.

In recognizing productive zones in multilayered formations, the possibility that these zones may occur higher in the hole on the oil and gas logs than on the electric logs must be kept in mind; this occurs with gaseous layers of great thickness as a result of an upward movement of the gas in returning drilling mud. From (Fig. 78) is is obvious that the Sarmation gas-bearing zone is sufficiently well indicated by the electric log data. However, according to the gas log, the top of this zone is 8 m. higher than it is according to the electric log. This is caused by the buoyant rise of the free gas with respect to the drilling mud during its upward movement to the top of the well. The interval of gas peaks indicated on the log cannot be subject to doubt, because this interval was determined by simultaneously logging in two field units, an automatic one and a semiautomatic one. This example is not unique because an analogous phenomenon is also observed in other cases.

It should be noted that the distorting effect of this factor increases as the viscosity of the drilling fluid decreases. Thus, if increase in the mud viscosity is a negative factor in attaining optimum conditions for degasification, it plays a positive role in attaining greater accuracy in locating productive levels. A viscous drilling mud localizes the intervals of gas manifestations better and, hence, facilitates determination of the depth of productive zones.

As investigations of oil and gas logs show, the residual content of gas in the drilling fluid has practically no significance in locating productive levels if the mud is degassed at normal atmospheric pressure without thermal treatment. In this case the concentration of combustible gases in the drilling fluid falls to the background value after the productive level is passed, and this occurs on nearly all logs, with few exceptions. In work with the thermovacuum degasifier, this circumstance obviously cannot be ignored.

In some cases the residual gas content may raise the background somewhat as is actually observed; however, this does not complicate locating the bottom of the oil or gas zone if the latter does not continue to manifest itself after it has been passed. It is true that, in practical logging work, distortion of the bottom of the productive zone occurs as a result of the efflux of gas and oil from a higher layer, induced by a decrease in hydrostatic pressure, but this phenomenon has nothing in common with the residual gas content.

Absolute values of gas peaks on the diagram are not only functions of the gas-oil ratios and reservoir pressures but are, at least to the same

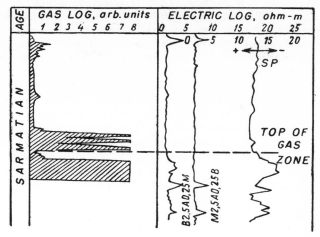

Fig. 78. Advance of free gas in the drilling mud returning
up the hole.

extent, functions of the drilling procedure (primarily the rate of penetration). It is quite natural that when a productive zone is drilled through,
maximum concentrations of combustible gases will correspond to maximum drilling rates, other conditions being equal, because a smaller quantity
of drilling mud flows past the bottom of the well per unit time at higher
rates of penetration than at lower rates.

In Fig. 79 is shown a typical curve of the content of combustible gases
in the drilling mud and the corresponding curve of the rate of penetration
observed on drilling through a layer uniformly saturated with oil, at rates
which are different from top to bottom.

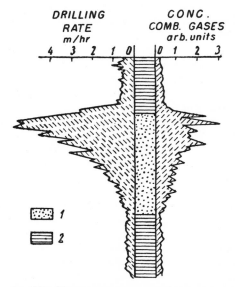

Fig. 79. Variation in the concentrations
of combustible gases with rate of penetration. 1—productive zone; 2—clay.

If such diagrams are interpreted only from the point of view of absolute values, we would be obliged to state that the oil content decreases from the top of the interval to the bottom. Actually, the zone is uniformly saturated with oil, and the decrease in absolute concentrations is caused exclusively by the decrease in the rate of penetration and, therefore, by the increase in the mud rate flowing past the bottom of the well.

It is especially necessary to take the drilling procedure into account under the conditions of platform formations, where the absolute concentrations of hydrocarbons are low in comparison with geosynclinal formations. Therefore, absolute concentrations are not a decisive criterion for judging the practical significance of gas anomalies. From this, it becomes clear that in the interpretation of oil and gas logs, a complete analogy in the configurations of gas and electrical anomalies is not to be expected, particularly in those cases in which the drilling procedure changes abruptly, or in which the reservoirs are carbonate rocks.

Under the conditions of the Northern Caucasus, there are many cases in which intervals with evident petroleum possibilities according to electric logging data produce water on perforation, while on the other hand, intervals with water-bearing characteristics according to electric logs produce oil or gas on testing. This occurs because carbonate rocks containing either oil or water have about the same electrical characteristics. Furthermore, the presence of highly mineralized waters (interstitial water) in productive levels sometimes lowers the apparent resistivities. Because of this, it is very difficult to distinguish oil-bearing zones from water-bearing ones on electric logs under such geological conditions.

Considerable difficulties also arise in the interpretation of electric logs, in the case where a section of the well contains rocks of appreciable density, which are characterized in electrical logging by apparent resistivities as high as those found in oil-bearing levels.

As a result of the penetration of fresh water muds into a water-bearing layer, the electrical characteristics of the latter are greatly changed (the resistance increases). On the other hand, the infiltration of salt water muds into a productive layer leads to the contrary result, the resistance decreases opposite the productive zones. This circumstance also complicates the selection of productive intervals by means of electric logs. Under these conditions, the importance of oil and gas logging becomes particularly great, because it is the only direct geochemical method which permits judgment as to the presence or absence of oil or gas in a particular stratum.

It follows from an analysis of oil and gas logs that the gas "peaks" of narrow width and low amplitude which are located above major production objectives must be evaluated very carefully, because they characterize zones that also contain commercial quantities of oil and gas, possibly on account of permeation by fluids from the main reservoir below.

As mentioned previously, the geologist must also reckon in the interpretation of some logs with the possibility of the introduction of errors in the data of oil and gas logging by bottom waters saturated with hydrocarbons. There are cases where the concentrations of combustible gases do not drop to background value after the main productive zones have been drilled through; instead, a very stable gas anomaly appears due to a series of layers which, for the most part, contain water saturated with hydrocarbons.

Distinguishing Between Oil and Gas Zones

One of the important problems in the interpretation of oil and gas logs is
that of locating purely gas-bearing formations and distinguishing them from
"purely" oil-bearing strata. At present, this problem cannot be solved
because of the lack of sufficient data, but it may be said that, in drilling
through "dry" gas zones, the resulting anomaly consists exclusively of the
methane fraction, while in penetrating oil pays, the proportion of heavy
hydrocarbons in the composition of the gas is greater and in some cases
approaches 50%. It must be stated that there are exceptions where oil-
bearing formations that are easily recognized by means of data on total
combustible gases are almost indistinguishable on the curve of heavy hydrocarbons. The weakly differentiated nature of heavy-hydrocarbon curves
on oil and gas logs is not quite clear, because when oil zones are opened,
the fluid passing into the mud consists mainly of gas dissolved in oil.
Heavy hydrocarbons must predominate in the composition of this gas on
account of their great solubility in comparison with methane.

In some cases, on the other hand, the concentration of heavy hydrocarbons is improbably high with respect to total combustible gases (it
sometimes amounts to 90 - 95% of the total). It is possible that such a
high content of the heavy fraction, as has been noted, resulted from the
presence of hydrogen sulfide and hydrogen in the natural gases of the oil
formations. The presence of hydrogen has been considered by foreign investigators to be a favorable index in prospecting for oil and gas. In gas
logs prepared by foreign investigators, the hydrogen maximum precedes
the maxima of hydrocarbon gases as a rule. This distribution of hydrogen
and hydrocarbon-gas anomalies is generally logical, since hydrogen, being
the lightest gas, must occupy a correspondingly higher part of the structure
containing the gas pool.

At the same time A. F. Dobryanskii in his work, "Geochemistry of
Petroleum", categorically denies the possibility of the presence of hydrogen in the natural gases of oil formations. In the opinion of this author (12),
indications of the presence of hydrogen in the gases of oil formations are
pure misunderstandings resulting from errors in analytical determinations.
It seems to us that such misunderstandings might indeed occur in the determination of microquantities of hydrogen. However, there are indications that hydrogen is present in the natural gases of oil formations in
macroquantities, and the analytical determinations of large quantities of
hydrogen are probably not the result of errors. For example, V. A.
Sokolov (17) states that the content of hydrogen in the gas from a well in
Tataria amounted to 30% or more. If hydrogen is actually present in the
gases of oil formations, its presence, together with that of hydrogen sulfide, which quite often is found in natural gases, must increase the content
of heavy hydrocarbons, since hydrogen and hydrogen sulfide burn at a
lower temperature than methane or heavy hydrocarbons (H_2 and H_2S burn
at about 250°, heavy hydrocarbons burn at about 600°, and methane burns
at 800 - 1,000° C). It follows from this that, in the presence of hydrogen
and hydrogen sulfide in petroleum gases, the determination of the ratio of
heavy and light components by existing methods of analysis is almost impossible.

In the interpretation of the oil and gas logs of wells that have opened
formations containing heavy oil, additional difficulties arise due to the

negligible magnitude of the gas-oil ratios. In contrast to heavy oils, light oils quickly release their dissolved gases when the pressure falls (in proportion to their movement toward the top of the well).

The saturation pressure, i.e., the pressure at which the main mass of gas is held in the dissolved state, is 52 atm. (12). When oil pays are opened, part of the gas dissolved in the oil goes over to the gas phase as a result of the decrease in pressure. However, the main mass of gas that is dissolved at high pressures (particularly with weighted muds) remains in the dissolved state until the pressure decreases to the saturation point, i.e., 52 atm. In drilling with a mud having a specific gravity of 1.2 - 1.3, pressures at a depth of 450 - 500 m. reach the saturation level, and the main mass of dissolved gas begins to pass into the gas phase in ever-growing amounts.

As investigations have shown, the process of evolution of dissolved gases, in the case of light oils, is almost entirely completed as the mud moves to the top of the hole. When zones bearing heavy oil are opened, however, this process is considerably delayed, especially under winter conditions.

In the absence of free gas in the productive layer, anomalies on the gas log are due solely to hydrocarbon gases dissolved in the oil. The method of incomplete degassing used in some cases often leads to overlooking production zones in a well section that contain heavy oils. This circumstance is one of the causes of the discrepancies between the data of oil and gas and electrical logging.

One of the most important and, at present, least clear aspects in the interpretation of oil and gas logs is the problem of ascertaining the presence of commercial accumulations of oil or gas and distinguishing them from non-commercial pools. The only correct approach to this problem is a complete analysis of oil and gas and other logging data considered in the light of all existing geological factors (especially the porosity and permeability of the reservoirs). In oil and gas logging work, large gas seeps which correspond to rocks with very moderate reservoir properties are often encountered. It is easy to err in evaluating the significance of such gas anomalies without detailed analysis of other types of logs and data from the examination of cuttings and cores for porosity and permeability.

This danger must be considered especially in distinguishing commercial pays on logs made in areas of dispersed oil and gas saturation (e.g., Maikop, diatomaceous layers, etc., which are oil and gas bearing to a greater or lesser degree everywhere in the Caucasus). An alternation of thin sand and sandstone beds intercalated in a predominantly shaley formation sometimes causes a distinct gas anomaly to appear on the well logs, although electrical and mechanical logging and the testing of cores for porosity and permeability may not give positive results.

The discrepancies between oil and gas logging and other types of logging may often be resolved by taking a side-wall core from the interval in question. Here, however, it must be kept in mind that side-wall cores do not always solve the problem unambiguously. Samples taken from productive zones sometimes do not show visible signs of oil, because they have been flushed by the continuous circulation of the drilling fluid.

A combination of oil and gas, electrical, mechanical, and luminescence logging makes it possible to interpret the results of the investigations with confidence, since oil and gas and luminescence logs indicate the presence or absence of oil or gas in the well sections, while mechanical and electrical logs show the correct locations of productive zones. These data should be supplemented by a lithological section, compiled from drill cuttings, side-wall cores, and other parameters (porosity, permeability).

Interpreting Automatically Recorded Data

In gas logging with automatic equipment, the parameters of interest to us (gas analysis, rate of penetration, mud pump speed, mud lag) are automatically recorded on a single paper strip. These data are also recorded manually in the logging record by the operator attending the equipment. Interpretation of a great number of gas logs and comparison with hand plotted data show that in the normal operation of the field laboratory, the gas curves and other parameters agree very well.

In some cases the gas-content curve on the paper strip is substantially different from that of the same curve constructed from manually-recorded data; however, the gas-bearing zones coincide exactly. Some discrepancy in the configuration of gas anomalies on the automatic record and on the manual logging diagram is quite natural, because the records are not obtained simultaneously.

Rather than presenting a detailed discussion of methods of interpretating automatic records (which interested persons may obtain elsewhere), we shall only note that gas anomalies on the automatic log must be especially carefully analyzed and compared with manually recorded data.

In the analysis of an automatic record, it must be kept in mind that both the configuration of a gas anomaly and the interval in which it appears are greatly altered when the rates of penetration are not constant. For an exact determination of the interval to which a gas anomaly actually belongs, a correction for the lag of the drilling mud must be applied. As is evident from (Fig. 80), the width of gas peaks either increases (Fig. 80, a) or decreases (Fig. 80, b), depending on the configuration of the traverse lines, or in other words, depending on the rate of penetration.

In the treatment of automatic records it is necessary to introduce the concepts of visible (or apparent) and true width. By the visible or apparent width of gas anomalies is meant that width which is directly recorded on the strip by the self-recorder (w) (Figs. 80, 81). By the true width is meant that width which is obtained graphically after applying the correction for the mud lag. The true width may prove to be greater than the apparent width ($w > w_2$), less than the latter ($w < w_1$), or equal to the latter ($w = w_3$) (Figs. 80, 81).

As is evident from the graph, if the top of the productive zone is drilled at a higher rate than the bottom, the true width of the interval of gas manifestations is greater than the visible width. On the other hand, if the top of the productive level is drilled at a lower rate than the bottom, the true width of the gas anomaly proves to be less than the visible width (Fig. 80). In those cases in which the productive intervals are penetrated more or less uniformly, or in other words, where the traverse lines are parallel to each other and uniformly spaced, the visible width of the interval of gas manifestations is equal to the true width (Fig. 81).

The interpreter must remember that automatically recorded data are not always complete and, in some cases, productive zones may be overlooked altogether or only partially recorded. Such effects are observed,

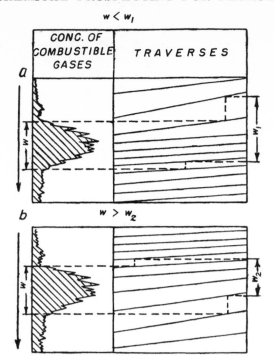

Fig. 80. Determining true width of a gas
anomaly on an automatic record. w—apparent width; w_1 — and w_2—true widths.

for example, in those cases where a pay zone has been penetrated and the
drilling stops before the circulating mud corresponding to this section has
reached the surface and passed through the degasifier. In these cases the
mud enriched in combustible gases is discharged without leaving any trace
on the automatic record, because after the drilling stops, the automatic
self-recorded no longer operates. (Data are recorded on the paper strip
only while penetration takes place.)

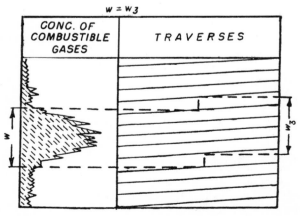

Fig. 81. Determining true width in the case of
uniform penetration of a productive zone.

However, there are also other cases in which productive levels that are sufficiently well distinguished on the automatic record (strip), for some reason leave no trace on the manual record. The causes of such discrepancies have not been adequately studied and are not understood. It follows from what has been stated, however, that in the interpretation of oil and gas logs, manual records must be supplemented with automatic ones and final conclusions regarding the well being studied can be drawn only after this is done.

Among the data on the automatic record, the curve showing the number of strokes of the mud pump per minute is of interest. Very often, maximum pumping rates correspond to intervals of the section in which absorption of the drilling fluid by porous rocks is observed.

The interpreter must remember that operation of the pump at a high rate can and sometimes actually does lead to a reduction in the concentration of combustible gases in the drilling mud as a result of the increase in the volume of mud flowing past the bottom of the well per in unit time.

Summarizing what has been said with regard to automatic logging, we emphasize that manual and automatic records are not to be treated separately, but must be interpreted together, since they essentially supplement one another.

Data Necessary in Oil and Gas Logging

Owing to the lack of a single, generally accepted method of expressing oil and gas logging data, graphic results from various regions cannot always be interpreted without ambiguity. Although no single method of presenting gas logging data can be suggested for all regions, some procedures must be standardized, and factual material necessary for the interpretation of gas logs must be uniform. For a complete and sound log interpretation, it is necessary to have the following data:

1. Geological section, compiled from analysis of cores and cuttings and electrical and mechanical logs.

2. Intervals where cores, side-wall cores, and paleontologic data were obtained if any.

3. Electric log data: spontaneous potential and the normal and lateral resistivity curves.

4. Drilling rate or rate of penetration.

5. Luminescence determinations on drilling mud, cuttings, cores, and side-wall cores.

6. Physical properties of the drilling mud (specific gravity, viscosity).

7. Filtration of the drilling mud: volume (V) of filtrate in ml., thickness of the mud cake in mm., the presence of chloride ions in the filtrate and its pH.

8. Chemical treatment and additions to the drilling mud (in particular, additions of oil).

9. Intervals of new drilling fluid (partial and complete changes).

10. Porosity and permeability of reservoirs, mainly for intervals of gas manifestations.

11. Interruptions in mud circulation (with indication of the duration of non-circulation, especially after penetration of the first productive zone).

12. Diameter and type of bit used in each interval of hole and the degree of bit wear (at the time of changing).

13. Readings of the "drillometer" in units through fixed intervals of penetration.

14. Readings of the pressure at the mud pump or stand pipe.

15. The number of revolutions of the rotary table according to geological-technical reckoning along with the actual number.

16. Geological age of the clay used in preparing the drilling fluid, with an indication of the presence or absence of combustible gases in the original mixture.

17. Intervals in which drilling mud was lost.

18. Lag of the drilling fluid in strokes of the mud pump, etc.

The data indicated above do not answer all the questions that may arise in the interpretation of oil and gas logs, but in most cases, they are quite sufficient for an unambiguous interpretation of results.

It is necessary to construct a geological log of the well being studied from data obtained with drill cuttings, cores, and side-wall samples, as well as additional data from mechanical and electrical logging, in order to compare it with the oil and gas logs and discern intervals that are being traced. Such a complex assemblage of different types of logs facilitates the correlation of logs and gives a better basis for selecting commercially productive zones.

In expressing the results of oil and gas logging according to light-oil and heavy-oil zones on a single diagram, several scales must be used because the absolute values of the concentrations of combustible gases in zones containing light oil are much greater than those of heavy oil. Analogous conditions occur in platform formations, where the oil found in Permian strata is heavy and oxidized, while that in the Carboniferous and Devonian is relatively light.

Lateral resistivity data are especially valuable in those regions where mud infiltration into the strata is observed (i.e., in regions with low pressures). Here, the resulting invaded zones are characterized on the electric log by high resistivities if the mud is made with fresh water, or by low resistivities if salt water is used.

Data on porosity and permeability may, for the sake of descriptiveness, be plotted as profiles opposite those intervals which they characterize.

On the gas logging diagrams submitted in the final report, the false effects of the highest productive zone on lower zones must be eliminated and the logs submitted in "pure form". Gas anomalies caused by the highest zone and their intensities must be indicated by arrows opposite the interval where they were observed, drawn to an appropriate scale. When oil and gas logging is conducted without allowing for the mud lag with sufficient accuracy, such gas anomalies may be erroneously ascribed to lower intervals that are not productive.

Interpreting Mechanical Logs

One of the advantages of automatic and semiautomatic field laboratory units lies in the fact that they permit not only the determination of combustible gases in the drilling fluid but also the acquisition of data characterizing the resistance to drilling of the component rocks of the well section being studied. The resulting curve of the mechanical log is an invaluable aid to the geologist in locating oil- and gas-bearing intervals.

However, the mechanical log may be intelligently used for interpretation only where there are data affecting the rate of penetration. The chief factors affecting mechanical logs are: (1) pressure of the drill bit at the bottom of the well; (2) type and wear resistance of the bit; (3) revolutions of the rotary table per minute; (4) pressure developed by the mud pump, etc. As investigations have shown, the rate of penetration is substantially increased by an increase in bit pressure.

Practical interpretation of mechanical logs has shown that reservoir rocks may give rise to maxima on the logs (Fig. 82, b), as well as minima (Fig. 82, a) depending on the rate of penetration and type of bits used. In deep-drilling practice, the RKh bit is often used. This bit easily penetrates argillaceous beds, giving rise to maxima in the rate of penetration, but when dense layers of rock (sandstones) are encountered, zones of minima appear on the log.

However, when these same intervals are drilled with cutting bits, the inverse effect is obtained. In intervals where sands and sandstones are encountered, maxima are obtained on the mechanical logs, while minimum rates of penetration correspond to argillaceous rocks, which is quite natural (Fig. 82, c). From this it becomes clear how unreliable an interpretation based only on the separation of maximum and minimum rates of

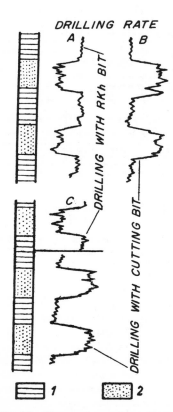

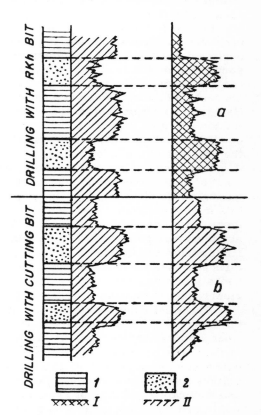

Fig. 82. Change in configuration of mechanical log depending on type of bit used. 1—clay; 2—sands and sandstones.

Fig. 83. Effect of different bits on mechanical logs. 1—clays; 2—sands and sandstones; I—curve of drilling time; II—curve of rate of penetration.

penetration is without an analysis of the drilling procedure. Since different types of bits are used in different intervals during deep exploratory drilling, the interpretation of mechanical logs becomes very complicated (Fig. 82, a).

To simplify reading the mechanical logging curve in those intervals which were drilled with an RKh bit, the rate of penetration may be indicated together with its reciprocal, namely, the drilling time curve. In this way sand and sandstone strata will also be represented on the diagram by maxima (Fig. 83, a). In this method of plotting data, there will always be maxima corresponding to potential reservoirs regardless of the type of bit used (Fig. 83, a and b).

However, the degree of wear of the bits is also important in the interpretation of mechanical logs. Absolute values of the rate of penetration are greatly decreased when a worn bit is used for drilling. If mistakes are to be avoided, the time of each bit change must be noted in the records and on the logs, lest the relative increase in the rates of penetration after changing the bit be interpreted as changes in the mechanical properties of the rocks (Fig. 84).

In order to allow for the effect of bit pressure on mechanical logging, more experimental data must be accumulated (observations on the rate of penetration with various loads on the bit) and used to calculate correction factors, which are as yet unknown. Using a correction factor, the rates of penetration could be reduced to uniform load conditions, which would considerably simplify the analysis of mechanical logs.

The speed of rotation of the rotary table must also be included among factors influencing mechanical logging. In deep-drilling this may vary from 150 to 300 r.p.m. or more. However, the effect of this factor does not seem so great because the r.p.m. of the rotary table usually decreases on drilling through dense rocks. Intervals where dense rocks are encountered will stand out more clearly on the drilling time curve (18).

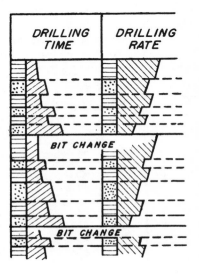

Fig. 84. Effect of bit wear on mechanical logs. 1—dense rocks; 2—soft rocks.

Practical experience has shown that mechanical logging is of use to the interpreter only if observations are made regularly. Regular observations of the pressure reading at the mud pump give an indirect indication of the rocks penetrated by the bit. As a rule, increases in pump pressure correspond to argillaceous intervals in the section of the well, where "clay collars" are often formed. Therefore, observations of mud pump operation and accurate recording of mud pump data are necessary in order to insure intelligent final interpretation of mechanical and oil and gas logs.

In. Figures 85, 86, and 87 are given examples of the interpretation of mechanical logs in which layers of sands in an otherwise predominantly argillaceous section stand out quite clearly.

Mechanical logging is especially important in regions where there are dense, unproductive rocks that have the same electrical characteristics as oil- and gas-bearing zones. As a result of this circumstance, there unproductive intervals are sometimes recommended for testing as likely objectives based on the electric log data. It is possible to eliminate such misinterpretations with the aid of mechanical logs and cuttings analyses in conjunction with oil and gas logging through a definite interval of penetration.

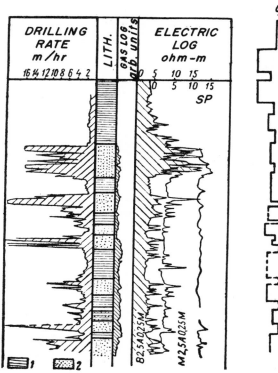

Fig. 85. Division of the Sarmatian into separate lithological units according to the data of mechanical and electrical logging. 1—clay; 2—sands, sandstones with heavy oil.

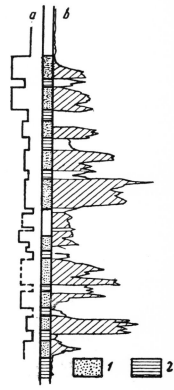

Fig. 86. Distinguishing productive zones in Kirmakin strata. 1—oil sands; 2—clays; a—mechanical log; b—gas log.

Interpreting Luminescence Logs

The data of luminescence analyses of drilling muds, cuttings, and cores is of considerable interest in the complex investigation of well sections. Luminescence logging is especially important in regions where light oils occur together with heavy ones, making detection of the latter by oil and gas logging very difficult. Regular observations on the appearance of oil in the mud and drill chips are also of substantial aid to the interpreter in separating productive intervals on the oil and gas logs into purely gaseous and oil zones.

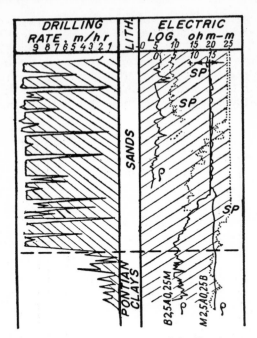

Fig. 87. Location of the top of the Pontian
argillaceous beds by electrical and mechanical logs.

No one type of logging can alone provide an unambiguous solution to
the problem of deciding the petroleum content of a given productive interval through which a well passes. Only by complex interpretation of the
data of oil and gas, luminescence, and other types of logging is it possible
to approach the solution to this problem. Thus, for example, investigations
have shown that when purely gas-bearing strata are penetrated, hardly any
luminescent substances are observed in the drilling fluid; however, when
oil-bearing reservoirs are penetrated, both drilling fluid and mud are
luminescent.

Investigations show that zones of heavy, tarry oil, which are quite
easily detected by luminescence logging of drill cuttings, may be overlooked on oil and gas logs. However, when luminescence examinations are
made, additional difficulties arise in connection with the non-uniform
motion of the rock particles in the mud.

Comparatively large chips are difficult to correlate accurately to the
well section, especially when drilling at great depths with a mud of low
specific gravity and viscosity. This explains the diffuse character of gas
and luminescence anomalies on logs (particularly, the lower limits of oil-
bearing zones). If a slight displacement is observed in a luminescence
anomaly and the mud lag has been taken into account, the anomaly should
be related to the nearest interval for which anomalous values have also
been observed by other types of logging (oil and gas, electrical, and mechanical).

Another inconvenience in the luminescence logging of cuttings is the
presence of large gaps in the log opposite argillaceous intervals where the

sampling of drill chips is impossible, because particles of clay pass into the mud and increase its viscosity. Owing to the occasional absence of data opposite clays and shales, luminescence anomalies lack significance within the limits of reservoirs. Hence, it is not possible to give a comparative evaluation of separate lithologic units along the entire section of a well. Although there is only a relatively small amount of information at present, the existing data show that in some cases it is possible to recognize the stratigraphic unit to which an interval of oil anomalies belongs by its luminescence characteristics. Thus, for example, the sharp difference in the luminescence characteristics of heavy, tarry oils and light, paraffinic oils sometimes makes it possible to ascertain without error the stratigraphic section to which the cuttings, core sample, or side-wall cores belong (there are said to be formations, within the limits of which there are zones of both light and heavy oil).

Examinations of the hydrocarbon extracts of core samples reveal that the nature of the luminescence in an interval of a given section varies depending on the lithology of rocks. The luminescence characteristics of sediments of different lithologies apparently are different because of changes in the amounts of tars and asphaltenes in the oils. It is possible that a change in the amount of tars in the oils of different layers included in a single series of strata may be explained by changes in both the thicknesses and sorption properties of the argillaceous beds scattered throughout the section (20).

As is evident from the above, it is very desirable to conduct luminescence analyses in conjunction with oil and gas logging, because it substantially supplements the data of other types of logs. For convenience in reading luminescence logs, they should be recorded on the same diagram as the results of oil and gas and other types of logging (21). The luminescence data are usually expressed by columns opposite those intervals from which samples of drilling mud, cuttings, or cores were taken (Fig. 88). The length of the column characterizes the quantitative content of oil or bitumen, while the qualitative composition is expressed by various colors or arbitrary signs. Besides the qualitative and quantitative characteristics of bitumens, it is recommended that the bituminous textures also be shown on the diagram.

Comparison of the lithologic-stratigraphic column drawn on the basis of the complex study of all existing data concerning the well being investigated with the results of luminescence and other types of logging makes possible a more reliable and well-founded selection of likely intervals for testing (21, 22).

Characteristics of Well Logs From Various Types of Rocks

Clays and Shales. A fluctuation of combustible gas content within the limits of background values corresponds to argillaceous rocks in the well bore if the drilling fluid is degassed under normal atmospheric pressure without thermal treatment. According to mechanical logging data, either minima or maxima may correspond to clays and shales, depending on the type of bits used. Sometimes argillaceous layers are characterized by a long drilling time, especially at considerable depths. Generally, other conditions being equal, drilling rate in this type of sediment decreases with depth because of an increase in density. Clays and shales on electric logs

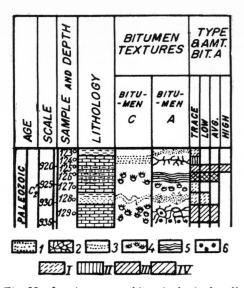

Fig. 88. Luminescence-bituminological well section in coal deposits (according to V. N. Florovskaya). 1—uniform; 2—fissured; 3—punctate; 4—biomorphic; 5—lamellar; 6—cavernous; I—light bitumen A; II—oily bitumen A; III—bitumen A of intermediate composition; IV—tarry-asphaltenic bitumen. Evaluation of the quantitative composition of bitumen A: traces—less than 0.005%; low—from 0.005 to 0.05%; intermediate—from 0.05 to 0.5% high—over 0.5%.

show maximum values of potential, i.e., a positive SP anomaly, and a low apparent resistivity (from 0.2 to 10 ohm-m.). The apparent resistivity of clays increases with increase in their density and, therefore, with decrease in their porosity. According to luminescence logging data, argillaceous sediments, with a few exceptions, contain only traces of oil or bitumen and this is usually taken as background.

Marls. According to oil and gas logs, marls are quite variable owing to changes in their porosities and permeabilities. Oil and gas anomalies of considerable intensity often correspond to marls having high porosity. Marls show up differently on mechanical logs, depending on their density; dense marls are marked by minima on the rate of penetration curve. According to luminescence logs, fissured marls may have a high content of oil bitumens. The electrical resistivity of marls varies from 5 to several hundred ohm-m. When fissured marls are interbedded among clays, the marls appear on the SP curve as quite well defined negative anomalies.

Productive sands. On oil and gas logging diagrams, productive sands are distinguished by a considerable increase in the content of combustible gases. When purely gas-bearing intervals are penetrated, the gas consists, as a rule, exclusively of methane and very insignificant amounts of heavy hydrocarbons. Opposite oil-bearing sands, anomalies in the content of both methane and heavy hydrocarbons are observed. Heavy hydrocarbons may make up as much as 50% of the total combustible gases. According to mechanical logging data, friable sands in the well section are distinguished by high drilling rates, regardless of the type of bits used. The curve of drilling time is quite comparable with the SP curve. On luminescence logs, oil sands are very clearly located by the appearance of oil in the cuttings and in the drilling mud.

According to electric logging data, oil-bearing sand is distinguished by a considerable increase in the apparent resistivity and by a negative anomaly in the SP curve, as in the case of water-bearing sand. However, cases often occur in the Caucasus in which drilling muds prepared from sea water, invade the oil-bearing sands during a prolonged drilling process and lower the resistivity so much that the peaks opposite oil layers vanish completely. On the other hand, when muds that have been prepared from fresh water invade water-bearing levels, the resistance may be greatly increased.

Productive sandstones. Productive sandstones appear the same as productive sands on oil and gas logs, and they are very easily located on a mechanical log. Dense sandstones show a marked increase in drilling time. On an electrical log, resistivities from tens of ohm-m. to several hundred ohm-m. are found for sandstones (depending on their density or degree of cementation). Besides this, the resistivity of sandstones increases depending on their content of oil or fresh water. According to luminescence logging, sandstones containing oil are quite easily distinguished, because large pieces of rock sometimes pass into the cuttings, in which the presence of oil may be established visually.

Carbonate rocks. According to electric logging data, limestones and dolomites containing heavy oil differ with changes in the content of the gaseous fractions in the heavy oil (23). On mechanical logs, carbonate rocks show maxima on the drilling time curve, regardless of the type of bit used. Among the carbonates, friable limestones and coquinas have the lowest drilling time, while silicified limestones and dolomites have the highest.

On the luminescence logs, cuttings from productive intervals of carbonate rocks are characterized by a high oil content. On the electric log, carbonate rocks show an increase in the apparent resistivity, the magnitude of which depends largely on the density of these rocks and their content of oil, gas, or highly mineralized waters. Opposite carbonate rocks lying within an argillaceous layer, the SP curve gives negative anomalies.

Clays and sands. Oil and gas logs in predominantly argillaceous strata containing thin, intercalated bands of productive sand and sandstone (Maikop and diatomaceous layers in the Caucasus) are very complex. This is obviously connected with the regional petroleum characteristics of these deposits and the peculiar conditions of their formation (24). The Maikop argillaceous sediments are characterized by very intense gas anomalies, although the reservoirs in these cases are thin beds of sand and sandstone of no practical significance. On mechanical logs, such deposits have the same characteristics as clays (the drilling time curve is the same for both). On electric logs, these deposits also have similar characteristics, with values of apparent resistivity between 5 and 10 ohm-m. On luminescence logs, predominantly argillaceous strata alternating with thin beds of oil-bearing sands give the same type of record as homogeneous, productive layers. However, if the sandstones contain gas but no oil, the luminescence data are the same as for argillaceous strata.

From the various data given above, it is evident that no single logging method can be used alone in the area where the rocks and their characteristics have not yet been determined by drilling. Only interpretations based on oil and gas logging combined with several other types of logs can assure success in deep exploratory drilling.

Correlation of Oil and Gas Logs

The correct correlations of results is of substantial importance in interpreting the data of several different types of logging. In contrast to electric logging, in which the recorded parameters (ρ and SP) are practically constant, the data of oil and gas logs vary substantially, depending on the drilling procedure.

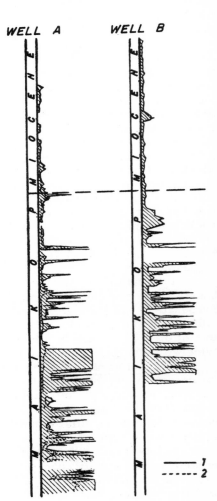

In view of the lack of reliable methods of correcting adequately for the drilling procedure, a detailed correlation of oil and gas logs, even of wells located close together, sometimes becomes intricate. However, the logging characteristics of large stratigraphic units, such as the Maikop, which is the productive formation on the Apsheron peninsula, are so similar that correlation is possible without difficulty (Fig. 89). Another example is the correlation of intervals of Maikop and Sarmatian strata in wells in which the gas logging characteristics are nearly constant (Fig. 90). As is evident from the graph, the upper limit of Sarmatian and Maikop beds is easily correlated in wells located at a considerable distance from one another. In such comparisons, however, one should not look for a complete agreement in the configuration of gas anomalies; but, in the first stage of comparison, one should correlate the broad zones of oil and gas anomalies, as indicated in the example given.

Sometimes in correlating logging data, the qualitative composition of the gas is of substantial importance because there must be some stratigraphic levels in which the composition of the gas is more or less constant. Thus, for instance, gas from the Sarmatian zone in the example given above consists exclusively of methane, but when the Maikop is exposed in both wells, the proportion of heavy hydrocarbons in the gas increases to 50 - 60%.

A composite correlation of gas logs

Fig. 89. Correlation of oil and gas logs. 1—total combustible gases; 2—heavy fraction.

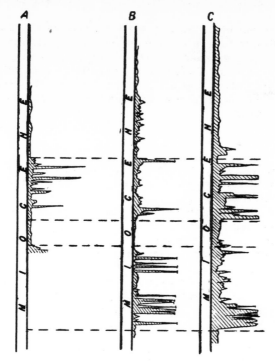

Fig. 90. Correlation of gas logs.

is most effective when data from other types of logging are also used. In such cases it should be kept in mind that shales, which form in relatively deep water, should be more uniform than other rocks (sands, sandstones). Correlations of argillaceous strata should therefore be much more accurate on mechanical and electrical logs.

In comparing an oil and gas log of a productive zone with the log of the same zone in a dry hole, we encounter the same difficulties that usually arise in the correlation of electrical logging resistivities. In analogous cases, the correlation must be carried out using mechanical logging data and the SP curve, because their configurations do not depend on the productivity of the rocks being studied.

A detailed correlation of oil and gas logs is possible only when there is a sufficient amount of information on hand to permit carrying out a series of successive correlations from well to well. When comparing gas and electric logs where a series of alternating beds of sand and sandstone less than 2 m. thick are located among clay formations (Maikop, diatomaceous layers, etc.), considerable difficulties arise as a result of the limited ability of electric logs to discern thin productive layers. According to I. I. Potapov (25), layers of sand less than 2 m. thick on the Apsheron peninsula, ''have irregular electrical characteristics and hence are inaccurately recorded on the electric log because of: mud penetration, increase in the well diameter due to erosion which is more pronounced than for thick layers, the effect of cable stretching, the rate of ascent of the proble, the small logging scale, etc.'' Therefore, discrepancies found in some cases in the correlation of electric with oil and gas logs may be explained in part by these circumstances.

The most suitable beds for correlation, besides clays and shales, are the regionally uniform layers of dense sandstones, carbonate rocks, and marls, which are distinguished by maxima on the drilling time and apparent resistivity curves. Thus, the most reliable method of interpretation is a composite correlation that utilizes the data of all types of logging. As a result, the correlation of formation boundaries becomes more accurate and better substantiated.

BIBLIOGRAPHY

1. V.G. Vasil'ev and K.V. Vysotskii. Geological, geophysical, and geochemical observations of investigation in the drilling of gas wells. Gostoptekhizdat, 1949.
2. V.A. Sokolov. Direct geochemical methods of prospecting for petroleum. Gostoptekhizdat, 1947.
3. Z.A. Tabasaranskii. Composite geological interpretation of oil and gas logging diagrams. Geokhim. metody poiskov nefti, Gostoptekhizdat, No. 2, 1954.
4. V.A. Uspenskii, A.S. Chernysheva, and Yu.A. Mandrykina. On the disperse form of the occurence of hydrocarbons in various sedimentary rocks. Izv. Akad. Nauk SSSR, ser. geol., No. 5, 1949.
5. G.A. Mogilevskii. Gasometry of wells. Byull. neftyanoi geofiziki, No. 4, 1937.
6. V.A. Sokolov. Gas analysis. Gostoptekhizdat, 1951.
7. G.A. Mogilevskii. Investigation of the gas content of rocks by the method of core and circulation gasometry of wells. Razvedka nedr, No. 4, 1940.
8. M.I. Subbota. New method of core-gas surveying. Geokhim. metody poiskov nefti i gaza, No. 1. Gostoptekhizdat, 1953.
9. V.G. Vasil'ev. Drilling muds in test drilling. Gostoptekhizdat, 1947.
10. Yu.M. Yurovskii. On some results of the development of gas logging work. Polevaya i promyslovaya geokhimiya, No. 2, 1953.
11. E.M. Geller. On relating samples of drilling mud and cuttings to depth. Geokhim. metody poiskov nefti i gaza, No. 1, Gostoptekhizdat, 1953.
12. A.Ya. Dobryanskii. Geochemistry of petroleum. Gostoptekhizdat, 1948.
13. N.A. Eremenko and S.P. Maksimov. Investigations of natural oil and gas manifestations. Gostoptekhizdat, 1953.
14. N.A. Eremenko. On the regularities of the distribution of crude oils according to specific gravity in the section of the formations of the Apsheron pneinsula. Neft. prom. SSSR, No. 3, 1941.
15. M.F. Mirchink. Industrial petroleum geology. Gostoptekhizdat, 1946.
16. V.N. Shchelkachev and B.B. Lapuk. Subsurface hydraulics. Gostoptekhizdat, 1949.
17. V.A. Sokolov. Essays on the origin of petroleum. Gostoptekhizdat, 1949.
18. V.N. Dakhnov. Interpretation of logging diagrams. Gostoptekhizdat, 1948.
19. V.N. Dakhnov. Industrial geophysics. Gostoptekhizdat, 1947.
20. N.A. Eremenko. Change of several properties of petroleum in a formation depending on the conditions under which pools were formed. Vest. Mosk. Universiteta, No. 9, 1948.

21. V.N. Florovskaya. Brief guide to luminescence-bituminological
    analysis. Gostoptekhizdat, 1949.
22. V.N. Florovskaya and V.G. Melkov. Introduction to luminescence bi-
    tuminology. Gosgeolizdat, 1946.
23. G.G. Grigor'ev and V.A. Frolov. Experiment in the use of gas logging.
    Goekhim. sb., No. 1. Gostoptekhizdat, 1951.
24. M.V. Abramovich. Exploration and prospecting for oil and gas pools.
    Azgostoptekhizdat, 1948.
25. I.I. Potapov. Electric logging in petroleum geology. Aznefteizdat,
    1948.

CHAPTER SEVEN

Bitumen Methods

Bitumen methods of prospecting for petroleum formations are based on the determination in rocks, soils, and waters of oil bitumens, i.e., oil and its solid conversion products. The dispersed form of these substances is of major importance.

In the first place, dispersed oil bitumens may be situated in oil-bearing strata outside the limits of producing reservoirs. These rocks contain that part of the oil which did not collect in the reservoir, traces of secondary migration, and products of partial decomposition of the pool under the influence of formation waters. These substances may also be transformed into solid bitumens. The discovery of substances of a similar nature is very important in evaluating the oil-bearing prospects of new regions, and it makes it possible to ascertain the presence of petroleum formations.

In the second place, oil bitumens may be situated above pools. These are traces of the diffusion and filtration of oil from the pool through the cap rocks (vertical migration). They may be encountered in cap rocks as far away as the surface layers and the soil. They may be the result of the migration of particles from the oil itself, partly or wholly converted to solid bitumens; they may also be products of the polymerization of hydrocarbon gases emanating from an oil reservoir. Apparently, the products of polymerization of gases are of primary significance here. The finding of oil bitumens in rocks, soils, or waters over oil-bearing sediments may indicate the presence of petroleum (oil and sometimes, gas) directly below.

In the third place, oil bitumens may be located within the reservoir itself. The determination of productive, oil-bearing zones may be accomplished with the aid of bitumen methods (bitumen logging) when such zones have already been penetrated and there is no visible evidence of commercial production.

There are three chief problems in the bitumen methods of prospecting and exploring for petroleum: (1) prospecting for oil-bearing formations during reconnaissance work in little known regions and the study of deep strata which do not crop out at the earth's surface; (2) predicting the presence of oil (and gas) pools below definite areas; (3) establishing whether or not particular strata contain oil after they have been drilled.

The first two problems are complicated by the fact that in addition to oil bitumens, rocks and soils contain other bitumens that are not related to oil. It is not easy to distinguish oil bitumens from those unrelated to petroleum. This difficulty may be surmounted only by special, detailed investigations which cannot be conducted on a mass scale. In a number of special cases, this problem is simplified and may be solved using elementary determinations. But in any case, interpretation of the results of bitumen investigations requires considerable knowledge of bituminology (the distribution, composition, and origin of bitumens). Therefore, a great deal of attention is devoted to these questions in the present chapter.

Bituminological investigations conducted in the course of oil prospecting are not easily separated from those carried out to determine the origin of oil. The former, which are of a practical nature, developed from purely theoretical investigations. Therefore, it is difficult to assign a definite date to the introduction of bitumen methods in propsecting for oil and gas formations. According to the best estimate, V. E. Levenson in 1926 first undertook the study of dispersed bitumens in rocks in Baku while trying to determine whether or not the rocks contained oil. In 1937 a bitumen asphalt survey was conducted in the U.S.A. specifically for the purpose of prospecting for oil deposits.

A new stage in the development of bitumen methods began in 1939 when N. A. Shlezinger in the USSR suggested the use of luminescence analysis for the detection of bitumens. Since that time the use of luminescence methods has become widespread. Since 1942 bitumen methods have also been applied to exploration work in the form of luminescence logging of drill cuttings and drilling muds.

In view of the special nature of bitumen-luminescence methods and their particular importance, a description of these methods is given in a separate chapter. The present chapter contains general information about bitumens and a description of those methods in which luminescence analysis is not used.

BASIC INFORMATION ON BITUMINOLOGY

Bitumens were described by Pliny the Elder (24-79 A.D.). "Bituminology" has existed for a long time as a separate science. However, the outlines of this branch of knowledge were obscure, since the meaning of the very word "bitumen" was ambiguous. Up to the present time not one textbook on bituminology has appeared. Until recent times the main object of bituminology consisted of bitumens existing in the form of masses in high concentrations: the various asphalts, asphaltities, ozokerites, coal bitumens, etc.

Contemporary bitumen methods of geochemical prospecting for petroleum involve the study of dispersed bitumens in rocks and soils. These bitumens, which exist in the form of microconcentrations, have only been studied since 1925, and very little is known about them. The greater part of bituminological data is concerned with large agglomerations of asphaltic substances. A study of dispersed bitumens requires familiarity with these data also, because a knowledge of the composition and origin of concentrated bitumens can be of great assistance. A direct, detailed study of dispersed bitumens without preliminary work on large concentrations is extremely difficult. Furthermore, study of the bulk form of bitumens is also of definite value in prospecting for oil. Therefore, the basic facts that are known about the concentrated as well as the dispersed forms of bitumens are given below.

Definition of the "Bitumen" Concept

The word "bitumen" is used in several different ways. In highway and other construction, "bitumens" are a kind of building material, but in its application to natural substances, this word is ambiguous. Firstly, all

caustobiolites,[1] which are clearly genetically related to oil, are usually
called bitumens. In this definition physicochemical properties are not taken
into consideration. Secondly, all natural substances that are soluble in
neutral organic liquids, including substances which are constituents of coal,
sapropelites, and the like, are called bitumens. In this case the definition
is based solely on the physicochemical properties of the substances and
does not depend on their origin. Such ambiguity leads to misunderstandings.
The need for eliminating this ambiguity is generally realized today.

It is essential that the word "bitumen" have a single, definite meaning. In this book the practice followed in the bitumen and bitumen-luminescence methods of oil prospecting has been adopted. This practice is based
on the solubility properties of bitumens as a characteristic that may be
used for separation and identification. Substances that do not dissolve in
the usual solvents (some carboids) may be genetically related to crude oil,
but they remain outside the scope of the bitumen methods of prospecting.

From this standpoint, the concept "bitumen" should be based on
physicochemical properties, namely, on solubility. Therefore, the following
definition of the term, "bitumen", is used in this book: a bitumen is a
natural organic substance soluble in neutral organic liquids under normal
conditions of temperature and pressure. This definition includes substances formed from oil as well as substances of different origin. Those
bitumens which evidently are genetically related to oil should be called oil
bitumens in order to distinguish them from others. All natural organic
substances that clearly are genetically related to petroleum, regardless of
their solubility and other properties, should be called oil-type caustobiolites
to avoid confusion. Thus, not all bitumens are of the oil-type, and not all
oil-type substances are bitumens, but all oil bitumens are simultaneously
bitumens and oil-type substances.[2]

The definition given above of the term "bitumen" has chemical as well
as diagnostic significance. Bitumens are composed chiefly of neutral organic compounds of relatively low molecular weight, oxidized to a slight degree, and having a low content of polar groups (carboxylic, hydroxylic, and
the like).[3] These substances are soluble in neutral organic liquids (according to the rule, "like dissolves in like").

[1] A "caustobiolite" (or caustobiolith) is a general term for a combustible sediment
resulting from geochemical activity in the biosphere. Caustobiolites are further subdivided
into: (1) humites (or humus), (2) liptobiolites (or the residual waxes, resins, fats, and oils
that resist decomposition under land or marsh conditions), and (3) sapropelites (or the
residual decay products of water organisms). See "Geochemistry" by K. Rankama and
Th. G. Sahama, Univ. of Chicago Press, 1950, pp. 342-350. Ed.

[2] V. A. Uspenskii and O. A. Radchenko (1), and also V. S. Veselovskii (2) suggest
that the term "bitumen" should signify all oil-type caustobiolites regardless of their solubility. Substances soluble in neutral organic liquids should, according to V. S. Veselovskii,
be called "bituminous substances", or according to V. A. Uspenskii and O. A. Radchenko,
"bituminogens". The name, "bituminous substances", cannot in its direct sense have any
significance different from that of "bitumens". The word "bituminogens" is to some extent hypothetical; the theory of the authors on the formation of petroleum from dispersed
bitumens alone is not generally accepted and not proved. For these reasons, the terms
"bituminous substances" and "bituminogens" are not suitable.

[3] Sometimes bitumens are described as substances with a "substantial proportion
of hydrocarbons in their composition". However, this is not at all correct: firstly, non-
hydrocarbon compounds may constitute a very large part of the total composition of the
bitumens (see, for example, Chapter I); secondly, hydrocarbons may constitute a "substantial proportion" of the composition of insoluble caustobiolites, as in many coals.

Among the solvents of bitumens are petroleum ether, benzene, chloro-form, acetone, ethyl ether, alcohol-benzene, carbon tetrachloride, carbon disulfide, and others. For the substance to be a bitumen, it is sufficient that it be soluble in any one of these liquids. Alcohols are not included among the neutral solvents. The alcohols dissolve such substances as "hematomelanic" acid, which is not a bitumen but a humic substance (soluble in alkalies). Organic bases (pyridine, quinoline, etc.) have great dissolving power and are farther from neutral. Alcohol-benzene (a mix-ture of one part ethyl alcohol and one part benzene) is just barely neutral, and it dissolves substances of transitional type such as tar acids, which are arbitrarily classified with the bitumens.

Classification of Bitumens

The majority of bitumens in their natural state are closely associated with a non-bituminous organic substance, i.e., one that is insoluble in neutral solvents. This is the case with coal bitumens, bitumens from syngenetic organic substances in rocks, etc. There is no doubt concerning the genetic relationship between bitumens and the other organic substances surround-ing item. Therefore, the type of organic material constituting the main mass of a given caustobiolite (whether in concentrated or dispersed form) may be used as a basis of classifying the bitumens. Oil bitumens should occupy a special place in such a system because they are exceptional in not being associated with any non-bituminous organic substance.

Bitumens in the main organic mass may be classified as follows:

1. Oil bitumens: (1) oils (including mineral tars, as well as naph-thenic salts, etc., in waters), (2) ozokerites, (3) asphalts, (4) kirs,[4] (5) asphaltites.[5]

2. Sapropel-humus type bitumens: (1) plant bitumens, (2) soil bitu-mens, (3) peat bitumens, (4) sapropel bitumens, (5) humic brown-coal bi-tumens, (6) boghead and sapropelite ("oil-shale") bitumens, (7) coal bitu-mens.

3. Dispersed syngenetic[6] bitumens: (1) bitumens in contemporary deposits, (2) bitumens in ordinary sedimentary rocks: arenaceous, argil-laceous, and carbonaceous rocks.

4. Bitumens of carboid minerals (kerites).

5. Bitumens of liptobiolites (succinites).[7]

Oil bitumens, as a rule, are independent agglomerations of organic sub-stances in an inorganic environment. Only insignificant amounts of insolu-ble substances (carboids, etc.) are ever present in organic accumulations. Oil bitumens are all closely interrelated genetically and gradual transitions from one form to another exist. The remaining bitumens are not independent

[4]"Kir" is the name given to an indurated natural asphalt that occurs with earthy materials. See "Asphalts and Allied Substances" by H. Abraham, 5th edition, Van Nostrand, New York, 1945, page 237. Ed.

[5]I.e., substances similar to asphalt with a C/H ratio over 10; about 15 forms of asphaltites have been distinguished (3).

[6]Dispersed epigenetic bitumens belong either to the oil bitumens, or to the bitumens of carboid minerals.

[7]This classification does not include bitumens formed in soils through the action of hydrocarbon gases from the underlying oil deposits. (Succinite is fossil amber. Ed.)

minerals, but only secondary components of organic agglomerations. Vegetable, soil, peat, sapropel, coal, and sapropelite bitumens are fractions that are soluble in neutral organic liquids of the corresponding vegetation, soil humus, peat, coal, "kerogen", and oil-shale.

Plant bitumens (fats, waxes, tars, essential oils, and the like) should, perhaps, be classified separately as part of living matter. However, from the practical point of view, this is beside the point. It is impossible to draw a sharp line between plant bitumens and soil bitumens, because the soil contains undecomposed vegetable remains. Furthermore, plant bitumens are also included in soil-bitumen survey analyses.

Syngenetic bitumens dispersed in sediments and rocks are also soluble components of the dispersed organic matter. In this respect they resemble bitumens of the sapropel-humus type. The proximity of these classes emphasizes the presence of transitional forms; oil-shale bitumens are an intermediate link between the bitumens of homogeneous caustobiolites (coals) and the bitumens of common rocks (i.e., those which are low in organic matter). Soil bitumens are also a transitional form. However, the special conditions for the existence of dispersed bitumens (the influence of the mineral environment) require that they be placed in a separate class. Furthermore, dispersed bitumens are the most important indicators in prospecting for petroleum.

The genetic relationships among the various sapropel-humus bitumens and also between these and dispersed syngenetic bitumens are more or less clear. Plant bitumens are the original source, and the others correspond to various stages of their conversion under different conditions. These correlations are represented schematically (Fig. 91).

Carboid bitumens and liptobiolites are also only fractions of certain caustobiolites. The carboids are largely sublimation products of various organic substances of the sapropel-humus type and, in some cases, of the oil type. These bitumens, apparently, are relatively rarely encountered.

Finally, the great difference between oil bitumens and bitumens of other classes should be emphasized. Oil bitumens occupy quite a unique position. The genetic relationship between oil bitumens and non-oil bitumens (if a few rare carboid bitumens are not considered) remains obscure. All non-oil bitumens (except carboids) are syngenetic with the rocks that contain them. At present, according to the eminent bituminologists, V. A.

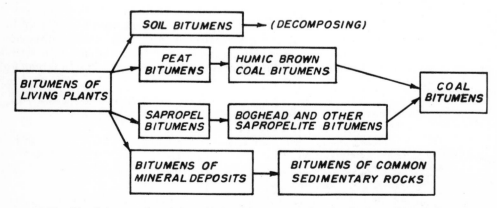

Fig. 91. Scheme of genetic relationships among the chief types of bitumens.

Uspenskii and O. A. Radchenko, no authentic cases of the occurrence of oil bitumens are known that are not under secondary conditions of deposition (1).

Characteristic Properties of Bitumens

A necessary condition for using bitumen methods in petroleum prospecting is the feasibility of recognizing the oil bitumens and distinguishing them from other bitumens. However, this is not easily done and, sometimes it is necessary to make use of a number of properties. Diagnostic data are given in Table 24 and may be used as a basis for distinguishing among the various bitumens. (Characteristics are given only for those bitumens whose properties are sufficiently well known.) Therefore, carboid bitumens and dispersed bitumens (discussed separately below) are not listed. The reader should bear in mind that the bitumens described in the table have not been studied with equal thoroughness. This inequality is qualitative as well as quantitative, because different bitumens have been studied by different methods.

Consideration of Table 24 leads to the following conclusions.

1. The primary difference between all sapropel-humus bitumens and all oil bitumens, as has been stated, is the ratio of the bitumen to the entire organic mass. Oils, asphalts, ozokerites, etc. consist almost entirely of bitumens; whereas, in peats, coals, and sapropelites, bitumens comprise not over 25% of the organic mass. Carboid minerals contain no more than 10% bitumen, while succinites contain no more than 25%.

2. Definite differences in the elemental composition of the two main kinds of bitumens also exist. Sapropel-humus bitumens (especially soil and peat types), on the one hand, may contain less than 70% carbon, while oil bitumens always contain more than 70% carbon. On the other hand, oil bitumens may contain more than 12% hydrogen, while others may not. The differences in the content of oxygen and other elements are particularly essential. The total (O+S+N) content of oil bitumens may be less than 6%, but the (O+S+N) content of other bitumens is always greater than 6%. Differences in the C/H ratio are insignificant, but the C/(O+S+N) ratio is more important. In sapropel-humus bitumens the latter ratio does not exceed 9 and may be less than 2; whereas, for oil bitumens this ratio is never less than 4 and may be greater than 9.

If the C/H and C/(O+S+N) ratios are plotted on the diagram suggested by V. A. Klubov for the classification of caustobiolites (4), it may be seen that the oil bitumens and sapropel-humus bitumens occupy different areas (Fig. 92). Oils and ozokerites on the one hand, and soil bitumens and peat bitumens on the other, are widely separated from one another. However, the area of the asphalts and asphaltites overlaps that of coal bitumens to a significant degree.

3. Data on acid and iodine numbers are very incomplete. However, some conclusions may be derived from them. Apparently, negligible acid numbers are possible only for oil bitumens (although data for coals are lacking); acid numbers over 65 are encountered only in the case of the sapropel-humus bitumens. Iodine numbers over 35 apparently exist only in the case of oil bitumens (for oils and ozokerites they must be less than for asphalts).

4. Only oil bitumens can have negative melting points.

5. Solubility data show the least variation, but the solubility differences

TABLE 24. Characteristic Properties of Various Bitumens [8]

Properties	Sapropel-humus bitumens						Oil bitumens			
	Soil bitumens	Peat bitumens	Humic brown-coal bitumens	Boghead and sapropel-humus coal bitumens	Coal bitumens	All sapropel-humus bitumens	Crude Oils	Asphalts, asphaltites, and kirs	Ozokerites	All oil bitumens
Proportion of bitumen in the organic mass	2–10	3–30	3–20	1–12	0–3	0–30	100	90–100	100	90–100
Elemental composition:										
%C	58–66	68–72	72–82	76–80	65–83	58–97	80–88	74–88	80–87	74–88
%H	8–10	9–10	7–9	10–12	6–9	6–12	10–14	6–12	11–15	6–15
% (O + S + N)	25–33	18–22	15–21	8–13	6–17	6–33	0–8	0–16	0–5	0–16
C:H	6.5–10	6.8–8	8–10.5	6.3–7.3	8–12	6–12	5.6–9	8–11.5	5.6–6.2	5.6–13
C:(O + S + N)	1.8–2.6	3–4	3.4–5.5	7–8	6–9	1.8–9	>12	>4.3	>16	>4
Acid number	—	46–70	8–87	50–63	(8)	8–87	0.01–2.0	2–64	—	0–64
Saponification number	—	20–200	45–380	87–184	8–9	8–380	—	3–140	—	(3–140)
Iodine number	—	(23–30)	12–174	(12–27)	—	12–174	—	(20–38)	—	(20–33)
Melting point, °C	—	57–84	45–320	70–86	—	45–320	<20	36–320	34–100	0–320
Solubility:										
in alcohol-benzene	100	100	100	100	100	100	100	90–100	100	90–100
chloroform	—	—	50–100	0–10	Up to 100	0–100	100	(100)	100	Up to 100
benzene	—	(10)	20–100	1–14	Up to 100	0–100	100	10–100	100	10–100
carbon disulfide	—	100	100	100	100	100	100	92–100	100	100
petroleum ether	—	—	0–40	<40	—	0–40	70–100	0–78	Up to 85	0–100

[8]Data in parentheses are known to be incomplete.

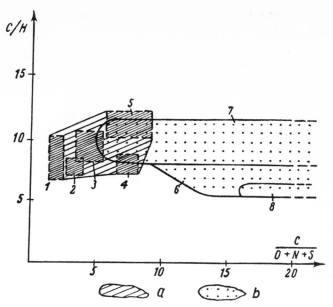

Fig. 92. Diagram of the elemental composition of bitumens.
1—soil bitumens; 2—peat bitumens; 3—humus-lignite bitumens; 4—boghead bitumens; 5—coal bitumens; 6—oils;
7—asphalts and asphaltites; 8—ozokerites; a—bitumens
of the sapropel-humus type; b—bitumens of the oil type.

in petroleum ether[9] should be pointed out. High solubility in petroleum
ether is almost always a direct index of oil bitumens. The solubility of
sapropel-humus bitumens in petroleum ether does not exceed 40%, while
oil bitumens may be completely soluble (the total bitumen content is determined by alcohol-benzene extraction). That is, if the (petroleum-ether extract)/(alcohol-benzene extract) ratio for oil bitumens is 0.5 or more, then
for sapropel-humus bitumens it cannot exceed 0.4. The differences in benzene solubility are also substantial. A lower solubility in benzene is
usually more characteristic for the sapropel-humus bitumens than for oil
bitumens. However, this is not a very clear relationship. In view of the
great importance of this question, the most characteristic differences between the properties of oil bitumens and sapropel-humus bitumens are
listed in Table 25.

Consideration of Tables 24 and 25 leads to the following general conclusion. The greatest possible number of properties must be examined accurately to determine to which class a given bitumen belongs because many
of the properties of different bitumens coincide. Also, the characteristics
given in Tables 24 and 25 are not necessarily applicable in all cases.

---

[9]Petroleum ether is a light gasoline fraction boiling at 60-65° C and not containing
aromatic hydrocarbons.

TABLE 25. Principal Distinguishing Characteristics of Oil Bitumens
and Sapropel-humus Bitumens

Properties	Oil bitumens	Sapropel-humus bitumens
Content of bitumen in the entire organic mass	100%	< 30%
Content of carbon.	> 70%	———
Content of hydrogen	———	< 12%
Total content of (O + S + N).	———	> 6%
C/(O + S + N)	> 4	< 9
Acid number	< 65	———
Iodine number	< 35	———
Solubility in petroleum ether.	———	< 40%

Fractional Composition of Bitumens

Bitumens may be separated into fractions by selective solution and selective adsorption.[10] Different schemes have been worked out for the fractional separation of oil bitumens on one hand and sapropel-humus bitumens on the other. The following fractions are usually taken for oil bitumens:

1. Oils — that part of the bitumen which is soluble in petroleum ether, not adsorbed by silica gel, and consists mainly of hydrocarbons.

2. Tars — that part of the bitumen which is soluble in petroleum ether and adsorbed by silica gel. They consist mainly of neutral compounds containing, besides carbon and hydrogen, oxygen, sulfur, and nitrogen (see Chapter I).

3. Asphaltenes — that part of the bitumen which is insoluble in petroleum ether, but soluble in alcohol-benzene and chloroform. In composition, asphaltenes are similar to tars but are distinguished from the latter by their high molecular weight.

4. Carbenes — that part of the bitumen which is soluble only in carbon disulfide. They consist of compounds having the highest molecular weights of all those entering into the composition of the bitumens. Molecular weight and the C/H ratio increase in the following order: oils —→ tars —→ asphaltenes —→ carbenes.

Liquid oils contain light-colored fractions that are less dense than bitumen oil. In asphaltites, on the contrary, there may be an admixture of substances heavier than carbenes. These are carboids and may be derived from carbenes by polymerization. Carboids are not soluble in any of the non-polar solvents; consequently, they are not bitumens. Bitumen as a whole is a complex system in which particles of substances of higher molecular weight form colloidal solutions with those of low molecular weight.

There are several other schemes of fractional separation for soil,

---

[10]Often the composition of a bitumen determined by methods of selective solution and adsorption is called "component composition", while the corresponding analysis is known as "component analysis". The word "component" could refer to elemental or any other composition. Therefore, it is more correct to speak of fractional composition and fractional analysis.

peat, and lignite bitumens. First, the bitumen is divided into waxes and tars; the waxes are insoluble in ethyl ether (some of them are insoluble in acetone as well), while tars are soluble in it. Secondly, the tars are divided into the benzene group (soluble in benzene) and the alcohol-benzene group (insoluble in benzene but soluble in alcohol-benzene). Soil, peat, and lignite "tars" are not the same as the "tars" of oil bitumens, because oil tars dissolve completely in benzene and petroleum ether,[11] while coal tars, etc., dissolve only partially. This latter group also contains significantly more oxygen in the form of acidic compounds (tar acids); these last are the chief constituents of the alcohol-benzene tar fraction. Waxes consist of hydrocarbons and neutral oxygen compounds (complex ethers and the like).

Coal bitumens are more similar to oil bitumens, because hydrocarbons predominate in them. Apparently, oxygen compounds are decomposed in the metamorphism of coals and the proportion of hydrocarbons increases.[12]

Bitumens Dispersed in Rocks

Bitumens dispersed in common sedimentary rocks, such as clays, sandstones, limestones, etc., are usually only an insignificant part of the total organic substances dispersed in these rocks. Therefore, it is incorrect to use the phrases "dispersed bitumen" and "dispersed organic substance" ("kerogen")[13] synonymously as is sometimes done.

According to P. D. Trask, the average content of organic carbon (clarke) in common sedimentary rocks (i.e., without taking into account rocks enriched in organic matter, such as the so-called oil shale) is about 1%, based on 7000 determinations. The average content of organic matter as a whole, according to the same data, is 1.7%.

V. A. Uspenskii estimated on the basis of 668 analyses that the average content (clarke) of the bitumen in sedimentary rocks is about 0.03% (6). Thus, of the entire mass of dispersed organic matter, the dispersed bitumens constitute only 1 or 2%. V. A. Uspenskii also estimated the average content of organic matter and bitumen in various types of rock (6). These data are given in Table 26.

The data in Table 26 are not sufficiently complete and, in the opinion of V. A. Uspenskii, represent rocks with an above-average content of organic matter. Nevertheless, some conclusions can be drawn from them. First, it is evident that the contents of organic matter and bitumens are higher in clays than in siltstones and sandstones and are lowest in limestones and dolomites. Secondly, it is evident that the content of bitumen in the organic matter (the bituminosity of the organic matter), on the contrary, is highest in carbonate rocks, less in sandstones, and lowest in clays.

---

[11]Excluding the so-called asphaltogenic acids, which play a completely subordinate part.

[12]There is a vast amount of literature on peat and coal bitumens. The latest review of this literature may be found in the article by M. V. Kibler (5). For a bibliography, see the book by V. S. Veselovskii.

[13]The term "kerogen" has no clearly defined meaning (it may be thought that kerogen is not the total dispersed organic matter but only a certain part of it). Hence, its use is not to the purpose.

TABLE 26. Average Content of Organic Matter and Bitumens in
Sedimentary Rocks (according to V. A. Uspenskii)

Rocks	Number of analyses	Content of organic matter in rock, %	Content of bitumen in rock, %	Content of bitumen in organic matter, %	Organic matter bitumen
Clays and shales	50	3.3	0.1	3.0	33
Marls and argillaceous limestones	20	2.9	0.1	2.7	29
Sandstones and siltstones	20	1.7	0.07	4.1	24
Limestones and dolomites	120	0.55	0.03	6.1	18

The relation between the content of bitumen in the organic matter, on the one hand, and the total content of organic matter and carbonates in the rock, on the other, was especially investigated by V. A. Uspenskii for a large number (270) of samples (7). He established that the bituminosity of dispersed organic matter is not directly related to the carbonate content of the rock but depends only on the total content of organic matter. As a rule, the greater the organic content is, the less is the carbonate content. These relationships are shown graphically in Figure 93 using Uspenskii's data, and he explains them in the following manner. Carbonate facies are less favorable for the accumulation of organic matter, which is therefore present in lower quantities. However, the organic matter which is present in the carbonate facies contains a higher proportion of the more stable fractions. These are the bitumens.

Up to this point only the quantity of dispersed bitumens has been discussed, but the facts already given demonstrate the syngenetic character of nearly all dispersed bitumens. This is shown by their association with the entire organic mass and the association of the latter with the inorganic part of the rocks.

The syngenetic character of nearly all dispersed bitumens does not mean that rocks are wholly lacking in bitumens acquired by secondary deposition. Dispersed oil bitumens are of the latter kind (and merit the closest attention), but they are encountered either relatively rarely or in very small quantities. Furthermore, it must be kept in mind that the data given above were obtained by quantitative extraction. Using this method it is not possible to determine the lightest, lowest-boiling fractions (see below), and the oil bitumens may be represented by just such fractions.

Qualitative data on dispersed bitumens are very scanty. Chemical investigations of materials occurring in such low concentrations (less than 0.03% of the rocks) are exceedingly difficult. The direct application of data obtained for rocks enriched in organic matter to the dispersed forms, is inadmissible. The organic matter of "oil shales" is practically identical to the material of the corresponding coals, humic or sapropelitic (8).

Some indications of the nature of the dispersed organic matter,

ALL ROCKS

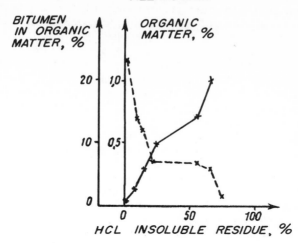

CARBONATE ROCKS

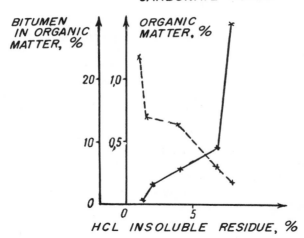

Fig. 93. Variation of the organic matter and bituminosity
of organic matter with the carbonate content of sedimentary
rocks.

including bitumens, may be given by a determination of the nitrogen in the
rock. The content of inorganic nitrogen in sedimentary rocks is quite
negligible. Therefore, the total nitrogen content characterizes organic
nitrogen and may also be a measure of the quantity of organic matter. The
value of the ratio of organic carbon to nitrogen (C_{org}:N) may characterize
the organic matter qualitatively. First, the C_{org}:N ratio is sedimentary
rock must correspond in the main to the C_{org}:N ratio in the water of the
basin in which these sediments were deposited. In the ocean this value is
about 10, while in bodies of fresh water it is as high as 30 (9). Secondly,
according to Trask (10), this value increases in the vicinity of oil pools;

if the C_{org}:N ratio in sedimentary rocks is usually less than 15, then near an oil formation this ratio is often greater than 15. Consequently, a C_{org}:N ratio greater than 15 in rocks of marine origin indicates the probable presence of oil bitumens.

Some information on the character of dispersed bitumens is given by a rough determination of selective solubility (the "solubility spectrum"). Thus, investigations of a similar type carried out by A. A. Kartsev showed that the main part of the dispersed bitumens in sandy argillaceous rocks are usually very similar to coal bitumens. Oil bitumens are comparatively rarely found in such a background (11, etc.).

V. A. Uspenskii recently conducted a quantitative investigation of the bitumen of Cambrian laminated clay from a region known to be non-oil bearing (12). From a clay sample weighing 800 kg. and containing less than 0.001% bitumen, he extracted the latter and determined that petroleum ether dissolves 37% of this bitumen and that the bitumen contains 82% C, 11% H, 7% (O+S+N) and has an acid number of 35. Comparison of these characteristics with the combined data of Tables 24 and 25 reveals that the given bitumen approximates the sapropel-humus type but differs from it in that the value of C/(O+S+N) is equal to 12. Further investigation of the composition of dispersed bitumens in various rocks is a very urgent task.[14]

Bound Bitumens

All that has been stated refers to free bitumens that can be extracted directly from rocks by solvents. Sometimes, after such extraction, treatment of the rock by acid makes it possible to remove an additional quantity of material using solvents. This material is bound bitumen.[15] Such bitumen is encountered in coals and common sedimentary rocks. In most cases the bound bitumen content is many times less than that of free bitumen. A different situation is observed in carbonate rocks where the bound form often predominates. Bound bitumens are essentially salts (mainly calcium and magnesium ones) of organic acids, and they are formed by the reaction of bitumens (including oils) with cations absorbed from the rock. Furthermore, bound bitumens may be represented by particles of bitumen located within crystals of inorganic minerals (e.g., calcite). Bound bitumens may or may not be related to oil.

---

[14]In an article published in 1954, N. A. Eremenko gives some data on dispersed bitumens in the Tertiary strata of the Caucasus and, on the basis of these data, arrives at a conclusion on "the genetic relationship of oils and bituminous substances dispersed in rocks" (13). However, the data given in Table 1 refer to tarry sandstones, and it is indicated in the text that, except for tarry sandstones, there are no bitumens in those sandstones which have been investigated.

[15]In the literature the terminology suggested by F. Fisher for coal technology is still encountered: free bitumen called bitumen A, bound bitumen called bitumen C, and coal components dissolving only at high temperatures and pressures (i.e., potentially a great many coals) called bitumen B. Use of this terminology with its wholly arbitrary and broad interpretation of the word "bitumen", lack of relation to oil, and lack of meaning is futile.

METHODS OF QUANTITATIVE ANALYSIS

In applying the bitumen methods to prospecting and exploration for petroleum, two important conditions should be satisfied as nearly as possible.
First, a very large quantity of data must be obtained in very brief periods
of time. Therefore, the quantitative techniques used must be very simple.
Secondly, data on the presence or absence of oil bitumens must be obtained,
since the bitumen methods of prospecting are based on recognizing these
substances. Simultaneous fulfillment of these two conditions is always difficult and sometimes impossible.

Those indices must be determined which are relatively easy to obtain
and which indicate the presence or absence of oil bitumens. The most important of these are the ratios: [1] (bitumen)/(C_{org}); [2] (C_{bit})/(C_{org});
[3] (petroleum-ether extract)/(alcohol-benzene extract); [4] (C_{org})/N. The
anomalous distribution of bitumen content and the solubility of the bitumen
in benzene are also rather significant. The methods of analysis used to
obtain these data are briefly described below.

Determination of Organic Carbon

The basic method of determining organic carbon in soils and rocks is that
of Knop. It consists of the oxidation ("wet combustion") of organic carbon
by a sulfochromic mixture ($C_rO_3 + H_2SO_4$) to carbon dioxide gas, which is
removed in an ordinary CO_2 adsorption train. The U-tubes in the adsorption train are filled with caustic potash and are weighed before and after
the oxidation. Carbonates must be decomposed beforehand by means of
sulfuric or hydrochloric acid and the carbon dioxide so formed, completely
removed.

If the organic matter is considerably metamorphosed, (as is, for example, anthracite), it is not oxidized by the above method. However, as a
rule, the method gives satisfactory results. The analysis is conducted in
a special apparatus consisting of a flask in which is placed a sample of
pulverized rock (1 - 10 g.), a coil (or bulb) condenser, and the adsorption
train. The oxidizing agent is poured into the flask through a dropping funnel and sulfuric acid (1:1) is added. This is followed by a solution of
chromic anhydride (50 g. C_rO_3 in 100 ml. water), and the reaction continues for 5 - 10 min. After 1 hour, air is passed through the apparatus,
and the U-tubes are then disconnected, dried, and weighed. The Knop
method cannot be used under field conditions.

Determination of Nitrogen

The determination of total nitrogen in soils and rocks is usually accomplished by the Kjeldahl method. This method essentially consists of the
decomposition of the nitrogenous organic compounds by sulfuric acid and
the conversion of the nitrogen to the form of ammonium sulfate, followed
by back-titration of the excess acid with alkali. The determination is carried out in a special Kjeldahl apparatus on a 5 - 30 g. sample of pulverized
rock. It consists of the following operations: (1) decomposition of the organic matter by sulfuric acid on heating; (2) decomposition of the resulting
ammonium sulfate by alkali; (3) expulsion of the ammonia thus formed and
adsorption thereof by sulfuric acid (in a receiving flask); (4) titration by

alkali of the excess sulfuric acid in the receiving flask. The method gives
sufficiently accurate values, except when the rock contains significant
amounts of absorbed ammonia or ammonium sulfate. It should be noted
that the method is distinguished by being very unwieldy.

Determination of Bitumens by the Weight Method

A weight determination of the bitumen in rock is usually accomplished with
the aid of the standard Soxhlet extraction apparatus. The determination is
carried out in the following manner. A rock sample (10 - 50 g.) in a paper
shell is put into the extractor and the solvent extraction is begun. The extraction is continued until the solvent flowing from the sample is no longer
luminescent in ultraviolet light. The extraction is then transferred to
another flask, and the solvent is partly evaporated on a water bath. The
concentrated extract is evaporated to dryness in a porcelain dish and the
bitumen residue from the evaporation is weighed.

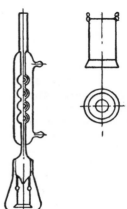

Fig. 94. Zaichenko ex-
traction apparatus.

The entire determination requires from 3 to 10
hours. Extraction may be carried out with any solvent. Successive extractions are possible, for example, with petroleum ether followed by alcohol-
benzene. In this way, qualitative characteristics of
the bitumen can also be obtained. The Zaichenko
apparatus (Fig. 94), in which the extractor is quite
close to the source of heat, makes it possible to
shorten the time of the determination to 1 - 2 hours.
The Movsesyan apparatus is designed for the study
of large samples (up to 7 kg.), yet extraction in this
apparatus requires 7 hours less time than with the
Soxhlet (14).

The weight method of determining bitumens has
two fundamental defects. First, the considerable
complexity of the analytical operations makes it impossible to carry them out under field conditions.
Secondly, the lightest fractions of the bitumens are
not taken into account, because they are lost in the
evaporation of the solvent. Although these losses are hardly great in a
quantitative sense, they are very serious because the light dispersed oil
escapes detection. This substance apparently spreads out to great distances in rocks and is a valuable indicator of petroleum.

Determination of Bitumens by the Colorimetric Method

Colorimetry makes it possible to simplify and expedite the determination
of the content of bitumen in rock. The method, which consists of a cold extraction in test tubes, has acquired the name "test tube method". The determination itself consists of comparing the color of the extract with that
of a standard of known concentration. This method was suggested by L. V.
Khmelevskaya for the examination of the total dispersed organic matter and
the determination by means of a parallel extraction using various solvents
for the "solubility spectrum" of the organic matter of rocks (15, 16).

The test tube method is very simple, permits determinations en masse,
and is readily usable under field conditions. However, it is not sufficiently

sensitive, because under the conditions proposed by L. V. Khmelevskaya (i.e., in daylight), the determination of bitumen concentrations less than 0.1% in rock is not possible. Therefore, this method is usable only for rocks which are considerably enriched in bitumens. The sensitivity is increased to a perfectly satisfactory level by the application of luminescence analysis.

APPLICATION OF BITUMEN METHODS

There are two principle ways of applying bitumen methods in petroleum prospecting. The first is the investigation of geological sections for the purpose of finding oil-bearing strata. This is used in reconnaisance work, and the determination of bitumens in subterranean waters also touches on this application (see Chapter IX). The second application is in the area survey which is conducted for the purpose of predicting the presence of oil pools within a limited location. This is used in detailed prospecting work.

Prospecting for Oil-Bearing Strata

Bitumen methods of prospecting for oil-bearing strata may be used in two main ways. First, the search may be carried out in regions in which the petroleum possibilities have not been investigated. In these cases either the presence of oil may be entirely unknown, or the original source of existing oil shows may be unknown. Under these conditions the following must be conducted: (1) bitumen route surveys; (2) investigations of highly concentrated caustobiolites (in veins, etc.). Such conditions exist, for example, in extensive areas of the Asiatic part of the USSR.

Secondly, searches for oil-bearing strata may be conducted in places where the petroleum possibilities are well known for some parts of the section but entirely unknown for other parts, such as sediments located at great depths that do not outcrop. Here the main application of bitumen methods will be to examine the cores of test wells. This is the case, for instance, in the lower Paleozoic strata of the Russian platform.

In each of these cases the problem consists of establishing the presence (or absence) of oil bitumens in a particular rock stratum. The evidence may consist of traces of dispersed oil, accumulations of asphalt-type minerals, etc. If there are macroscopic concentrations of bitumens, these should be studied in detail (determination of elemental and fractional compositions, acid and iodine numbers, etc.) in order to determine whether they are oil bitumens or belong to another type. If only dispersed bitumens are present, a great number of determinations will be required, such as: (1) the ratio of the content of bitumen in the rock to the total content of organic matter; (2) the ratio of the yield of petroleum-ether extract to the total amount of bitumen in the rock. Unfortunately, systematic determinations of these quantities are not carried out in large numbers.

If the presence of oil bitumens is established, the problem of their connection with some stratigraphic unit must still be solved. Both the areal and cross-sectional distribution of bitumens must be studied to accomplish this. If a definite stratigraphic correlation is established, the oil-bearing stratum may be considered found. In the contrary case, the possibility of a connection between bitumens and fissures must be considered. This is especially necessary if the bitumens discovered occur in the form of veins, streaks, etc. (or as components of other vein caustobio-lites).

Establishment of the presence of an oil-bearing stratum is very important in guiding further prospecting and exploration work. However, the oil-bearing stratum containing dispersed oil bitumens does not necessarily contain commercial quantities of oil. Other conditions are necessary for the latter, such as traps, etc., about which bitumen methods can give no information.

The absence of dispersed oil bitumens in a given stratum does not necessarily mean that no petroleum is present. Negative results may be due to inadequate precision or care in the analysis. It should be remembered that the light dispersed oils, which are very important, are lost in any weight determinations. Furthermore, the dispersed oil bitumens may have been converted to insoluble forms, such as carboids; yet, at the same time, the oil pools may have been preserved. Where the pool has been formed by vertical migration alone, the oil zone outside the limits of the commercial reservoir may be practically devoid of dispersed oil bitumens. It must also be kept in mind that the absence of bitumens reveals nothing concerning the possibility of a commercial gas field.

Bitumen Area Surveys

In the bitumen area survey, the distribution of bitumens in the surface layers (soils, alluvium, and bed rock) is determined in order to predict the possibility of petroleum beneath the surface.[16] It is assumed that the presence of petroleum is indicated in surface layers, including soils, by increased concentrations of bitumens, or bituminous anomalies. The formation of bituminous anomalies may occur in two ways:

1. Crude oil may migrate from a pool to the earth's surface either by diffusion through a layer of rock or by bulk movement through fissured zones. According to the calculations of V. A. Sokolov, the rate of diffusion of oil hydrocarbons (lubricating oil fractions) is several thousand times less than for hydrocarbon gases (17). The coefficient of diffusion of methane through water-saturated clay, according to Sokolov, is about 10^{-6} (18). This means that the diffusion of methane molecules through a layer of clay 1,000 meters thick requires several million years. In the case of crude oil, such long periods of time are required for diffusion that it is difficult to evaluate its practical significance. A much greater part is played by the movement of oil through fissures. The presence of numerous surface seeps resulting from migration of oil in fissured zones serves as graphic demonstration of the occurrence of this process. In addition to these well known macroseeps of oil, there must be microseeps of a similar kind. However, the maximum depth from which crude oil can rise in this way remains unknown.

2. Another source of bituminous anomalies over oil pools may be the polymerization of hydrocarbon gases migrating from the pools to the earth's

---

[16] Bitumen surveys of alluvium and bed rock were conducted in the USSR using luminescence analysis; soil bitumen surveys were carried out without luminescence methods by ordinary extraction determinations (this division was purely accidental). Here general information is given and a soil bitumen survey is described.

surface. The occurrence of this process was revealed by finding "paraffin dirt" near gas seeps on the shore of the Gulf of Mexico.

"Paraffin dirt" occurs widely in the region of the Gulf Coast. It occurs in the top layer of the soil as yellow-brown, amorphous masses consisting mainly of carbohydrates. (Its composition does not correspond at all to its name.) There is no doubt that this substance is formed from hydrocarbon gases. It is found only where there are gas seeps, and the size of the dirt deposits is directly proportional to the size of the seeps (19).

Consequently, the simplest hydrocarbon gases may be converted to complex organic substances. This is apparently the result of bacterial activity. The biochemical nature of this process is demonstrated by the following. The ability of bacteria to assimilate methane, ethane, propane, etc. is well known, and the intermediate, collateral, and final products of this assimilation may be bitumens. All authenticated occurrences of such substances that formed from gases have been in soils and never in bed rock. Therefore, the hypothesis depending on the catalytic activity of rocks is not confirmed, although it cannot be wholly rejected. Another hypothesis on the polymerization of ethane and propane by solar ultraviolet rays is also not confirmed by experimental data. This effect has been established only for very short wave lengths which do not reach the earth's surface (20). Hence, the polymerization of hydrocarbon gases in the soil is apparently a biosynthetic process.

The soil bitumen survey is based on the detection of substances formed from gases. These bitumens are substances of a very special kind. They were not listed in the classification given above, because their properties are almost unknown and their origin differs greatly from that of other bitumens. It must be kept in mind that their properties may be entirely different from those of oil bitumens because they are a non-oil type. A significant part of these substances is apparently composed not of bitumens but of substances of another kind. Nevertheless, they are indicators of oil because they are obviously derived from petroleum.

The methods and techniques of field work in the soil bitumen survey are very simple. Profiles and points are distributed over the areas just as in gas and core-gas surveys. Soil samples are taken as in soil science work. Soil sections are obtained at a depth from 20 to 200 cm. (depending on the type of soil and the nature of the indicator to be determined). Analyses are made in the laboratory and include determinations of total organic carbon, bitumens and bitumen carbon. The results are plotted on profiles and maps (in the U.S.A.).

Three factors are used in the soil-bitumen survey as indicators of an oil potential.

1. The total bitumen content in soils may in some cases be used as an indicator. When the total bitumen content is high (compared with the background of common soil bitumens characteristic for the given region) and the location is geologically favorable for the presence of oil, one can speak of a bituminous anomaly. The coefficient of contrast for the anomaly must not be less that 2 - 3.

In exploring bituminous soil anomalies in the U.S.A. (sometimes, even without favorable geologic evidence), oil was obtained in a number of cases (21). However, at least as many positive predictions proved to be unjustified. These negative results were "explained" as follows: A bituminous anomaly in the soil may remain after the pool which gave rise to it has

disappeared, in much the same way that we see light from extinct stars long
after they have ceased to exist. Obviously, the idea of the great stability of
surface geological features, such as a soil profile, in comparison to oil
pools buried at great depths is ridiculous. It is mentioned here to enliven
the text.

The total bitumen content is a very unreliable index. The bitumen content in the soil necessarily includes soil bitumens having no relation to oil.
The amount of soil bitumen depends on the total content of organic matter
(humus) in the soil. This may vary widely depending on geomorphological,
geobotanical, and other conditions. Also, the total content of all bitumens
in the soil may vary. Such variations may readily be assumed to be bituminous anomalies, and geological indications cannot always eliminate this
danger. This explains the failure of many bitumen surveys of this type.

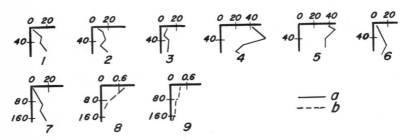

Fig. 95. Results of soil bitumen surveys (according to
M. M. Kononova). a—carbon content of bitumen in % of
total C_{org}; b—content of C_{org} in soil in %.

2. A more reliable index is the bituminosity of soil humus, i.e., the
content of bitumen, not in the soil as a whole, but only in the organic part
of the soil (humus). This index is defined as the ratio (bitumen)/(C_{org}) or
C_{bit}/C_{org}. The usual bitumen content in soil humus does not exceed 10%.
This is the soil bitumen background. When additional amounts of bitumen
appear because of an oil pool, this quantity must increase. Other significant sources of bituminization of soils are unknown. It is true that when
gases are polymerized in the soil, other substances besides bitumens may
be formed, and in this case, the indicator does not reflect all substances
derived from oil.

In the USSR soil bitumen surveys were conducted on an experimental
scale in Transcaucasia, the Volga region, and other areas. According to
data obtained by M. M. Kononova (22), the carbon content of bitumens
relative to the total humus carbon in the soil in various cases was as follows: over pools, 12 - 62%; at the limits of oil-bearing areas, 4 - 10%.
In every single case the values over pools were higher than in adjacent
areas. Several of the profiles obtained are given in the diagram (Fig. 95).

M. M. Kononova showed that, in soils of arid regions (gray desert
soils, etc.), a bituminous anomaly may appear in the very topmost layer,
while in black soils it appears only in the deeper layers. It may be that
the sorption properties of the soils also have a significant effect.

Anomalies in the bituminosity of soil humus combined with favorable
geological evidence are reliable indicators of the presence of oil pools (or
gas pools, because these may also give rise to bitumens in the soil resulting

from polymerization of methane). The absence of a bituminous anomaly cannot be considered a reliable negative indication (this is also true for gas anomalies). It has been shown that in some cases a bituminous anomaly only in fault zones, where existing conditions facilitated the movement of gases. The presence of a bituminous anomaly gives no indication as to whether the pool is large enough to be industrially significant or not.

3. In detecting bituminous anomalies M. M. Kononova suggested an additional criterion, the depth of the soil profile (22). This indication consists of the fact that the usual rapid loss of organic matter with depth is retarded by the upward infiltrating organic substances derived from petroleum. This tends to lengthen the soil profile. This phenomenon was established in several oil-bearing areas of the Apsheron peninsula (Fig. 95). This index is useful only in arid regions for soils poor in humus. For soils rich in humus, such as black soils and the like, it is too elusive. Its significance is also lost in the presence of buried soils.

P. S. Slavin notes that this factor depends on the direction of water currents in the soils and subsoils (23). According to data from the investigations of M. I. Subbota the bitumen content in the soil and subsoil also depends on atmospheric precipitation, which may carry bitumens downward through deeper strata to the level of the water table (24).

This brief discussion of the problem of interpreting the data of soil bitumen surveys shows that a considerable knowledge of the field of soil science is necessary for a successful solution of these problems.

BIBLIOGRAPHY

1. V.A. Uspenskii and O.A. Radchenko. Toward the question of a scheme of genetic classification of substances called bitumens. Izvestiya Akad. Nauk SSSR, ser. geol., No. 6, 1952.
2. V.S. Veselovskii. Testing of mineral fuels. Gosgeolizdat, 1951.
3. N.A. Orlov and V.A. Uspenskii. Mineralogy of caustobiolites. USSR Acad. Sci., 1936.
4. V.A. Klubov. Geochemical classification of caustobiolites. Sb. geol. rabot, posvyashch. pamyati akad. I.M. Gubkina. Gostoptekhizdat, 1950.
5. M.V. Kibler. Action of solvents on coals. Khimiya tverdogo topliva (sb.), v. I. IL, 1951.
6. V.A. Uspenskii, A.S. Chernysheva, and Yu.A. Mandrykina. On the dispersed form of hydrocarbons in various sedimentary rocks. Izvestiya Akad. Nauk SSSR, ser. geol., No. 5, 1949.
7. V.A. Uspenskii and A.S. Chernysheva. Material composition of organic material from lower Silurian limestones in the region of Mt. Chudovo. Tr. VNIGRI, nov. ser., No. 57 (Geokhim. sb., No. 2 - 3). Lengostoptekhizdat, 1951.
8. A.F. Dobryanskii. Oil shales of the USSR. Lengostoptekhizdat, 1947.
9. B.A. Skopintsev. Organic matter in natural waters. Tr. Gos. okeanogr. inst., No. 17 (29). Gidrometeoizdat, 1950.
10. P.D. Trask and H.B. Patnode. Source beds of petroleum. Tulsa, 1942.
11. A.A. Kartsev. The organic matter of the rocks of the Kirovabad oil-bearing region. Doklady Akad. Nauk SSSR, v. LXV, No. 3, 1949.
12. V.A. Uspenskii, A.I. Gorskaya, and A.S. Chernysheva. On the nature of laminarites from the Cambrian clays of the Baltic region. tr.

VNIGRI, nov. ser., No. 57 (Geokhim. sb., No. 2 - 3). Lengostoptekhizdat, 1951.

13. N.A. Eremenko. On the dispersed from of occurrence of bitumens in
Tertiary deposits of the northeast Caucasus. Tr. Akad. nefti.
prom., No. 1 Gostoptekhizdat, 1954.

14. S.G. Movsesyan. Attempt at rapid extraction of bituminous rocks. Az.
neft. khoz., No. 1 - 2, 1947.

15. L.V. Khmelevskaya. Method of determination en masse of organic
admixtures in sedimentary rocks. L., 1939

16. L.V. Khmelevskaya. Toward a method of lithological study of sedimentary rocks in oil-bearing regions and in oil prospecting. Tr.
17-i sessii Mezhd. geol. kongr., v. IV. Gostoptekhizdat, 1940.

17. V.A. Sokolov. Direct geochemical methods of petroleum prospecting.
Gostoptekhizdat, 1947.

18. V.A. Sokolov. Theory and method of the gas survey. Sb. "Geokhim.
metody poiskov nefti", No. 1. Gostoptekhizdat, 1950.

19. V.A. Uspenskii, A.I. Gorskaya, and I.P. Karpova. Genesis of algarites
and processes of anaerobic oxidation of oils. Izvestiya Akad.
Nauk SSSR, ser. geol., No. 4, 1947.

20. W.A. Noyes and P.A. Leighton. The Photochemistry of Gases. N.Y.,
1941.

21. S.J. Pirson. Critical survey of recent developments in geochemical
prospecting. Bull. Am. Assn. Petrol. Geol., vol. 24, No. 8, 1940.

22. V.A. Kovda and P.S. Slavin. Soil-geochemical indices of the oil-
bearing character of the depths. Akad. Nauk SSSR, 1951.

23. P.S. Slavin. On the soil-geochemical method of petroleum prospecting.
Geokhim. metody poiskov nefti i gaza, No. 1. Gostoptekhizdat,
1953.

24. M.I. Subbota. Seasonal variations of the indices of gas surveys and
methods of calculation thereof. Geokhim. metody poiskov nefti
i gaza, No. 1. Gostoptekhizdat, 1953.

CHAPTER EIGHT

Bitumen-Luminescence Methods

Bitumen-luminescence methods of prospecting and exploration for oil and gas formations are, essentially, bitumen methods. Their geological and geochemical foundations are generally the same as those of bitumen methods (see Chapter VII). The bitumen-luminescence approach differs from other bitumen methods only by the use of luminescence. Luminescence analysis is distinguished by its simplicity and its very great rapidity; yet at the same time, it has a very high sensitivity. These distinct advantages have led to the widespread use of bitumen-luminescence methods in prospecting for petroleum formations; indeed, they are more widely used than other bitumen methods.

Luminescence methods of detecting dispersed oil and bitumens in rock as an aid to prospecting were first suggested in 1939 by N. A. Shlezinger in Saratov (1) and shortly afterwards by M. Kh. Kleinman (2) and V. N. Florovskaya (3) in 1941. They were first applied in route (or reconnaissance) surveys and in the study of cores from exploratory wells. In 1942 K. P. Kozin suggested luminescence logging of drilling muds. Bitumen-luminescence methods became especially popular as a result of the work of V. N. Florovskaya and the publication of a special monograph (4). In the U.S.A., bitumen-luminescence methods came into use only in 1944 and were based on the work of Soviet investigators. The original application of bitumen-luminescence methods in the U.S.A. was in soil surveys in areas where detailed prospecting was needed (area survey).

At the present time, bitumen-luminescence methods of prospecting for petroleum are applied in the form of: (1) route surveys, (2) detailed area surveys, (3) studies of cores from supporting[1] and exploratory wells, (4) studies of underground waters, and (5) logging of drilling muds and cuttings. In addition, there are a number of secondary applications of luminescence analysis to exploration problems as, for example, in the correlation of well sections, etc.

BASIC INFORMATION ON LUMINESCENCE OF BITUMENS

The basis of luminescence analysis of bitumens is the ability of bitumens to luminesce. Therefore, the phenomenon of luminescence in general and the peculiatities of this property of the bitumens in particular will be briefly briefly discussed.

---

[1] ''Supporting'' wells are apparently shallow structure tests drilled to supplement surface geology data. Ed.

Luminescence, its Main Forms and Some Properties

The simplest definition of luminescence is the independent emission of light at normal temperatures.[2] But this definition is not quite accurate. According to the precise and concrete definition of S.I. Vavilov, luminescence is the excess of radiation over temperature radiation. This excess radiation must have an ultimate duration exceeding the period of light vibrations [as opposed to the reflection and scattering of light, radiation due to electrons, and the like. (5)].[3]

Depending on the nature of the source of excitation, the various types of luminescence are called photoluminescence, X-ray luminescence, chemiluminescence, etc. The source of excitation of photoluminescence is light. Photoluminescence is the radiation of light that is excited by absorption of light (7). For bitumen-luminescence methods only photoluminescence is significant and only this form will be further discussed.

Usually, fluorescence and phosphorescence are distinguished. Fluorescence differs from phosphorescence in that there is no afterglow; i.e., fluorescence ceases immediately upon cessation of excitation, while phosphorescence persists.[4] Fluorescence is chiefly characteristic of liquids, while phosphorescence is peculiar to crystalline substances. Fluorescence is of fundamental significance for bituminology.

The energetic yield of luminescence is the ratio of the energy of the luminescence to the absorbed energy. The wavelength (or frequency) distribution of the energy being studied is called the luminescence spectrum. If the luminescence spectrum lies in the region of visible light, it determines the color of the luminescence. The luminescence spectrum depends on the substance being excited and the nature of the source of excitation (i.e., the wavelength of the exciting radiation). The first factor is the basis of luminescence analysis (see below), and the second is of a statistical nature. This is more correctly expressed by Vavilov's Law: the exciting wave is transformed into one of greater length than itself (6). This situation is illustrated by the diagram (Fig. 96). Thus, shorter wave lengths must be used for excitation to obtain luminescence spectra in the region of visible light. Therefore, ultraviolet rays are usually used for excitation of luminescence.

In bituminology one deals mainly with solutions of bitumens in organic

---

[2] The physical foundations of the phenomenon are set forth here in the briefest, most elementary manner possible and only with regard to their applicability to bituminology.

[3] According to the more general definition of V. A. Levshin, luminescence is a proper, non-equilibrium radiation of excited, complex particles or substances formed by them ("proper"—as opposed to reflected and scattered light, "non-equilibrium"—as opposed to temperature radiation, "radiation of excited, complex particles"—as opposed to direct radiation due to electrons and the like) (6). The two definitions do not contradict each other because an excited state of particles already assumes a period of radiation exceeding that of light vibrations.

[4] The basic difference between fluorescence and phosphorescence, according to contemporary ideas, is that fluorescence is an independent radiation of discrete centers (molecules), while phosphorescence is a recombination radiation, i.e., a radiation of centers interacting with each other (in crystals) (7).

liquids. The brightness (intensity) of the luminescence depends on the luminescence yield. The yield of a solution depends in turn on the concentration of the luminescent substance ("luminogen") in the solution. However,
this relationship is not a simple one. Up to a certain limit the brightness
of fluorescence increases with increase of concentration, but above some
optimum concentration the radiation begins to fall off (Fig. 97). This phenomenon is called "concentration extinction" (quenching). The cause of
this is not quite clear. According to S. I. Vavilov, quenching occurs as a
result of the interaction (mainly through resonance) of excited fluorescent
molecules with non-excited and extraneous ones. When this occurs, the
energy of excitation goes over to another form (thermal), and the greater
the concentration, the more frequent such interaction (8). Evidently, association of molecules in concentrated solutions is also important, since
it converts the substance to non-luminescent forms. The phenomenon of
concentration quenching is very important in the analysis of bitumens.

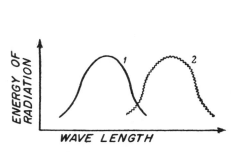

Fig. 96. Correlation of the spectra of
excitation and luminescence. 1—spectrum of excitation; 2—spectrum of
luminescence.

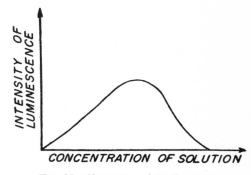

Fig. 97. Variation of the luminescence intensity of a solution with
concentration.

Principles of Luminescence Analysis

The fundamental indices of luminescence analysis are: (1) the brightness
of luminescence (quantitative index); (2) the luminescence spectrum (qualitative index). Chemically different substances have different luminescence
spectra. However, the latter, as a rule, do not consist of distinct lines but
are composed of more or less broad bands, sometimes having maxima at
various wavelengths. Also, the dependence of the spectra on the exciting
waves should be remembered. B. L. Levshin distinguishes two types of
luminescence analysis: (1) detection analysis, or the detection and investigation of various items (here the composition of the luminogen is already
known and it is necessary to determine its presence and sometimes its
quantity); (2) chemical luminescence analysis, or the determination of the
chemical composition of an unknown substance from its luminescence. The
second problem can be solved only in special cases under definite, restricted conditions. In bituminology, both types of analysis are used. The
bitumen must first be detected and its approximate quantity determined.
In many cases, it is then necessary to determine the composition of the
bitumens, even if only to a first approximation (fractional composition).

Luminescence analysis has come to be very widely used in the most diverse branches of science and technology and is applied in a great variety of ways (9). Besides bituminology and the oil-refining industry, this method has been used in such fields as coal petrography, mineralogy, prospecting for uranium and tungsten, paleontology, and hydrogeology (determining the direction of underground currents with the aid of luminescent substances). Luminescence analysis is also widely used in various branches of biology, medicine, chemistry, the food industry, detection of defects, legal chemistry, archeology, etc.

Luminescence of Bitumens

The luminescence of bitumens, like that of all organic substances, depends on the chemical structure. Luminescence is especially characteristic of compounds containing aromatic rings. On the other hand, saturated compounds do not luminesce at all. Nearly all bitumens contain aromatic rings, and therefore, nearly all of them luminesce. Some very light oils (for example, in Il'dokani) are exceptional. In compounds with identical or similar types of structure, luminescence depends on the molecular weight. As the molecular weight of a compound increases, its luminescence spectrum is shifted in the direction of longer wave lengths. The same thing occurs as the number of rings increases. Thus, the luminescence spectrum of benzene and its homologs (on irradiation with ultraviolet) is still situated in the ultraviolet region (i.e., invisible to the eye), whereas hydrocarbons of the anthracene and phenanthrene series have visible spectra.

Since nearly all bitumens are complex mixtures, their luminescence spectra, as a rule, do not have sharp maxima. The difference in luminescence between different bitumens is primarily determined by their fractional composition. Therefore, it is impossible to distinguish, for example, oil bitumens from coal bitumens in the general case. Those bitumens which contain large quantities of chlorophyll and similar substances occupy a special place because they are primarily soil bitumens. Chlorophyll has a characteristic sharp luminescence spectra in the region of red and orange colors (as do the porphyrins).

The luminescence of all "free" bitumens is of the fluorescent type. Bound bitumens are partially phospherescent (10). Aside from bitumens, living matter, and the decomposing remains of organisms, there are practically no luminescent compounds among natural organic substances. The luminescence of coals is entirely determined by their content of bitumens (11). There are many luminescent inorganic minerals, such as the uranyl minerals, scheelite, many calcites, fluorite, etc. But in contrast to the bitumens, they are insoluble in organic liquids.

Luminescence of Bitumen Fractions

As stated above, the luminescence of bitumens is determined by their fractional composition. The luminescence spectrum of a bitumen is made up of the luminescence spectra of its individual fractions. In conformity with the rule stated above, the heavier the fraction, the greater the wavelength of its luminescence sprectrum. Luminescence spectra of several oil fractions according to the data of V. N. Florovskaya and V. G. Melkov (very incomplete) are listed in Table 27.

TABLE 27.   Luminescence spectra of oil fractions (according to
            V. N. Florovskaya and V. G. Melkov)

Fraction	Interval of spectrum including more than 50% of energy, Å	Predominant color of radiation
Light oils	4100 — 5100	Blue
Heavy oils	4800 — 5100	Azure
Light tars	5100 — 5400	Green
Heavy tars	5800 — 6200	Yellow
Asphaltenes	——————	Brown
Naphthenic acids	4000 (sharp maximum)	Violet

Light colored fractions (kerosines, ligroins, gasolines) have a strong luminescence color. Light fractions often do not exhibit significant luminescence since they consist of saturates, lower naphthenes, and hydrocarbons of the benzene series, i.e., substances which either do not luminesce at all, or have ultraviolet luminescence spectra. This must be taken into account because part of the dispersed oil is probably of this nature. The luminescence spectra of crude oils, according to the data of F. M. Efendiev, generally lie in the 3700 - 5700 Å range and have the form of broad bands from 900 to 1600 Å wide with flat peaks from 20 to 400 Å wide (Fig. 98) (12).

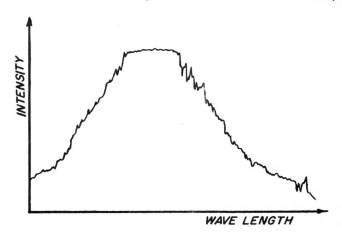

Fig. 98. Example of the luminescence spectrum of crude oil.

LUMINESCENCE ANALYSIS OF BITUMENS

In prospecting for petroleum formations, the following are the main objectives of luminescence analysis:

1. detection and determination of the total content of bitumens in rocks, soils, waters, and drilling muds;

2. determination of the general nature of the bitumens detected in rocks and soils and an approximate determination of their fractional composition;

3. determination of the fractional composition of crude oils and bitumens;

4. determination of the nature of the distribution of bitumens in rocks.

For these purposes, many forms of luminescence analysis have been developed: drop, test tube, capillary, quantitative-fractional, and others. Common to all these is the use of ultraviolet light for excitation of luminescence; hence, the same apparatus is used for production of these rays in all methods. A very brief account is given below.

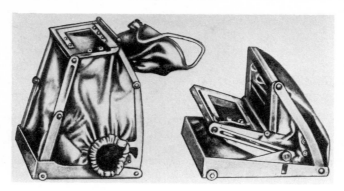

Fig. 99. Collapsible solar luminoscope.

Equipment

The equipment for luminescence analysis consists of sources of excitation and light filters. The source of ultraviolet radiation may be natural (the sun) or artificial (quartz-mercury arcs, spark discharges, and others). For the separation of ultraviolet light from other parts of the spectrum, light filters of nickel glass (Wood glass and the like) or, rarely, quartz monochromators are used.

Field (portable) and stationary apparatus are used. The first type includes solar luminoscopes, lamp luminoscopes, and others. The collapsible luminoscope of Melkov and Florovskaya (13) is distinguished by its maximal portability. It consists of a light-tight, cloth chamber provided with a Wood light filter and having an aperture for observation of the luminescent substance placed within, (Fig. 99). The device may be used anywhere in sunny weather.

The latest field equipment is the luminoscope of G. G. Grigor'ev (14). This is also a portable apparatus with which it is possible to make observations without a dark room. It requires a supply of electrical energy because the source of ultraviolet light is a quartz-mercury arc.

One type of laboratory apparatus is the analytical lamp (fluorescence analysis apparatus), which consists of a light-tight chamber, a quartz-mercury arc and Wood light-filters[5] (Fig. 100). Work with the lamp is done in a darkened room. This device can also be replaced by a common sun lamp. Recently a specially designed air-cooled lamp was suggested by S. P. Boravskii (15).

In the laboratory the GOI apparatus is used. Here the source of

---

[5]Made primarily for the determination of vitamins.

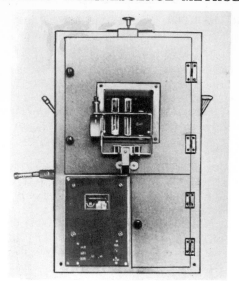

Fig. 100. Analytical luminescent
lamp L-80.

ultraviolet light is a spark discharge tube, but instead of a light-filter, a
quartz monochromator is required. This apparatus is complex and expen-
sive, but it makes possible the separation of long and short ultraviolet
wave lengths. This permits a more detailed analysis of the luminescence
of substances.

Drop Analysis

Luminescent-drop analysis, developed by V. N. Florovskaya, is based on
the approximate relationship between the bitumen content of a rock and the
shape of the luminescent spot produced by applying a drop of solvent to the
surface of the rock. Furthermore, it is possible to estimate approximately
the nature of the bitumen (fractional composition) from the color of the luminescent spot. As the bitumen content of the rock decreases, the shape
of the luminescent spot changes and may be classified as: uniform, non-
uniform, ring, points, or absent. When there is a uniform distribution of
bitumen in the rock (usually in carbonate rocks), the drop is applied to a
ground, flat surface of the sample, whereas with a non-uniform distribution,
it is applied to the surface of the powdered rock.

   According to V. N. Florovskaya it is possible to distinguish "light
bitumen", "oily bitumen", "bitumen of intermediate composition" and
"tar-asphaltene bitumen" by the color of the drop (13). From the point of
view of oil prospecting, the greatest interest lies in the so-called light bitumen, since it is the light bitumens that are most probably derived from
petroleum. However, owing to the lack of research on the luminescence of
the "light bitumens", it is impossible at present to reach any definite conclusions as to the significance of their presence (especially since "light
bitumens" have been found in places where there is no possibility of petroleum). Drop analysis is very inaccurate (16).

Test Tube Analysis

Test tube luminescence analysis[6] consists of: (a) cold extraction of bitumens from rocks, soils, or drilling muds (usually using chloroform), and (b) determination of the bitumen content by comparing the intensity of the luminescence of extracts with special standards. A sample of pulverized rock is carefully weighed and the volume of solvent used is measured before analysis. Standard solutions are prepared from crude oil or dispersed bitumen. The standard scale must cover an interval of bitumen content from 10^{-1} to 10^{-4}% (consisting of 15 standards, prepared by successive dilutions to half-strength). In general, several standard scales of various substances should be on hand. The intensity of luminescence is determined either visually or photometrically (the photometric method has not yet been developed in the USSR). F. M. Efendiev suggests the use of colorimetry by dilution in the Duboscq colorimeter (18).

The sensitivity of the method is at least 10^{-5}% bitumen in rock, which is quite adequate. The accuracy is adequate for a determination of the order of concentration. Complications result from: (a) differences in the luminescence colors of sample and standard; (b) the phenomenon of concentration quenching (as concentrations over 0.1%). In order to eliminate these complications, suitably colored standards must be selected and, in some cases, the extracts being studied must be diluted. Also, the solvent must be pure because, if impurities are present, the solvent itself may luminesce. Test tube analysis may be used in the field.

Capillary Analysis

Luminescent-capillary analysis is used to determine the approximate fractional composition of bitumen. A prepared extract is placed in a standard vessel and one end of a strip of non-luminescent filter paper is immersed in the solution. The bitumen rises along the capillaries and separates into fractions because the lighter ones rise correspondingly higher. After evaporation of the solvent, the resulting capillary extracts are examined under ultraviolet light. The width of the bands (zones) corresponding to individual fractions (distinguished by the color of luminescence), and total height of ascent are measured (Fig. 101). The values obtained are compared with standard paper strips.

The weight of rock sample, volume of solvent, size of the paper strips, and time involved in the extraction process must be accurately measured. The variety of bitumens strongly hinders comparison. According to K. F. Rodionova, capillary determination of the fractional composition of

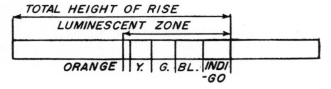

Fig. 101. Example of a capillary bitumen extract.

---

[6]"Standard" analysis according to V. N. Florovskaya (17).

bitumens by the capillary method is very inaccurate. This is especially true when the content of "oil" fractions is relatively low, because tars may entirely cover the oil zone on the paper (16). This method gives better results for crude oils.

Adsorption (chromatographic) Analysis

Luminescence-adsorption (chromatographic) analysis of natural bitumens was developed by A. F. Fioletova (19), P. F. Andreev, S. P. Maksimov (20), F. M. Efendiev (21), and others. The method consists in passing the extract through a glass tube filled with an adsorbent (powdered MgO, Al_2O_3, silica gel, etc.). The bitumen is thus fractionated and forms zones (just as in capillary analysis), the luminescence and width of which are determined. Individual fractions may be isolated and studied separately. Luminescence-adsorption analysis may be used in the field but isolation of fractions must be done in the laboratory.

Quantitative Fractional Analysis

Preliminary separation of bitumen into fractions, followed by a determination of the quantity and nature of these fractions by luminescence gives more reliable results than the total analysis of bitumens described above. An accelerated separation of bitumens into fractions in test tubes, followed by a determination of luminescence in the test tubes and capillary extracts, was developed by V. N. Florovskaya and N. D. Sakhovskaya under the name, "luminescent-component analysis" (17). A chloroform extract (in a test tube) is filtered and evaporated. The residue is treated with petroleum ether and then the petroleum-ether extract is filtered off. Asphaltenes remain in the residue. Their quantity is determined by redissolving them in chloroform and measuring the luminescence of this extract. Next, silica gel is added to the petroleum-ether extract, which contains oils and tars (neutral). The mixture is shaken at length (until the luminescence color of the extract is azure) and filtered. The amount of oils is determined from the luminescence of the filtrate. The silica gel is then treated with chloroform and the quantity of tars in this new chloroform extract is determined by luminescence. Thus, the quantities of oils, tars, and asphaltenes are obtained separately. The total quantity of bitumen may be determined by summation. Each fraction requires its own set of standards. Quantitative fractional analysis gives sufficiently accurate results. The analytical technique is very simple and may be used in the field.

This method of analysis is intended for the determination of petroleum bitumens. For other bitumens (for example, syngenetic dispersed bitumens in rocks), it is of value only for an accurate determination of the total bitumen content. The method of separation outlined above needs to be changed and improved. Changes and improvements were recently suggested by K. F. Rodionova (the use of alcohol-benzene as well as chloroform for additional extraction of the most acid components of the bitumens) (22).

Luminescence-Extraction Analysis

All of the various types of luminescence analysis considered here, except quantitative fractional analysis, reveal almost nothing on which to base any judgment as to the genetic nature of the bitumens. At best, soil bitumens may be identified by the red and orange tints of the luminescence of chlorophyll, which they contain in large amounts. In order to distinguish oil bitumens from non-oil ones, it is necessary to determine some other properties of the bitumens besides luminescence. One such property is selective solubility. Luminescence-extraction analysis is based on the simultaneous determination of solubility and luminescence (23). This consists in a parallel extraction of bitumens by different solvents (in test tubes) and the determination of the luminescence of each extract by comparison with appropriate standards (in test tubes or capillary extracts). A separate scale of standards is prepared for each solvent. Luminescence-extraction analysis gives the "solubility spectrum" of a substance, just as does the method of L. V. Khmelevskaya (see Chapter VII); but the luminescence determination greatly increases the sensitivity. Results are expressed by special graphs (Fig. 102). As a result of luminescence-extraction analysis, it was ascertained that the dispersed syngenetic bitumens of sandy, argillaceous rocks are, for the most part, considerably different from oil bitumens and quite similar to coal bitumens (24, et al.). The basis for distinguishing oil bitumens from non-oil ones is the ratio (petroleum-ether extract)/(alcohol-benzene extract).

However, in evaluating the results of luminescence-extraction analysis, several complicating factors must be taken into account. First, the intensity of luminescence may depend not only on the amount of bitumen in the extract but also on the nature of this bitumen or part of it. Therefore, comparison of the intensity of extracts sometimes may give an incorrect idea of the quantitative ratio of concentrations. Secondly, some data indicate that part of the syngenetic bitumens of carbonate rocks are very similar in their extraction characteristics to oil bitumens.

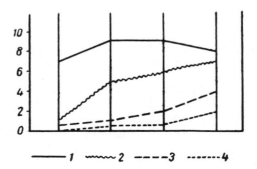

Fig. 102. Extraction characteristics of bitumens.
1—asphalt; 2—coal; 3—Maikop clay; 4—Akchagyl clay.

Luminescence-extraction analysis is in need of much further development. The range of applicable solvents must be increased, and the characteristics of the main types of dispersed syngenetic bitumens must be more firmly established. It is also desirable to combine luminescence-extraction analysis with quantitative fractional analysis, i.e., the separation of bitumen into fractions and the determination of their selective solubilities. This will increase the accuracy of results and will aid in the solution of the

main problem, the recognition of oil bitumens. The method recently developed by K. F. Rodionova (22) appears to be a long step forward in this
direction.[7]

Microscopic Luminescence Determinations

The purpose of a microscopic luminescence study of rocks is to learn the
nature of the distribution of bitumens in rocks (i.e., bituminous textures
and structures). The spatial relationships between the organic and inorganic parts of a rock form the bituminous texture of the rock. The special
relationships within the separate groups of organic substances themselves
make up the bituminous structure of the rock (13). V. N. Florovskaya
distinguished 11 types of bituminous textures and 14 types of structures.
For oil prospecting purposes, textures are more important. The luminescence study of bituminous structures is of interest in coal petrography (25).

Selectively impregnated, fissured, and cemented bituminous textures
(Fig. 103) indicate the secondary nature of bitumens in a rock. The bitumens of carboid minerals also exhibit a characteristic secondary nature.
The remaining bituminous textures (uniform, lamellar, punctate, etc.) cannot in themselves indicate whether a bitumen is primary or secondary.

It must be kept in mind that, if organic matter contains bitumen in a
finely dispersed state (such as certain portions of coal), it often has a luminescent surface under the microscope or hand lens (25). For these in-

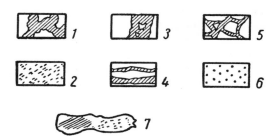

Fig. 103. Bituminous textures (according to
V. N. Florovskaya). 1—selectively impregnated; 2—uniform; 3—fissured; 4—lamellar;
5—cemented; 6—punctate; 7—luminescent
portions of rock.

vestigations, special fluorescence microscopes, as well as ordinary microscopes with quartz condensers are used; textures are studied with the
aid of binocular microscopes. The rocks are studied in powdered prepara-
tions, thin sections, and hand samples.

---

[7]See also E. S. Lysenkova, "Experiment in the use of luminescence analysis for
investigation of rock and oil samples". Grozny Book Publishing House, 1953.

APPLICATION OF BITUMEN-LUMINESCENCE METHODS

Route Surveys

Bitumen-luminescence route surveys are conducted during reconnaissance of new regions for the purpose of locating oil-bearing strata. These are conducted at widely spaced intervals. For example, surveys were conducted in the Northern Caucasus, along the Kuban and Terek Rivers, which covered an entire section of the Mesozoic and Cenozoic rocks (13). Good exposures are required for this type of work, since rock outcrops are studied. The frequency of sampling within the section may be varied.

The main types of analysis in bitumen-luminescence route surveys are the test-tube analysis and sometimes the drop analysis as well. It is quite possible to use the luminescence-extraction method. The determination of bituminous textures is also carried out. Bitumen-luminescence logs are compiled as the final result (Fig. 104).

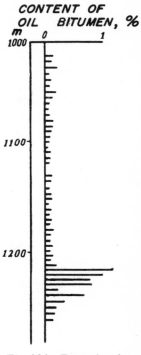

CONTENT OF OIL BITUMEN, %

The basic index in these surveys in the total bitumen content of the rocks strata with an especially high bitumen content (over 0.1%) are subjected to a more detailed study. Those strata in which extracts of the oil type or in which bituminous textures of a secondary nature are observed receive special attention. Detailed bituminological investigations are conducted by making quantitative determinations on a large number of rock samples from selected intervals. Thus, bitumen-luminescence route surveys are preliminary investigations which must be followed by more exacting work. Luminescence investigations of waters, discussed below,[8] and of cores from supporting wells are also included in route surveys.

Area Surveys

Detailed bitumen-luminescence surveys of specific areas are conducted for the purpose of predicting the presence of oil pools under some part of the area. There are two kinds of bitumen-luminescence area surveys: soil and subsoil. In the former, samples are taken from the soil layer, while in the latter, they are taken from alluvium and bed rock. The first variety has been developed in the U.S.A. (11); the second has been used in the USSR.

Fig. 104. Example of a bitumen-luminescence log.

The theory and methodology of bitumen-luminescence soil surveying does not differ from that of soil-bitumen extraction surveying which was discussed in Chapter VII. Anomalous values in the total bitumen content of the soil, as determined by luminescence and evaluated on the basis of

---

[8]Luminescence study of waters — see Chapter IX.

correlations with geological data are the primary indicators. Samples
containing bitumens with orange and red luminescence colors are obviously
not derived from oil and are excluded. This greatly increases the utility
of luminescence results in comparison with other results that are based on
the total weight of bitumens.

Bitumen-luminescence subsoil surveys of alluvium and bed rock
(partly including soils as well) have been conducted in a number of regions
of the Caucasus and in several other places (13, 26). Field methods are
basically the same as in the core-gas survey. Sampling points are arranged in a definite pattern. Samples are taken from shallow wells (up to
15 - 20 m. in depth), excavations, and ditches. A test-tube determination
of the total bitumen content in the rocks is the principal analytic technique.
Results are recorded on profiles and maps (Fig. 105). An anomalously
high total bitumen content is considered an indication of petroleum. According to V. N. Florovskaya, values exceeding 10^{-3}% are anomalous (27).

Bitumen-luminescence surveys conducted on subsoil samples have
given ambiguous results for the most part. This is apparently due to the
following:[9]

1. There is no firm theoretical foundation for subsoil bitumen surveys.
Bitumens are formed biosynthetically and photosynthetically from petroleum gases in the soil. Therefore, they cannot exist at deeper levels.
Aside from syngenetic bitumens, deep-lying rocks can contain only: (a) dispersed oil particles passing directly into pools, which is a rare case (see
Chapter VII); (b) bitumens formed by the polymerization of petroleum gases
due to the catalytic action of the rocks, which is purely hypothetical. Thus,
subsoil bitumen surveys are based on the determination of substances,
whose very existence is subject to doubt.

2. In subsoil bitumen surveys, there are no analytical criteria by
which bitumens derived from petroleum might be distinguished from those
of other origin. Although it may be possible in some cases to distinguish
syngenetic soil bitumens by the color of their luminescence, this criterion
is useless on bedrock samples.

3. In subsoil surveys it is often quite impossible to discern quantitative anomalies. If the area being studied contains rocks of different ages,

SCALE	BITUMEN CONTENT, %	SYMBOL
14—15	1,25—2,5	
11—13	0,156—0,625	
7—10	0,01—0,08	
4—6	0,00125—0,005	
1—3	0,000156—0,000625	

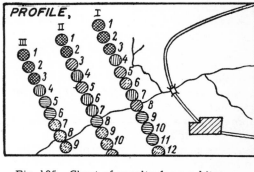

Fig. 105. Chart of results from a bitumen-
luminescence subsoil area survey (after
V. N. Florovskaya).

[9]These points represent the personal views of the author of the chapter.

the differences in their syngenetic bituminosity may be so great as to make all attempts to discern anomalous zones futile. This particular situation was encountered in a number of areas in the Northern Caucasus where, for example, surveys in a single area simultaneously found Paleogene rocks with a syngenetic bitumen content up to 1% ("anomalies") and Quaternary detritus with a bituminosity below 10^{-4}% (13). To distinguish "anomalies" of syngenetic bituminosity from anomalies due to oil pools is practically impossible.

The above demonstrates the lack of any serious basis for the bitumen-luminescence method of investigating subsoil horizons and the slight practical utility of the method. In those areas in which this method gave relatively good, well-defined results (for example, in Turkmenia), liquid petroleum had apparently migrated along fault zones.

The soil survey has marked advantages over the subsoil survey. As applied in America, however, the bitumen-luminescence soil survey is not quite satisfactory and needs to be perfected. At the same time the luminescence analysis is made, the content of organic carbon in the soil may be determined from which the ratio $(C_{org})/(bitumen)$ may be computed (see Chapter VII). Another way of improving results is to find more reliable criteria for distinguishing syngenetic subsoil bitumens and the substances formed in the soil as a result of the presence of an oil pool.

Study of the Cores from Deep Wells

It is necessary to distinguish between the bitumen-luminescence study of cores from supporting wells, on the one hand, and from exploratory wildcats, on the other. The methods and techniques are the same, but the problems are different. The study of cores from supporting wells has the same purpose as the route survey, to prospect for oil-bearing strata. The study of cores from wildcat wells has the same purpose as the area survey, i.e., to detect the presence of oil pools in the depths.

Predicting the presence of an oil pool at some greater depth from the bituminosity of cores is based on the hypothesis of the penetration of luminescent liquid bitumens into the cap rocks and the formation of halos of dispersed oil bitumens around pools. Similar phenomena were observed by V. N. Florovskaya in several regions of Tataria (4). In a carbonate cap rock, the quantity of bitumens gradually diminished with increased distance from the pool, while the bitumens became lighter (varying from an asphaltene-tar bitumen to a light oil bitumen). This indicates a natural fractionation of the bitumens, resulting from the fact that their motion occurred in the liquid and not the gas phase. These observations played a major role in the further development of bitumen-luminescence methods in general, although this case appears to be rare. Hardly any similar phenomena were observed in other regions. In order for a significant bitumen halo to be formed by movement of liquid particles, the rocks must have suitable properties (possibly existing most often in carbonate rocks). The movement of gases does not leave any traces of bitumens in the rocks. It will be recalled that the lightest fractions of the liquid hydrocarbons do not luminesce. The limited amount of coring in exploratory drilling also hinders the development of a method of detecting oil pools by studying core luminescence.

In the study of a core, (from either wildcat or supporting wells) by luminescence, the main methods of analysis employed are: test tube, capillary, luminescence-extraction, microscopy, and possibly quantitative fractionation. The results are assembled in columns for individual wells (basically similar to those for route surveys, but with an indication of depths).

Luminescence Logging

Bitumen-luminescence logging of drilling muds (and to a lesser extent of cuttings) has recently become especially important. This is an exploratory method used with exploratory drilling in areas where the petroleum possibilities are still unknown or have been established only for some horizons. The purpose of luminescence logging is to establish the oil-bearing nature of individual strata as they are drilled. The logging of drilling fluids consists in a luminescence analysis of the mud flowing out of the well during the entire drilling process. The data obtained are then correlated with the sell section.

Most of the luminescent bitumens in mud occur as oil films and finely emulsified oil particles which have passed into the mud as it moves past oil zones. Other bitumens, such as dispersed syngenetic types come out in the cuttings when the rock is drilled but do not pass into the mud. A certain amount of bitumen, present in the clay from which the mud is prepared, luminesces only in the extract (in this case, forming a "background" which is perfectly uniform and therefore does not interfere). Oil films luminesce even without extraction.[10] These circumstances greatly simplify luminescence logging because the problem of distinguishing between oil and non-oil bitumens practically disappears. Therefore, this method is sometimes also called oil logging. Luminescence logging (like gas logging) may be conducted either by an intermittent sampling of the mud or by a continuous sampling using an automatic gas logging unit.

Luminescence analysis of drilling muds may be conducted by various methods, with and without extraction. Analysis without extraction gives good results when oil films are present in the mud. The oil content of the mud is evaluated from the shape of films on the surface of the suspension which are compared with standards prepared from known concentrations of local crude oils (as in the drop analysis of rocks—see above.) This method is very simple because it does not even require sampling. In an automatic logging unit, the determination is carried out in an inspection tank equipped with a stationary source of ultraviolet light. The drilling fluid is examined continuously with this setup, but unfortunately, the data obtained are unreliable.[11]

Analysis with extraction is more accurate. Drilling mud samples are taken, and the determination is conducted by the test tube method (see above) with a ratio of solvent to sample equal to 1:10 (by volume). F. M. Efendiev recommends the use of centrifugation in extraction analysis (18).

The content of oil in clay suspension is defined by the equation:

---

[10]It must be kept in mind that tarry oils luminesce very weakly.

[11]See footnote 10 of this chapter.

$$D = \frac{Bm}{n} \%,$$

where, B is the content of oil in a standard solution,
m is the number of milliliters of solvent,
n is the weight of the sample of drilling mud,
D is the oil content of the drilling mud.

Values obtained in this way also include: (a) the bitumens which are actually part of the mud (and must be determined beforehand); (b) several other substances, such as soaps, which come from water-bearing levels.

A serious complication in evaluating the data of luminescence logging is the contamination of the drilling mud by petroleum lubricants used in drilling. If these substances are significantly different in their luminescence characteristics from the crude oils encountered in the hole, false interpretations can be avoided. Luminescent-capillary analyses of these and other substances are necessary for control. If the lubricants are composed of oils similar to those present in the strata, luminescence logging cannot be used successfully. Recently, a method of eliminating the luminescence of lubricants by the addition of special quenching agents has been developed.

Logging results may be expressed in diagrams on which the oil content is shown along the well section (Fig. 106). This makes it possible to recognize oil-bearing zones in the well bore, but these will not necessarily be oil pools. Oil in the drilling mud indicates the presence of these zones. When large sections of the well contain dispersed oil (i.e., where the local background is high) productive zones are marked by a sharp increase in the oil content of the mud.

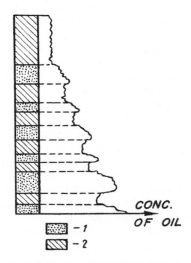

Fig. 106. Luminescence log of drilling mud. 1—oil-bearing sands; 2—clays.

Natural gas pools may be distinguished from oil pools by combining gas and bitumen-luminescence logging. Zones containing only gas do not show up on luminescence logs. This method also makes it possible to discover oil pools that contain very little gas and are therefore missed by gas logging. Estimating the commercial value of pools from luminescence data is an intricate operation.

The need of recording the luminescence of drilling mud continuously and automatically is a serious problem. In automatic luminography it is desirable to eliminate visual examination and obtain luminograms of wells directly, similar to electric logging, gas logging, etc. This method is now being developed.

Luminescence logging of drill cuttings has been used relatively little. It has its shortcomings because of the technical difficulties of collecting the cuttings, quartering them, and the necessity of using solvents. The presence of syngenetic bitumens in the cuttings also complicates the evaluation of data, especially for rocks of low oil content.

Correlation of Well Sections

There are two methods of correlating well sections according to the luminescence results. The first method consists in correlating productive zones within the limits of individual formations according to the nature of the luminescence of the oils from different levels. A procedure for this type of correlation was developed by V. N. Florovskaya (28), N. P. Moskalev, N. A. Eremenko, ans S. P. Maksimov (20). Luminescence by capillary, adsorption, and fractional analyses of oils constitutes the basis of comparison (see above).

According to Z. M. Tabasaranskii and N. B. Vassoevich, this method may be employed only with great caution. Even within the limits of individual pools, the nature of the luminescence may vary considerably. This is explained by the fact that the luminescence is related to the fractional composition of the crude oils, which often varies as a result of gravitational segregation and other processes (see Chapter I). This kind of correlation gives more reliable results in areas of fairly uniform, undisturbed strata (platform conditions).

The second method of correlating luminescence results is to compare the nature of the luminescence of dispersed syngenetic bitumens in well sections. This comparison may also be made for wells that are spread out over long distances. The method was suggested by M. D. Semina and V. N. Florovskaya.

Luminescence analysis (capillary, quantitative fractional) may also be used for a preliminary evaluation of the physical properties of oils obtained from test wells. These determinations, which may be made very quickly, make it possible to foresee problems of oil storage, transportation, etc.

BIBLIOGRAPHY

1. N.A. Shlezinger and L. Novozhenova. Fluorescence method of discovering petroleum in geological prospecting work. Byull. Vses. khim. o-va. No. 4, 1941.
2. M.Kh. Kreinman. Application of luminescence analysis. Razvedka nedr, No. 6, 1941.
3. V.N. Florovskaya. Luminescence method of detecting bituminosity in rocks. Doklady Akad. Nauk SSSR. 31, No. 4, 1941.
4. V.N. Florovskaya and V.G. Melkov. Introduction to luminescence bituminology. Gosgeolizdat, 1946.
5. S.I. Vavilov. Preface to the Russian translation of P. Pringsheim, "Fluorescence and Phosphorescence". IL, 1951.
6. V.L. Levshin. Photoluminescence of liquid and solid substances. Gostekhizdat, 1951.
7. P. Pringsheim. Fluorescence and Phosphorescence (transl. from Engl.). IL, 1951.
8. S.I. Vavilov. Microstructure of light. Akad. Nauk SSSR, 1950.
9. MA. Konstantinova-Shlezinger. Luminescence analysis. Akad. Nauk SSSR, 1948.
10. A.F. Fioletova. Determination of the bituminosity of rocks by the method of luminescence analysis. Zhur. analyt. khimii, v. II, No. 1, 1947.
11. J. De Ment. Fluorochemistry. N. Y., 1945.

12. F.M. Efendiev and Kh.I. Mamedov. Spectroscopic investigation of the luminescent radiation of crude oils. Izv. Akad. Nauk AzSSR, No. 1, 1952.

13. V.N. Florovskaya. Brief guide to luminescence-bituminological analysis. Gostoptekhizdat, 1949.

14. G.G. Grigor'ev. Portable field luminoscope. Field and industrial geochemistry, No. 1. Gostoptekhizdat, 1953.

15. S.P. Boravskii. Analytical quartz-mercury lamp with air-cooling. Geochem. methods of prospecting for oil and gas, No. 1. Gostoptekhizdat, 1953.

16. K.F. Rodionova and O.B. Vagner. Towards the characteristics of bitumens by the method of luminescence analysis. Sb. "K geologii tsentr. oblastei Russkoi platformy". Tr. VNIIGAZ. Gosgeolizdat, 1951.

17. Directions for luminescence-bituminological analysis. Lengostoptekhizdat, 1951.

18. F.M. Efendiev. Luminescence method of investigating petroleum and bitumens. Aznefteizdat, Baku, 1953.

19. A.F. Fioletova. Luminescence analysis of bitumens. Izv. Akad. Nauk SSSR, ser. fiz., 13, No. 2, 1949.

20. N.A. Eremenko and S.P. Maksimov. Investigations of natural manifestations of gas and petroleum. Gostoptekhizdat, 1953.

21. F.M. Efendiev. Development of the luminescence-chromatographic method of investigation of petroleum. Izv. Akad. Nauk AzSSR, No. 3, 1952.

22. K.F. Rodionova and K.A. Novikova. Comparative data of bituminological investigations of sedimentary rocks by chemical and luminescence methods. Sb. "Voprosy geologii i geokhimii nefti i gaza" (Tr. VNIIGAZ). Gosgeolizdat, 1953.

23. A.A. Kartsev. Extraction characteristics of caustobiotites. Doklady Akad. Nauk SSSR 65, No. 2, 1949.

24. A.A. Kartsev. Organic matter of the rocks of the Kirovabad oil-bearing region. Doklady Akad. Nauk SSSR 65, No. 3, 1949.

25. I.I. Ammosov and V.P. Ermakova. Luminescence microscopy as a method of study of sapropel coals. Doklady Akad. Nauk SSSR 74, No. 2, 1950.

26. E.N. Elizarova. On the luminescence-bituminological survey. Geochem. methods of prospecting for oil and gas, No. 1. Gostoptekhizdat, 1953.

27. V.N. Florovskaya. On anomalous values of bituminosity as an indication of oil-bearing character. Sb. "Geokhim. metody poiskov neft nefti", No. 1. Gostoptekhizdat, 1950.

28. V.N. Florovskaya. Results of luminescence analysis of petroleum. Sb. "Pam. akad. I.M. Gubkina", Akad. Nauk SSSR, 1951.

CHAPTER NINE

Hydrochemical Methods

Hydrochemical methods of exploration for oil and gas formations are based on the determination of the saline composition of water.[1] The saline content of waters as well as some single components, salts and ions, can be used as indications of the presence of petroleum. The saline compostion of waters in a number of cases may also help to clarify the geological structure. Hydrochemical oil indicators are either direct or indirect.

The study of the composition of waters of oil-bearing strata began in the 1870's and 1880's. At this time, A. Potylitsyn determined that a low sulfate content is characteristic of waters from oil-bearing strata (1). Later, K. V. Harichkov considered the naphthenate content of these waters (2). Initially, the use of hydrochemical indicators in oil exploration was to a large degree incidental, and even today, hydrochemical exploration methods are not proven techniques.

The study of hycrochemical indicators and methods of predicting the presence of petroleum were worked out primarily by V. A. Sulin and his collaborators, A. A. Varov, L. A. Gulyaeva, and others from 1932 to 1942 (3). Thanks to the works of these researchers and others, the Soviet science of the theory and methodology of prognosis of crude oil from hydrochemical data is, at the present time, far ahead of that in foreign countries.

Indirect hydrochemical methods of oil exploration (in the form of surveys and other works) were first used in the U.S.A. starting in 1937. This was primarily for the clarification of geological structure. However, the American work is characterized by incomplete analysis of the water, because the Americans usually used only a single indicator. In USSR, structural hydrochemical surveys and other similar works have been more fully developed by the use of a variety of methods (the works of the school of V. A. Sulin, V. A. Kovda and others).

At the present time, hydrochemical methods of oil and gas exploration are used under different conditions at different stages of the work for different purposes. In reconnaissance exploration, hydrochemical methods are directed mainly towards the prediction of the presence of oil reservoirs in a given region. For detailed mapping, they can be of considerable help to geological surveys and geophysical work in the explanation of the deep tectonics. In exploration, the role of hydrochemical methods consists, first of all, in estimating the oil content of separate horizons and sections. It is also useful in explaining some details of geological structure. Finally, hydrochemical investigations solve a number of technical problems in the exploitation of an oil field.

---

[1] The gases dissolved in water and the bacteria present in water are not considered hydrochemical indicators. They are discussed in other chapters. (Gases in Chapter 10 and bacteria in Chapter 13.)

[237]

DIRECT HYDROCHEMICAL INDICATORS OF PETROLEUM

Direct hydrochemical indicators of petroleum are those materials dissolved in water (salts, ions, etc.), which enter the water from the oil itself, i.e., water soluble constituents of crude oil. To this category belong: (1) soluble bitumens (naphthenates), (2) iodine, and (3) ammonia. These materials are not indicators of gas. Of greatest value are the bitumens.

Dissolved Bitumens (Soaps)

Bitumens dissolved in water can be considered both as hydrochemical and as bituminous indicators. However, since they are salts (organic), it is more convenient to consider them as hydrochemical indicators. The bitumens dissolved in natural waters are represented as salts of organic acids (soaps), primarily naphthenic acids. Sodium is the principal cation associated with these naphthenates. Usually, all these materials are called "naphthenic acids" (abbreviated NA), which is not correct. The naphthenates may be classified into three groups depending upon the composition of the water in which they are in contact. If the primary cation is sodium, sodium naphthenates will be formed (A_1), if calcium and magnesium, the corresponding naphthenates (A_2). If the water is free of salts, free naphthenic acids can in general be dissolved in water (A_3) but only in small amounts.

The soaps can be formed in the crude oil itself and can also be formed in the water when the acids enter from the oil. The acids can either be originally in the oil or they can be formed as a result of oxidation. Entering the water, the naphthenic acids react with sodium in compounds such as bicarbonates, carbonates, bisulfates, etc., forming soaps (see Chapter I).

The nature of soaps dissolved in natural waters is not well known. From available data (4, 5, and others), the naphthenic acids have acid numbers usually from 250 to 330 which indicates 10 to 15 carbon atom molecules. These naphthenic acids are characterized by formulas $C_9H_{17}COOH$ - $C_{14}H_{27}COOH$ (the general formula $C_NH_{2N-1}COOH$). Such acids in oils are present in the kerosene fractions. An example of the structural formula of the corresponding soap will be of the form:

$$H_3C-\overset{\displaystyle H}{\underset{\displaystyle |}{C}}-\overset{\displaystyle H}{\underset{\displaystyle |}{C}} \diagup \overset{CH_3}{}$$

Apparently, among acids with 14 and 15 carbon atoms, there are bicyclic naphthenic acids of the general formula $C_NH_{2N-3}COOH$. The presence in the waters of soaps of naphthenic acids of lower molecular weight, characterized by the acid numbers, 340-430, was also determined. Such acids have formulas from $C_6H_{11}COOH$ up to $C_8H_{15}COOH$ and in the oils they are found in the gasoline-ligroin fractions. These soaps are found in the waters less frequently.

In addition to naphthenic soaps in waters, there occur also soaps of aliphatic acids. They occur far less frequently. This is explained by insignificant content of aliphatic acids in the oils themselves, insignificant as compared with their content of naphthenic acids. Very little is known about fatty soaps in natural waters. F. F. German reported comparatively larger amounts in waters of the oil reservoirs of Turkmenia.

The presence and quantity of soaps in waters depend upon the nature of the oil as well as upon that of the water (3). Usually, the more naphthenic acids in the oil (more exactly, in its light fractions), the more soaps there are in the water of the given oil-bearing horizon, under otherwise similar conditions. A considerable content of naphthenic acids is characteristic for crude oils especially rich in naphthenic hydrocarbons. In this class of oils, there is observed a direct connection between the content of (naphthenic) acids, resins, and specific gravity (Fig. 107). This connection is explained, most probably, by the common origin of both acids and resins (partly) through oxidation of hydrocarbons.

The content of soaps in the water depends also upon the general character of the salinity of water. In hard waters, there can only be calcium and sometimes magnesium naphthenates. Calcium soaps have low solubility and therefore cannot be present in the water to any considerable extent. They precipitate from solution and enter into the composition of the rocks, primarily as bound bitumens. As a result, soaps occur very seldom in hard waters.

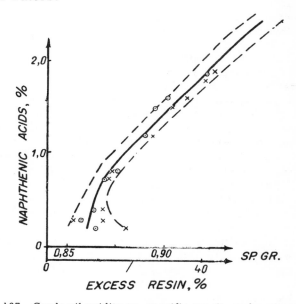

Fig. 107. Crude oil acidity vs. specific gravity and resin content.

The situation is entirely different in alkaline waters. Here it is possible to have highly soluble naphthenates of sodium. Therefore, in alkaline waters, large amounts of soaps (up to 5 g/l) sometimes accumulate. In extreme cases, they even dominate all the other salts (Maikop, Norio) and are of commercial interest.

The largest amounts of soaps in water occur where there are both naphthenic oils and alkaline waters. Such a situation is characteristic, for instance, for the Apsheron Peninsula (within the lower part of the productive layer), Western Azerbaidzhan, Georgia, parts of the Northern Caucasus, and elsewhere. Ural-Volga oil-bearing regions show opposite conditions: aromatic-methanic oils and hard waters. Soaps are rare in the waters of Second Baku and their content is insignificant.

The hardness of water is the main obstacle to the accumulation of soaps. In the Embensk Oil Province, despite the richness of oil (especially Neocomian) in naphthenes, there is little soap in the waters due to the absence of alkaline waters. At the same time, in the Grozny formations, even in strata with typical paraffin oils, soaps are present since the waters are alkaline. It is possible that in such cases a considerable part of the soaps are aliphatic. This problem still awaits an explanation.

Implications of Presence or Absence of Dissolved Bitumens

The significance of dissolved bitumens as indicators of petroleum is explained by the fact that the only source of the materials in water is crude oil. There are no known bitumens of other than oil origin.[2] This strongly increases the value of bitumens contained in water as compared with bitumens found in rocks. In addition to the bitumens in natural waters, other dissolved organic materials are found, such as humates, i.e., soaps of humic acid. There are especially plentiful in marshy waters. In underground waters, the content of humates is negligible. Besides, their presence does not hinder the determination of bitumens. The humates do not dissolve in neutral organic liquids, but bitumens dissolve in these liquids.[3]

Bitumens, and in particular naphthenates, in waters are direct and unique (indisputable) indicators of petroleum. The amount of bitumens in the water has no special significance. A negligible content will suffice for a definite prediction (especially for hard waters).[4] Moreover, a very high content of bitumens in water (especially the presence of oil emulsions) indicates a rather considerable disintegration of reservoirs by oxidation (or even by erosion). This sometimes leads to the loss of economic value of the reservoirs, for instance, in some regions of Georgia and Western Azerbaidzhan. Thus, the presence of bitumens in the water does not indicate anything about the commercial significance of an oil accumulation.

The absence of bitumens in waters cannot in general be used as a criterion for the absence of petroleum, particularly in hard waters. The absence of soaps in alkaline waters is somewhat more indicative. In this case, it is important to have data about the possible nature of oil in the region and the horizon under investigation. For instance, on the Russian platform, in Paleozoic rocks, there are only aromatic-paraffinic oils containing few acids. Therefore, the absence of bitumens in Paleozoic waters

---

[2] In addition to dissolved oil bitumens (soaps and others) oil emulsions can also occur. The problem of natural emulsions is at present not well known. Apparently, they can be present only in sufficiently mobile waters that are destroying the oil reservoir. Emulsified oil is obviously an important indicator.

[3] The determination of the general content of organic materials in water is commonly based on the oxidizability of water.

[4] Recently, E. A. Bars found in surface and ground waters substances analytically inseparable from naphthenic soaps. Apparently, these are derivatives from plants and other organisms.

is not conclusive. In Neogene folded regions, oils predominate which are rich in acids. Therefore, the absence of soaps, for instance, in alkaline waters of Maikop deposits of Transcaucasia, can be though of as a negative criterion having, however, a very relative and limited value. Thus, in searching for petroleum, the absence of soaps in waters has considerably less value than their presence.

A scheme for estimating the presence of petroleum from the naph- thenates in waters under different conditions is given in Table 28. The scheme of interpretation given in Table 28 is only approximate. In particu- lar, one should not attempt to assign a range of validity for the predictions. Predictions are made only for aquifers containing dissolved bitumens. If the oil potential of a given area has not yet been established, the presence of bitumens in the waters of a single horizon indicates the presence of petroleum in the area as a whole. No quantitative predictions may be made, however. Furthermore, the connection between dissolved bitumens and the oil of the horizon where they are discovered is not always obvious. This problem is solved only when tectonic features are taken into account. In the presence of faults, it is possible to have "secondary" extraction of dis- solved bitumens at the expense of inflowing waters from lower horizons.

TABLE 28. Petroleum Predictions Based on Naphthenates in Waters

Naphthenates	Water	Expected Character of Oil[5]	Conclusion
Present	. . . .	. . . .	Oil present
Absent	Hard	Paraffinic	?
Absent	Hard	Naphthenic	?
Absent	Alkaline	Paraffinic	?[6]
Absent	Alkaline	Naphthenic	No oil

The area covered by a negative prediction in a given horizon should be very small. It should not exceed several kilometers or go beyond the limits of the plane of the given tectonic uplift (if one exists) or a block bounded by faults. It is also not possible to judge the distance from the point of obser- vation to the reservoirs from the quantity of bitumens dissolved in the water. However, in a detailed study of a region, it may be possible to make such a prediction.

Phenols and their Derivatives

Phenols were discovered recently (6) in waters of oil-bearing sediments. A study of phenols in waters has not been undertaken. However, postula- tions can be made about the utilization of these substances as indicators of oil. Phenols in water can originate only from oil. Therefore, their ex- ploratory value is similar to that of naphthenates. The main difference is

----

[5] By comparison with other regions of the same province or with other geologically related regions (see Chapter I).

[6] Here, probably, soaps of fatty acids are present.

that the amount of phenols both in oils and waters is considerably smaller than the quantity of naphthenates. This is the main reason that the phenols have not received previous attention.

The phenols in waters can be present either in free form or as phenolates. Many phenols and especially phenolates are highly soluble in water (for instance, sodium phenolate, 24 per cent). These phenols can exist both in alkaline and hard waters. This property strongly increases the possibility of using phenols as indicators of oil. The existing methods of determining phenols in waters have a sensitivity sufficiently high for exploratory purposes. The investigation of the distribution of phenols and their derivatives in waters of oil-bearing sediments is important in petroleum prospecting.

Iodine

Iodine is present in water in the form of iodides, probably as sodium iodide (class A_1). The iodine in waters is an important and well-known indicator of petroleum. As contrasted with bitumens, iodine in waters is not a substance exclusively of oil origin. It is present in almost all natural waters. However, the quantitative differences are significant. In most natural waters, the content of iodine is negligible. In fresh surface waters and in fresh groundwaters, the iodine content is from 10^{-5} to 10^{-3} mg/l, in sea water about 5×10^{-2} mg/l, in underground saline waters 10^{-1} to 1 mg/l, in Devonian brines in Moscow it reaches 5 mg/l (3). The latter amount is close to the maximum observed in non oil-bearing regions. At the same time, in the waters of oil-bearing sediments, the content of iodine, as a rule, is higher than 3-10 mg/l, reaching tens of mg/l, and in extreme cases (Chusov region) it exceeds 100 mg/l. Some oil reservoirs are also industrial iodine deposits.

In oil-bearing sediments, iodine is more concentrated than in fresh waters by a factor of 10^4 to 10^7. It is more concentrated than in brines by a factor of 10 to 10^4. The amount of iodine in excess of 1 to 5 mg/l, rather than its mere qualitative presence, is used as an oil indicator. This lower limit of anomalous concentrations is not fixed but should be considered in the light of different conditions.

In the waters of oil-bearing sediments, the major part of iodine comes from oil. Little is known about the content of iodine in crude oils. The iodine present in petroleum probably comes from seaweeds which have concentrated the element. Obviously, the iodine in oil is present in the form of complex organic compounds.

The iodine content is apparently higher in other natural organic substances as well as in petroleum. Such problems as distribution of iodine in waters of coal-bearing and similar sediments, and the influence of other factors upon the accumulation of iodine in water, remain unclear. The available data on the content of iodine in the waters of coal deposits show that the quantity is very small, (for instance, in Tkvarchel it is 0.1 mg/l(7)). Such a difference between oil and coal waters can be explained by a higher iodine content in crude oils as compared with coals, or by a larger solubility of oil fractions containing iodine as compared with iodine-containing substances of coal. In addition, it is possible that the influence of the water plays a part.

The accumulation of oil is aided by hydrogeological closure of the oil reservoirs, which hinders the removal of iodine (8). The closure can also explain the relatively high concentration of iodine in waters of the oil-bearing Devonian of Moscow, since the content of this element in Devonian rocks does not exceed its Clarke (9). This influence may also explain the observed differences in iodine content of waters of different oil regions. A clear connection between the content of iodine and general mineralization of waters of oil-bearing layers has not been discovered, but maximum concentrations of iodine are known only in metamorphic brines corresponding to the highest closure. Further investigation of the distribution of iodine in underground waters is necessary.

At the present time, we assume that an iodine content greater than 5 mg/l under any conditions is a positive indicator of petroleum. Therefore, the Paleocene and Eocene around Essentuka where such magnitudes are observed may be described as oil-bearing (10). If waters have a low total mineral content, an iodine concentration less than 1 mg/l may still be considered a criterion of oil. The connection between the minimum content of iodine which is still an indicator of oil and the total mineral content of water should be investigated. The region within which predictions based on the iodine content of waters may be made is determined the same as in the case of the naphthenates (see above).

Ammonia

Ammonia in waters occurs mainly in the form of chloride and is a primary salt. Ammonia has been almost unused as an indicator of petroleum until recently, and its distribution in the waters of oil-bearing sediments has been little investigated. However, in many respects it is analogous to iodine. Apparently, almost all ammonia in natural waters is of organic origin. In surface and ground waters, ammonia does not exceed several mg/l (usually it is considerably smaller) or it is totally lacking. The presence of ammonia in these waters is due to biochemical soil processes or artificial contamination. There are very few data about the content of ammonia in underground waters. There is a basis for thinking that with increase in depth, degree of closure, and metamorphism of the waters, the content of ammonia increases. In Devonian brines of Moscow, the ammonia content is about 60 mg/l (8). Dispersed organic materials in the rocks are the main source of ammonia in the waters of oil-bearing sediments. Stagnation and reducing conditions cause ammonia to remain in the water.

The ammonia content in waters of oil-bearing sediments often exceeds 100 mg/l (for instance, in Devonian waters of the formations of the Second Baku, it is never less than this amount (8)), sometimes reaching 500 mg/l and even more. Such large amounts are not encountered outside oil deposits. Most of the ammonia in the waters of oil-bearing sediments originates from petroleum. The ammonia enters the water during decomposition and subsequent solution of nitrogen compounds of the oil.

Thus, like iodine, a major concentration of ammonia occurs in the waters of oil-bearing sediments. Therefore, the increased content of ammonia in water is an indicator of oil. As was the case for iodine, the smallest concentration that may be considered anomalous varies under different conditions. Apparently it depends primarily upon the degree of metamorphism of the salt content of the water. For deep lying metamorphosed

Devonian brines of the Russian platform, the anomalous content of ammonia indicating oil in a given area should be about 100 mg/l. In other cases, the minimum significant amount can be considerably smaller.

There are almost no data on the content of ammonia in waters of coal deposits. The only available data show an absence of ammonia in these waters (7). One reason for the absence of ammonia is that there is no nitrogen in gases from coal beds (11). Both N_2 in gases and NH_4 in waters should be present if the decomposition of nitrogen compounds of coal were taking place. The reason for the absence of ammonia in waters of coal deposits is apparently the stability of nitrogen compounds in coals (as compared with oil). Is is possible that the relative degree of compaction of these coal deposits for which data are available plays a certain role, i.e., their permeability is enough to prevent the retention of ammonia.

Thus, the anomalous increase in the content of ammonia in water is a direct indication of petroleum. Oil pools may be located by using the ammonia content of waters in the same way that iodine is used.

INDIRECT HYDROCHEMICAL INDICATORS OF PETROLEUM

Indirect hydrochemical indicators of petroleum are salts and ions dissolved in waters (or some combinations of salts and ions), which are not generally derivatives of oil substances (like naphthenates, iodine, ammonia). In one way or another, they are connected with crude oil or with conditions favorable for the presence of oil reservoirs.

The indirect hydrochemical indicators of oil are diverse and manifold. They can be divided into two groups. To the first group of indirect indicators belong the products and results of chemical reactions between oil and salts dissolved in water. Among these are: (1) Hydrosulfides and other reduced compounds of sulfur, (2) absence of sulphates and (3) soda. Although the lack of sulfates in water is closely connected with the presence of sulfides and other reduced sulfur compounds, these indicators should be treated separately for a number of reasons. They may have several meanings. In contrast to the direct indicators considered above, they can also originate without any connection to a petroleum environment.

The other group of indirect hydrochemical indicators is represented by substances which usually accompany oil pools although they are formed quite independently of the oil. Here belong (1) calcium chloride and (2) bromine. These substances cannot in general indicate directly the presence of oil. They can only indicate conditions favorable for the presence of oil reservoirs.

Hydrosulfides and Other Reduced Compounds of Sulfur

The reduced forms of sulfur are important and well known indicators of oil. All compounds of sulfur except sulfates are reduced. In natural waters, several reduced forms of sulfur occur. These are: (1) hydrosulfide ion (HS^-), (2) thiosulfate ion ($S_2O_3^{--}$), (3) sulfite ion (SO_3^{--}), and (4) molecular dissolved hydrogen sulfide (H_2S).[7] Of basic importance are hydrosulfides

---

[7]Theoretically, there may be such ions as HSO_2^- $HSO_3^=$ $HSO_4^=$

and H_2S. There is an equilibrium between these substances which depends on the pH of the water:

$$H_2S \rightleftharpoons HS^- + H^+.$$

Sodium hydrogen sulfide, which has primary alkalinity (A_1), occurs in alkaline waters. Only calcium (and sometimes magnesium) hydrogen sulfide, which has secondary alkalinity (A_2), can occur in hard waters. For pH < 6, there can be no hydrosulfides in the water and the reduced forms of sulfur are represented by molecularly dissolved H_2S.

The distribution of hydrosulfides in the waters has been little studied. Such studies were made almost exclusively for balneological purposes. Usually only H_2S is determined in the water, that is, the sum of the reduced forms of sulfur, both ions and dissolved gas. The highest hydrosulfide content known is in waters of oil-bearing Chokrak limestones on the Kerchen Peninsula, 247 mg/l (equivalent to 8 per cent) for $HS^-/H_2S > 2$ (12). The content of $S_2O_3^{--}$ and SO_3^{--} amounts usually to about one per cent of the content of HS^-.

Almost all subsurface waters with a significant content of hydrosulfides (and H_2S) are from oil-bearing regions and oil-bearing formations. In a number of places, where sulfur waters have long been known, oil formations were subsequently discovered ("Goryachii Klyuch", Sergievsk). In Matsesta, for instance, in the opinion of some investigators, oil formations once existed but disintegrated as a result of the oxidation caused by sulfates (13). The same can be assumed about Essentuki. Finally the same holds for oil deposits which are not necessarily of industrial value. The presence of even dispersed oil or pure gas accumulations is sufficient.

The formation of most hydrosulfides and other reduced forms of sulfur in subsurface waters is caused by the reaction between the oil hydrocarbons and dissolved sulfates in the presence of bacteria. In addition, these substances can sometimes be formed during decomposition of sulfur components of the oil (see Chapter I). The formation of these reduced compounds of sulfur in subsurface waters makes possible their use as indicators of oil and gas.

However, there are underground waters with hydrosulfide and H_2S that are not connected with oil. Here belong, first of all, springs connected with magmatic processes. The springs of the Pyrenean French resorts are typical examples of these. These springs, which are in zones of fracture between metamorphic and magmatic rocks, are characterized by very high temperatures, insignificant mineralization, and quite unusual composition (predominance of silica at the expense of heavy metals (14)). Such waters have nothing in common with waters of oil-bearing sediments.

The H_2S waters of the resort Krainka (at Oka) occurring in Quaternary alluvium are a special case. According to A. N. Buneev, reduction of sulfates takes place in the waters of Krainka not owing to hydrocarbons but to hydrogen given off during cellulose fermentation in surface waters (15). The reduction of SO_4^{--} should follow the formula: $SO_4^{--} + 3H_2 \rightarrow HS^- + 3OH^- + H_2O$. The accumulation of reduced forms of sulfur is small, however, (up to 40 mg/l).

It is not clear whether the reduction of sulfates in large quantities is due solely to oil hydrocarbons or whether other forms of natural organic substances such as coals, etc., may also be reducing agents. Experimental data show that reduction of sulfates due to dissolved humates does not take

place (15). However, one should not forget that in coal deposits methane
is sometimes present in tremendous quantities. It is possible that in deep
deposits, the reduction of sulfates may be caused by methane (16). This
question deserves more attention.

Thus, excluding regions of magmatic activity and zones of surface geochemical activity, a considerable content of hydrosulfides and other reduced
forms of sulfur can be considered a positive indication of oil (including gas
of coal origin). However, when an especially large content of reduced
forms of sulfur in water (more than 200 mg/l) is observed, the deposits
are generally in an advanced state of disintegration and are not of great
importance (Chokrak, Kamskii Kungur).

The absence of hydrosulfides and similar compounds in water does not
indicate absence of oil and gas. Hydrosulfides cannot be in the waters of
pH<6, and many waters of oil-bearing strata are of this type. Negative
predictions cannot be made because extensive reduction of sulfates does
not take place in every oil deposit. (The same is true for decomposition of
sulfur-containing fractions of oil.) Consequently, the waters of oil formations do not always contain reduced forms of sulfur.

Absence of Sulfates

The absence or very low content of sulfates in the water reflects the presence of hydrosulfides and other reduced sulfur compounds. The sulfates
are reduced by oil, giving hydrosulfides and similar substances. Therefore, lack of sulfates in waters can also be a positive indicator of oil. This
has long been known. Until recently, it was used much more often than the
presence of reduced forms of sulfur. The reason is that determination of
the sulfate ion, as one of the six main ions of natural waters, may be done
anywhere. However, lack of sulfates in water is not a unique indicator of
oil and gas. Lack of sulfates need not have any relationship to oil or to
sulfate reduction processes. The precipitation of sulfates from solution
when the concentration exceeds the solubility is an example. In this case,
the sulfates do not decompose. They merely precipitate from the water
and enter into the composition of the rocks.

The solubility of sulfates depends on the cations present and the nature
and concentration of other dissolved salts. Calcium sulfate is least soluble;
its solubility is especially low in the presence of calcium chloride (i.e., in
waters of calcium-chloride type). Calcium-chloride waters can contain
only the sulfate of calcium. As a result, in waters of this type, there can
be only an insignificant amount of SO_4. The solubility of sulfates of magnesium and, especially, sodium is much larger than of calcium sulfate.
However, in underground brines, in some cases, magnesium sulfate may
be precipitated. In addition, under conditions of high pressure and absence
of calcium sulfate, the magnesium sulfate apparently can react with limestone according to the equation of Heidinger[8] and consequently is also removed from the water.

Thus, lack of sulfates in water may have no connection with petroleum.
This is possible especially in the case of deep brines of the calcium-

---

[8]$MgSO_4 + 2CaCO_3 \rightarrow MgCO_3 \cdot CaCO_3 + CaSO_4$

chloride type.[9] Surface waters and waters of the upper horizons (exposed zone), as a rule, have a relatively large content of sulfates. The fresh waters in the areas of magmatic and thoroughly flushed sedimentary rocks (for example, in high mountains), are an exception.

A special case is that of surface and groundwaters of Central Yakutiya. According to V. P. Shugrin and A. A. Kartsev, there is an anomalous lack of sulfates in the water of this region. They are either absent or almost absent and the ratio SO_4/Cl is less than one. The presence of chlorides quite clearly shows that the rocks are not fully flushed and are not free of salts. On the contrary, there are salt-bearing layers.

Apparently this phenomenon may be explained by two basic factors: (1) permafrost and (2) the presence in the section of salt-bearing layers. On the one hand, the permafrost layer strongly inhibits the leaching of salts from the rocks. Here the leaching of the sulfates, present in the form of highly insoluble gypsum, will be especially low as compared with the highly soluble chlorides. On the other hand, the chloride concentration of the waters (including magnesium chloride) is greatly increased by the thick salt-bearing Cambrian beds. As a result, the waters belong to the magnesium chloride type. This means that in these waters there can be no highly soluble sodium sulfate. The waters are either free of sulfates or contain sulfates in a smaller amount than chlorides: SO_4/Cl is less than one.

Thus, the lack of sulfates in water cannot always be considered an indication of oil and gas. In brines of the calcium chloride type, this indicator is of little value. This same is true of fresh waters draining practically salt-free rocks and also of the frozen waters of the permafrost zone. In all other cases, this indicator is of great importance.

The presence of sulfates in waters (in larger or smaller quantities) in general indicates the absence of oil in a formation. However, a negative prediction may not always be made. First of all, it is necessary to take into account the nature of the rocks (3). In the presence of considerable masses of gypsum and anhydrites, the amount of sulfates in water can partly be preserved despite reducing processes because the water can receive a continuous supply of sulfates from the rocks. Such a phenomenon occurs in a number of regions of the Second Baku.

Secondly, one also ought to take into account the possibility of "sterilization" of the waters by high temperature which prevents the biochemical reduction of sulfates. Such is the case in some strata of the Grozny formations where, at 70°C or higher temperatures, the sulfate content of waters is high (up to 10 per cent equivalence) even at the water-oil contact (see also Chapter I).

Furthermore, it appears that the biochemical reduction of sulfates cannot take place at very low pH and extremely high salinity. Thus, the sulfate content of water can be considered a criterion for the absence of oil and gas only if the rocks do not contain considerable masses of sulfates and there are no conditions inhibiting bacterial action, especially high temperatures. A scheme for evaluating the presence or absence of sulfates in the waters under different conditions is given in Table 29.

---

[9]However, the very presence of this type of water itself is an indicator of possible oil (see below).

TABLE 29. Petroleum Predictions Based on Sulphates in Waters

Case	SO_4 in Water	$CaCl_2$ in Water	SO_4 in Rock	Temp. °C	Conclusion: Oil and/or Gas	Remarks
1	No	No	Yes	-	Yes	It is impor-
2	,,	Yes	-	-	?	tant to con-
3	,,	No	No[10]	-	?	sider the
4	Yes	-	Yes[11]	<70	?	presence or
5	,,	-	No[11]	>70	?	absence of
6	,,	-	No[11]	>70	No	HS[1] and HS[2]

In some cases it seems possible to give an approximate estimate of the distance from the reservoir in a given stratum to the sample point by using the SO_4 content. Thus, in the reservoirs of the Apsheron Peninsula, according to the date of V. A. Sulin, D. V. Zhbrev, A. Ya. Gavrilov, and others, oil-bearing strata contain sulfates in small quantities at a distance of several hundred meters from the boundary of the reservoir; but closer than that, there are no sulfates.

Soda (Alkalinity)

Soda (sodium bicarbonate) can be formed by oxidation of hydrocarbons by sulfate (see Chapter I). Therefore, the presence of soda in water (which makes the water of the alkaline sodium bicarbonate type) may under certain conditions be considered a criterion of the presence of oil. Alkaline waters are characteristic of numerous oil-bearing strata. Apparently, most of the soda in waters of oil-bearing sediments was formed by oxidation of oil substances.

However, soda can occur in natural waters in other ways, unrelated to petroleum. Alkaline waters are also characteristic of regions where sodium-rich magmatic, metamorphic, and some sedimentary (arkosic sandstone) rocks occur. Secondly, they occur also in zones of solonetz development. Finally, alkaline waters can also be connected with volcanic regions where the soda is formed by CO_2 coming from the depths.

It is relatively simple to distinguish alkaline waters of the weathering zone draining salt-free rocks from alkaline waters of oil-bearing strata. The former are fresh and calcium carbonate is the most abundant salt they contain. The latter are salty and sodium chloride is the principal salt present.

The alkaline waters of the solonetz can usually be distinguished by the conditions of their occurrence. They can be only surface or groundwaters. However, ambiguous cases are possible. This is particularly true of waters in volcanic, or primarily volcanic, regions (for instance, Borzhomi).

Whether or not soda may form by oxidation of coal and similar caustobiolites (compare the hydrosulfides and others, above) is also unclear. In

---

[10]All sulfates, even if dispersed, are included.

[11]We consider here major masses of gypsum and anhydrites.

the upper zones of coal deposits, alkaline waters apparently are not found, and if found, their alkalinity is of inorganic origin (17, 18, and others). However, alkaline waters are known to occur in deep coal-bearing sediments, for instance in the Donbass (16). There the soda apparently is formed by reduction of sodium sulfate by methane.

Thus, soda in waters can be considered an indicator of oil and gas (including gas-bearing coal beds?) providing the waters are not from the weathering zone, the Solonetz, or do not have a volcanic origin. The absence of soda in waters is of no value in estimating oil potential. If one considers springs, the soda can be displaced by sulfates in the weathering zone. According to A. A. Kartsev, the oil-bearing Maikop deposits of Transcaucasia contain only alkaline waters at great depths. At the same time, springs at the surface, which originate from those deposits, do not contain soda. In considering oil formations, not only alkaline waters but also waters of the calcium chloride type are characteristic.[12]

Calcium Chloride

Calcium chloride in the water is the final product of metamorphism of the salt composition of subsurface waters. It forms by cation exchange between the water and the rocks. The process of metamorphism of brines leading to the formation of calcium chloride proceeds further the more stagnant the hydrogeological conditions. This stagnancy (hydrogeological closure) favors the preservation of the oil reservoirs. Thus, the most favorable conditions for oil deposits and dissolved calcium chloride coincide. Therefore, the presence of calcium chloride in waters (i.e., calcium chloride type of water) is an indirect indicator of possible oil and gas. In contrast to the indicators considered above, calcium chloride never has any direct connection with petroleum. Therefore, the presence of calcium chloride does not indicate the presence of oil itself but only favorable conditions for oil accumulation (hydrogeologic stagnancy). The existence of such conditions does not necessarily imply the presence of reservoirs. Other factors are necessary for this (the processes of oil formation, traps, etc.)

Waters containing calcium chloride have, as a rule, a very high mineral content. If the presence of calcium chloride is established in highly mineralized waters at considerable depths (or emerging from such depths) it may be concluded that stagnant conditions occur. If calcium chloride is detected in weakly mineralized groundwaters (or in rare cases, surface waters), there must be an inflow of water from depth, or from other horizons, and mixing of waters must occur. It is not always possible to determine the horizon from which the calcium chloride originates, in such cases.

The absence of calcium chloride in water does not indicate unfavorable conditions for preservation of oil accumulations. As is known, alkaline waters are also characteristic of oil-bearing strata.

Bromine

Bromine is present in natural waters in the form of bromides and especially as sodium bromide. Bromine has no direct connection with petroleum.

---

[12]In these and in hard waters, calcium carbonate is formed during the oxidation of hydrocarbons instead of soda (see Chapter I).

The value of bromine in oil exploration is due to the fact that it is found in high concentrations in waters containing calcium chloride. Thus, the role of bromine as an oil indicator is essentially analogous to that of calcium chloride. Large amounts of bromine indicate a high degree of metamorphism of the brines that are characteristic in particular for rocks containing commercial accumulations of oil. In some cases, the bromine content exceeds 1000 mg/l, a concentration high enough for commercial production of bromine. However, a high concentration of bromine (even high enough to be commercially valuable) occurs also in some salt lakes and has a purely surface origin. Moreover, in many alkaline waters of oil-bearing strata, the bromine content is small.

The Cl/Br ratio is of considerable interest. In ocean water it equals 292. In metamorphosed brines (subsurface as well as surface, i.e., lakes) the ratio Cl/Br<292; hence we have a concentration of bromine. In brines formed by leaching of salt (chloride) deposits, the ratio Cl/Br exceeds 292, reaching sometimes a value of several thousand. This ratio can be used to distinguish brines formed by the leaching of salt deposits from subsurface metamorphosed waters which are not connected with salt deposits. Thus, bromine is only an auxiliary indicator in oil exploration.[13]

General Characteristics of the Salinity of Brines

The general nature of the salinity of water is determined by a combination of dissolved salts. According to V. A. Sulin, this is described by the genetic type, group and sub-group, and the class of water (19).

Genetic Type. The genetic type of a mineralized water, according to V. A. Sulin, is determined by the presence in the water of special characteristic components connected with the environment of the water. There are four such characteristic salts: calcium chloride, magnesium chloride, sodium bicarbonate, and sodium sulfate. Accordingly, four genetic types of water are distinguished. The direct determination of the type of water depends on the Na/Cl, (Na-Cl)/SO$_4$, and (Cl-Na)/Mg ratios. Coefficients for different types are given in Table 30.[14]

If the coefficients are close to the limiting values, the waters are said to belong to transition types. For instance, if (Cl-Na)/Mg = 0.99, the water belongs to a type transitional between chloride-magnesium and chloride-calcium. Waters completely free of sodium and chloride should be placed in a special class. Such cases occur in groundwaters of the tundra, etc.

TABLE 30. Coefficients Characterizing the Types of Water

Type of water	Na/Cl	(Na-Cl)/SO$_4$	(Cl-Na)/Mg
Chloride-Calcium	<1	<0	>1
Chloride-Magnesium	<1	<0	<1
Bicarbonate-Sodium	>1	>1	≤0
Sulfate-Sodium	>1	<1	<0

---

[13]Recently data were obtained (L. A. Gulyaeva, V. G. Glezer, and others) indicating that there may be some direct connection between a part of the bromine in underground waters and petroleum.

[14]The coefficients are computed from equivalents.

In a number of cases some conclusions may be drawn from the genetic water type concerning the presence of oil and gas. The significance of chloride-calcium and bicarbonate-sodium waters was discussed earlier. Both these types are characteristic of oil formations. The chloride-calcium type indicates stagnant hydrogeological conditions favorable for the existence of oil and gas deposits. The bicarbonate-sodium type of underground waters may directly indicate the presence of oil, but only if the total mineral content of the water is high.

The chloride-magnesium type of water is not generally an indicator of petroleum. It does not indicate hydrological conditions either since it is connected primarily with rocks of a definite composition, i.e., with salt-bearing deposits. Nonetheless, this water type does not indicate the absence of oil. The sulfate-sodium type of water is characteristic of an open hydrogeological zone. Therefore, it is an unfavorable indicator (3) in oil exploration.

Group and Sub-Group. The group of a mineralized water is determined by the predominant anion and its sub-group by the predominant cation. The sub-group should be stated only if the predominant cation forms salts with the predominant anion, but not with other anions. In nature, there are three main groups of waters: chloride, sulfate, and bicarbonate waters. The chloride group, when present, is a favorable indicator of oil and gas, but only in the sense of indicating the possibility of an oil reservoir. The bicarbonate group (excluding its sodium sub-group) and the sulfate group are obviously negative indicators. A scheme for evaluating oil and gas prospects from the type, group, and sub-group of the water is given in Table 31.

The water class, according to V. A. Sulin, is determined by the predominant Palmer characteristic. A positive prediction can be made on the basis of the presence of classes S_1, S_2, and sometimes A_1, but there are too few of these indicators. Class A_2 is an absolutely negative indicator. Negative conclusions can refer only to those deposits in which the given waters occur. Positive predictions, however, still require stratigraphic confirmation.

Use of Combined Hydrochemical Indicators

Examples of the application of a number of indicators have been given above: the presence of naphthenate, sulfates, water type, etc. All of the indicators discussed must be used together for reliable predictions.

TABLE 31. Evaluation of Oil and Gas Prospects from the Type, Group, and Sub-group of Water. (+, oil prospects; -, no oil prospects; x, case does not occur in nature.)

Type	Group and sub-group								
	Cl^-			$SO_4^=$			HCO_3^-		
	Na	Mg	Ca	Na	Mg	Ca	Na	Mg	Ca
$CaCl_2$	+	x	+	x	x	x	x	x	x
$MgCl_2$	+	x	x	x	-	-	x	-	-
$NaHCO_3$	+	x	x	-	x	x	+	-	-
Na_2SO_4	-	x	x	-	-	-	x	-	-

The presence of direct indicators (soaps and iodine) and, under some conditions, such indirect indicators as hydrosulfides, etc., is a positive indication of petroleum. However, these factors give no indication of favorable conditions for the existence of a pool. The oil accumulation may have no commercial value or the reservoir may have disintegrated. Such indirect indicators as calcium chloride, bromine, the chloride group, etc., indicate favorable hydrogeological and chemical conditions, but in this case, there also may be no oil (or gas).

Only the simultaneous presence of direct indicators[15] and indirect indicators of the second group (e.g., simultaneous presence in water of calcium chloride and a large amount of iodine, or the presence of naphthenates in water of the chloride group) can confirm the probable presence of commercial oil pools. A scheme for joint evaluation of the basic hydrochemical indicators is given in Table 32. The conclusions summarized in Table 32 refer only to those deposits in which the analyzed waters occur. Data on the composition of dissolved gases must also be included. This is especially important in exploration for gas fields, since there are no direct hydrochemical indicators of gas.

TABLE 32. Petroleum Predictions Based on a Combination of Hydrochemical Indicators

No.	Soaps, Iodine, Hydrosulfides, etc.	Calcium Chloride Bromine, Chloride Group, etc.	Conclusions
1	Present	Present	Oil present, probably in commercial pools
2	Present	Absent	Oil present, commercial pools not very probable
3	Absent	Present	Conditions favorable for commercial pools of oil and gas, but presence of oil uncertain
4	Absent	Absent	Oil potential unknown; unfavorable prospects.

Consideration of Hydrogeological Data

An appraisal of hydrochemical indicators of oil should take into account the environment and direction of flow of the waters being investigated. Several important types of environmental differences in waters can be distinguished. Autochthonous waters are waters which come from the reservoir in which they are found (stratum, massif, etc.). This case is the simplest. Conclusions on the presence of oil are made directly for a given reservoir (if it is a definite stratigraphic horizon, the conclusions hold for this horizon).

Allochthonous waters flow into the reservoir from outside and usually

---

[15]Here one should include such indirect indicators as hydrosulfides, etc. Such indicators as lack of sulfates and soda occupy an intermediate position.

from lower horizons. In this case the waters are mixed, and the observed
compounds (indicators of oil) come from below. The prediction is made
only for the underlying reservoirs. Exactly which reservoir the prediction
applies to must be determined from other data which are not always available. Finally, there may be "tectonic" (vein) waters in fissures of the
earth. The problem here is essentially the same as in the previous case.
Thus, the validity of the predictions depends on the conditions of the water
occurrence.

If the waters occur in a definite oil-bearing stratum (horizon, bed,
massif), the direction of water flow must be taken into account. If, in the
given stratum, there are direct hydrochemical indicators of oil (dissolved
bitumens, iodine), a more precise prediction may be made when the flow
direction of subsurface waters is known. The oil reservoirs should be in
a direction opposite to that of the water flow. This does not mean, however,
that they do not occur in other directions.

The direction of subsurface flow is important in another respect. A
study of the geochemistry of the waters of the Tersk-Dagestan province
shows that waters reaching a great depth (for instance, in the Alkhanchurt
depression), may be subjected to "sterilization" by high temperatures.
When the waters rise and cool, they may remain "sterile". This favors
the retention of SO_4. Therefore, the path that the sulfate waters have followed must be traced. If the water flows through large thicknesses of rock
(4 to 5 km), the presence of sulfate must be considered a negative indication.

WATER ANALYSIS (BRIEF TREATMENT)

In hydrochemical oil prospecting and exploration work, essentially the
same methods of chemical analysis are applied as in other hydrochemical
work. The basic salt components of water that are determined are listed
below:

1. Five fundamental ions define the salt composition of the water: (a)
chloride, (b) sulfate, (c) bicarbonate, (d) potassium, and (e) magnesium
(sodium is found by difference).

2. The so-called "micro-components"; (a) naphthenate, (b) iodine,
(c) ammonia, (d) bromine, (e) bisulfide, and others.

The pH of the water is of great importance. The analysis of gases dissolved in the water will be treated separately. (See below, Chapter X). The
water may be analyzed either in laboratories or by use of portable field
equipment. The methods of field analysis differ considerably from the
methods applied in the laboratory.

Laboratory Determination of Fundamental Ions

Chloride ion is determined by volumetric methods. Near pH 7, the chloride
ion can be determined by the Mohr method, and under any conditions by the
Volhard method. Mohr's method for the determination of chloride ion consists of titration of the chloride ion with silver nitrate using potassium-
permanganate as an indicator. (The silver can be replaced by mercury.)

Volhard's method also involves titration of the chloride ion with silver
nitrate, but an excess of this reagent is added. The solution is then back-
titrated with potassium thiocyanate until a blood red color is obtained.
(Ferric ammonium sulfate is used as the indicator.)

Bicarbonate ion is determined by titrating with hydrochloric acid using methyl orange as an indicator. Carbonate ion is usually absent, or present in only minute quantities, and is determined like bicarbonate ion except phenolphthalein is used as the indicator.

Sulfate ion is determined in the laboratory by a gravimetric method. The sulfate is precipitated by adding an acid solution of barium chloride. The precipitate is then ignited and weighed.

Calcium is usually determined volumetrically. Calcium and magnesium are separated by precipitating the calcium with an excess of ammonium oxalate and subsequently dissolving the precipitate of calcium oxalate. The solution is then acidified and titrated with potassium permanganate until a pink color appears. This method sometimes gives incorrect results. A gravimetric method can also be used.

Magnesium is usually determined gravimetrically in the laboratory. Magnesium is determined in the filtrate from the calcium precipitation, and an alkaline solution of sodium ammonium hydrogen phosphate ($NaNH_4HPO_4$) is added. The magnesium phosphate precipitate is subsequently ignited and weighed.

Determination of Dissolved Bitumens

Bitumens dissolved in the water can be determined either chemically or from their luminescence. The chemical methods consist in determining the anions of "bitumen" acids, primarily naphthenate ions. The volumetric method is the most convenient one for naphthenate ion determination. It consists of extracting the naphthenates with a neutral organic solvent (usually petroleum ether), transforming them into sodium salts by adding sodium hydroxide, and titrating the excess alkali with hydrochloric acid. Hydrogen sulfide in the water is first removed by aeration, and the precipitated sulfur is filtered out. If the water is highly mineralized, ammonium chloride and ammonium hydroxide are added prior to analysis.

Procedure. A sample of water is placed in a separatory funnel; a few drops of sulfuric acid (dilution 1:4) are added, followed by 40 ml of solvent. The sample is shaken for one minute, and the gas cautiously released. The water layer is drained into a glass and the extract is poured into a stoppered flask. The water is re-extracted two more times with 20 cc of solvent each time. The combined extracts are poured into a separatory funnel, washed five times with a saturated solution of sodium sulfate (added in portions of 15 ml and agitated) and poured into a flask. 15 ml of ethyl alcohol are added. A definite volume of 0.1 N solution of caustic soda is added until a bright pink color appears. The sample is shaken for one minute and the gas cautiously released. The solution is then titrated with 0.1 N hydrochloric acid, using phenolphthalein as the indicator. The naphthenate ions content is calculated by the formula:

$$A = \frac{(a-b)N \cdot 180 \cdot 1000}{volume\ of\ sample}\ mg/l$$

where a is the quantity of HCl to titrate the standard NaOH; b is the quantity of HCl for titration of excess NaOH; N is the normality of HCl.

The dissolved bitumens can also be determined by gravimetric methods. In one method, the extract (prepared as in the volumetric method) is placed in a water bath and then in a desiccator. The sulfate is evaporated and the residue is weighed. This residue represents the dissolved bitumen consisting basically of naphthenic soaps. The volumetric determination includes aliphatic acids and their salts as well as napthenates, just as the gravimetric analysis does.

The luminescence method for determining dissolved bitumens is simpler. It is fully applicable in the field and at the same time is sufficiently sensitive. This method consists of extracting the bitumen by an organic solvent (in simple cases, in a test tube) and the subsequent comparison of the brightness of the luminescence of the extract with a standard scale. The dissolved bitumen is determined like the bitumen in rocks (see Chapter VIII). The determination of the dissolved bitumen is facilitated by the fact that the naphthenates which are dominant among the dissolved bitumens, have a uniformly violet color or luminescence. It is important to note that fatty soaps are not luminescent, and consequently it is impossible to determine them by the luminescence method. The content of fatty soaps in water can be determined from the difference between the quantities obtained chemically and those obtained by the luminescence method.

Physico-chemical Methods. The so-called physico-chemical method was proposed by A. Abdurashitov as a special method of prospecting for oil (20). However, it represents essentially a simplified method of estimating the water's soap content. The decrease in surface tension of the water, which depends upon the concentration of soaps, is determined. Soaps are practically the only "surface active" substances in the oil-water system. They strongly decrease the surface tension at the oil-water interface. Salt water free of soaps (for example, sea water) has a surface tension (at the oil boundary) of about 20 to 30 erg/cm^2. For waters containing naphthenate salts, the values are about 1 to 3 erg/cm^2. One cannot determine the soap content exactly from the decrease in surface tension. But this is not necessary. The presence of bitumens in the water indicates oil. The surface tension of water is found very simply by using a tensiometer. Simplicity is the major advantage of this method over the chemical determination of dissolved bitumens.

Determination of Iodine

Iodine is determined in the laboratory and in large concentrations (tens of mg/l) is determined by the volumetric method of Frezenius. Low concentrations of iodine in water are determined either by the volumetric method of Dragomirova (21) or colorimetrically. Frezenius' method consists of the oxidation of iodides with sulfuric acid and sodium nitrite to free iodine, extraction of the iodine with chloroform, and titration with hyposulfite.

In Dragomirova's method, the concentration of iodine in water is determined as follows: (1) all water is evaporated, (2) the dry residue is heated, (3) this residue is subjected to extraction by alcohol, (4) the alcohol is evaporated, (5) the residue is dissolved in water, (6) the iodine is oxidized to iodate by adding an acidified solution of bromine water, (7) the iodate is reduced to molecular iodine by adding potassium iodide, and (8) the iodine is titrated from a microburet with a 0.001 normal solution of hyposulfite using starch as the indicator.

The colorimetric method of iodine determination (also using a solution made from dry residue) consists in determining the color of the sample in a mixture of 1 ml of 1N sulfuric acid, 0.3 ml of 5 per cent sodium nitrate, and chloroform. The color is determined by comparison with standard solutions of potassium iodide.

Determination of Ammonia

The ammonia content in water is usually determined colorimetrically by using Nessler's reagent. The sample (10 ml) is diluted with distilled water to 100 ml, and then Nessler's reagent and Seignette's salt are added (2 ml each). The same reagents are added to a standard solution of ammonia chloride (29.65 mg/l), of the same volume as the diluted sample. Then, in the colorimeter the colors of the sample and of the standard solution (content of NH_4 in the latter is 10 mg/l) are compared. The sample is diluted till the colors are identical. The ammonia content is computed from the difference in amount of the compared solutions. The distilled water used for ammonia determination has to be specially prepared by double distillation from an acid medium.

Determination of Hydrosulfides and Other Reduced Compounds of Sulfur

The determination of the total content of the reduced forms of sulfur in water (the so-called "total hydrogen sulfide") is done volumetrically. The analysis involves titration of the reduced forms of sulfur with a solution of molecular iodine containing an indicator (starch) in the presence of a reducing agent (potassium iodide). In alkaline water a preliminary neutralization with hydrochloric acid is necessary. Hydrosulfide can be determined by adding cadmium acetate to the water and subsequently determining the precipitated cadmium sulfide.

The amount of hydrosulfides and hydrogen sulfide can be determined separately from Auerbach's formula

$$(H_2S) = \frac{1.73S + c - 0.72b + \sqrt{(1.73S+c \times 0.73b)^2 - 2.92S\,(S+c-b)}}{1.46}$$

where (H_2S) is the free H_2S in millimoles; S is the total reduced S in millimoles; $c = \Sigma CO_2$ in millimoles; $b = \Sigma(HCO_3+CO_3)$ in mg-equivalents. The amount of HS^- is computed from the formula

$$[HS^-] = S - [H_2S]$$

Determination of Bromine

Bromine in low concentrations (up to 100 mg/l) is determined by the hypochlorite method or colorimetrically. In large concentrations, more exact results are obtained by electrometric titration.

Field Laboratories

Reznikov's Laboratory. Hydrochemical field laboratories are portable, and are used mainly on route surveys. In hydrochemical oil prospecting work, the laboratory designed by A. A. Reznikov is most often used. Although less portable than other field laboratories, it gives more reliable results. The equipment fits into a wooden box 43 x 14 x 30 cm. in size and weighs about 10 kg. In addition, there is a box with spare reagents weighing about 20 kg. All determinations are made by volumetric methods in test tubes, using small samples.

Chloride, bicarbonate ion, carbonate ion, and ammonia are determined in the same manner as in a permanent laboratory. Before determining magnesium, calcium must be precipitated out. This is accomplished by adding a weakly acid sodium oxalate solution. Then the sample is titrated with a neutral potassium palmitate solution with phenolphthalein as an indicator.

One does not determine calcium directly using Reznikov's equipment but finds the "total hardness" (the sum of calcium and magnesium). The calcium content is computed as the difference between the total hardness and the magnesium content. To determine total hardness the sample is aerated in an acidic medium to remove interfering carbon dioxide and then neutralized with sodium hydroxide. The sample is then titrated with potassium palmitate using phenolphthalein as an indicator.

Sulfate ion is determined in the same sample used for the "total hardness". The addition of barium chloride precipitates the sulfate ion as barium sulfate. The excess barium is titrated with potassium palmitate.

The N. N. Butyrin Laboratory. The field laboratory of Butyrin differs from that of Reznikov by its greater portability. Its weight is about 2 kg and its dimensions are 30 x 20 x 8 cm. The data obtained by using the hydrochemical laboratory of Butyrin are less accurate than those obtained by the methods described above.

Chloride, bicarbonate, and carbonate are determined by the usual volumetric methods (see above). Test tubes and microburets are used for titration. The samples are still smaller than in Reznikov's laboratory, i.e., 5 to 10 ml. This renders the analysis of highly mineralized waters very difficult.

The determination of calcium, magnesium, and sulfate ion is done by nephelometric methods. Solutions of standard turbidity are specially prepared (barium sulfate for determination of the sulfate ion, calcium oxalate for determination of calcium, and magnesium ammonium phosphate for magnesium determination). The degree of turbidity is determined by a turbimeter using the minimum height of the solution through which the contour of a drawing under the bottom of the container can be seen. Ammonia is determined colorimetrically.

Butryin's equipment is not widely used. The application of hydrochemical field laboratories is also possible in mining and exploratory drilling areas.

Determination of pH of Water

The pH is usually determined colorimetrically in the laboratory and in the field. Bromine-cresol purple is used as an indicator for pH = 5.6 to 6.4; bromine-thymol blue for pH = 6.3 to 7.2; phenol red for pH = 7.1 to 8.0; thymol blue for pH = 8.0 to 9.0. Samples to which an indicator is added are compared (in a comparator) with standard buffer solutions.

APPLICATION OF HYDROCHEMICAL METHODS

Hydrochemical methods of prospecting and exploration for oil and gas can be applied to the solution of various problems in different forms. There are two main groups of hydrochemical methods.[16] The purposes of the first group are: (a) prediction of the presence of oil in a given area, region, layer, section, or horizon; (b) prediction of the presence of favorable conditions for the existence of commercial oil and gas pools in a given layer or horizon; and (c) both of these types of predictions. This kind of work is done chiefly in deposits where the presence of oil is suspected. These are hydrochemical methods of petroleum prospecting in the narrow sense.

The second group includes hydrochemical studies that are directed only towards the clarafication of the geological structure, such as the tectonics and structure of the region. Here hydrochemical indicators that are not indicators of the presence of petroleum can be used. Such hydrochemical studies may be made not only in oil prospecting but also in exploring for other minerals and for various geological surveys. Since the main use of such studies is the explanation of the geological structure, they are called structural hydrochemical surveys.[17]

In practice, there are also cases where hydrochemical studies combining both groups of hydrochemical investigations are conducted. However, for purposes of exposition, it is convenient to separate them clearly. Therefore, below, we first describe the hydrochemical methods of exploration, in the proper sense of the word, and then the structural hydrochemical surveys.

There are several forms of hydrochemical investigations: (1) route surveys, (2) generalized prospecting investigations including the construction of stratigraphic hydrochemical maps, and (3) the study of waters for exploratory purposes. These categories are arbitrary but necessary for convenience in exposition.

In addition, hydrochemical investigations are also applied for auxiliary purposes in exploration and exploitation of oil and gas deposits including the solution of a number of technical problems.

Route Surveys

Hydrochemical route surveys are used for petroleum reconnaissance in areas where the oil potential is unknown or little known. The main aim of these surveys is to find indications of oil and to predict the presence of oil within the area in general or in some definite stratum. The main attention should be given to direct hydrochemical indicators of petroleum (dissolved bitumens, iodine) and to the indirect hydrochemical indicators of group I (sulfur compounds, soda) taking into account the total salt content of the water and hydrogeological and geological conditions.

The basic target should be deposits which are thought of as possibly

---

[16]In addition, there are also auxiliary studies.

[17]Hydrochemical investigations in sections under exploitation, whose purpose is the explanation of some details of geologic structure, are classified as auxiliary operations.

containing oil and gas. However, it is not always possible to obtain a sufficient number of observation points of these waters. Therefore, ground and
surface waters are sometimes investigated, especially where they are
thought to mix with deeper waters from possible oil-bearing formations.

The field work consists in taking samples of water from available water sources along the reconnaissance traverse. The course of the traverse
follows the valleys of the rivers or other convenient directions providing
the maximal number of water sources. Of fundamental interest, as stated
above, are deep artesian wells. In addition to the sampling of water, the
temperature of the springs should be measured, and the nature of the water
outlet should be observed. This is necessary to determine the stratigraphic
origin of the spring. The relationship of the spring to the stratigraphic
section cannot always be deduced if the exposures are poor or the spring
flows out through fissures. Recently hydrochemical route surveying has
been accompanied by water-gas surveying (see the following chapter).

Most of the water analysis during the hydrochemical route surveying
is usually done by means of a field laboratory. The results of the analyses
are plotted on hydrochemical maps. There is no generally accepted method
of making these maps. Several variations of such maps may be described:
(1) Water analysis results may be plotted on the map (preferably a geological one) using Tolstikhin circular symbols at sample points. The radius of
the circles may be made proportional to the mineral content of the water.
(2) Arbitrarily chosen symbols showing water type, group, etc. may be
placed near the sample point. Indicators such as naphthenates, iodine, hydrogen, sulfide, etc. should be shown on all hydrochemical maps. (3) Sometimes zones of identical water types (based on some particular identifying
characteristic) may be plotted along with the analytical data. Hydrochemical zones cannot always be distinguished, however. Often there are too few
observation points to permit interpolation. An example of one of these hydrochemical map types is shown in figure 108.

In interpreting the results of hydrochemical route surveys, different
cases have to be considered. If direct hydrochemical indicators of the
presence of petroleum are found where no signs of oil had previously been
observed, a positive result has been obtained. The result is considered
positive even in the case where the indicators cannot be correlated with
any definite stratum.

In other cases, hydrochemical indicators can be correlated with a
definite stratum. As a rule, correlation is possible only with a stratigraphic horizon of considerable thickness and not with a single reservoir.
Thus, an oil-bearing formation is detected. Finding the oil-bearing formation is important also when oil manifestations were already known in
the region but were not correlated with definite rocks.

Determining the direction of the water flow in oil-bearing strata may
sometimes help to make the prediction more precise by indicating the direction in which the reservoir should be sought.

If the presence of oil in a region is established and the oil-bearing
formation deduced, a study of conditions in the formation must be made.
The general nature of the salt composition of the water plays a conclusive
role. If enough sample points show stagnant and semi-stagnant conditions,
a positive prediction that commercial quantities of oil are present may be
made.

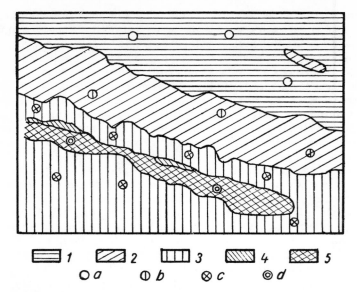

Fig. 108. Hydrochemical map of artesian springs. 1 —Akchagyl formation; 2 —Shirakh strata; 3 —Sarmatian; 4 —Middle Miocene; 5 —Maikop: a —Na_2SO_4 type, SO_4 group; b —Na_2SO_4 type, Cl group; c —$CaCl_2$ type, Cl group; d —$NaHCO_3$ type, Cl group.

Although the fundamental purpose of hydrochemical route surveys is to predict the presence of oil, these surveys can also serve to show the geological structure. This is especially important where not only oil is unknown, but also where the geological structure is not well known. The study of structural conditions from hydrochemical indicators of course facilitates oil prospecting. This will be discussed in greater detail below. Nowadays hydrochemical route surveys are an important link in oil prospecting. They are carried out primarily in regions where many artesian springs exist but where the oil potential has not been extensively studied.

Hydrochemical Prospecting

In regions where there are a considerable number of deeply drilled holes, many artesian wells, and where the geological structure and composition of underground waters are relatively well-known, systematic generalizations based on the available hydrochemical data are valuable. Hydrochemical investigations of this type are conducted in regions where the oil potential is, in general, already known. Their purpose is to show the most promising regions in a given province.

The generalized hydrochemical investigations are based essentially on water analyses already available that were done for different purposes. The basic data are given by the water analyses from deep drill holes. In addition, supplementary analyses are made. These are usually determinations of naphthenates and similar compounds for which data are either scarce or absent. Classical work of this kind was done by V. A. Sulin and his collaborators (A. A. Varov, L. A. Gulyaeva and others) in Azerbaidzhan, in the regions of the Second Baku and the Emba.

Since these investigations are usually conducted in areas where oil is

already known, most attention is devoted to finding areas where conditions
are most favorable for commercial oil production. Therefore, a fundamental role is played by such indicators as the general nature of the salts
in the waters, etc. A careful correlation of hydrochemical and geological
data is also made. Combinations of indicators (type, group, class, amount
of sulfates, and others) which show various conditions in a given geological
region most accurately are chosen. No standard procedure can be devised
for this purpose.

Small-scale hydrochemical maps are drawn from the indicator data,
and maps predicting the oil potential of the area are made on the basis of
these. Zones with major or minor prospects of commercial oil deposits
are then selected (Fig. 109). The main criterion used is the degree of
stagnancy of the water. One should however, keep in mind that the prediction of commercial value of individual oil-bearing zones on the basis of
hydrochemical indicators alone is not sufficient because the reservoir
properties of the rocks are not taken into account.

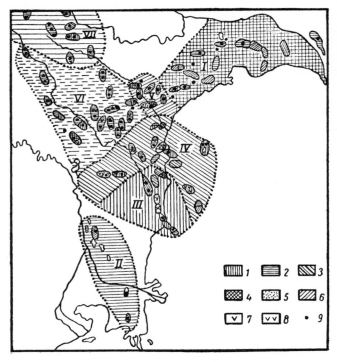

Fig. 109. Map for predicting petroleum from the composition of water (according to V. A. Sulin). I and II—important oil-bearing zones; III—oil prospects; IV—local
oil-bearing zone; V—oil possibly present locally; VI—
local oil-bearing zone; VII—prospect if suitable structures
and reservoirs are present: 1—bicarbonate (A_1 less than
15); 2—bicarbonate (A_1 more than 15); 3—sodium sulfate;
4—magnesium chloride; 5—calcium chloride (S_2 less than
15); 6—high calcium chloride (S_2 more than 15); 7—low
sulfate (less than 1.0 mg-equiv. SO_4 per 100 g); 8—sulfate (more than 1.0 mg-equiv. SO_4 per 100 g); 9—mud
volcano.

General hydrochemical oil surveys are possible in some cases in regions where oil is not known. A necessary and very rarely realized condition for this is a large number of deep wells. This situation occurs in the Kuzbass.

The investigations of G. M. Sukharev show that in some cases it is possible not only to predict oil and its commercial value but also to predict the nature of the deposits in a given zone (22). In zones where the water is highly mineralized and metamorphosed (stagnant zone), one should expect mainly an environment of gas or water drive. In semi-stagnant zones, with normal degrees of mineralization and metamorphism, one should expect a limited water-drive condition. Finally, at relatively low degrees of mineralization and metamorphism of water, the most probable condition is the typical water drive. Quantitative gradations between these conditions will depend upon various geological conditions.

The construction of small scale, hydrochemical stratigraphic maps in oil prospecting is another type of hydrochemical work. All possible oil bearing zones were considered together in the methods described above. In hydrochemical stratigraphic work only certain horizons are studied. This is possible only if a large number of wells has been drilled through the given horizon. The purpose of making hydrochemical maps of the strata is to delineate regions within a given horizon with the best prospects of commercial oil and gas. Such delineation is based on an interpretation of the hydrogeological conditions in the reservoir under investigation.

Large regions are included on the maps, on which the various hydrochemical indicators characterizing the waters can be plotted. Up to now, the total mineral content and the chloride content have been used. Points of equal concentration of the indicator are connected by isolines, such as "isocones" (lines of equal mineralization) and "isochlors". Such maps have

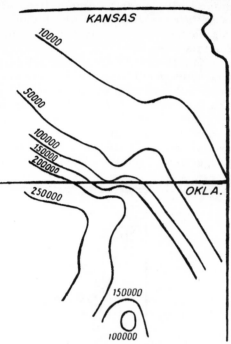

Fig. 110. Hydrochemical stratigraphic map. Isocones of waters of the Wilcox sandstone of Kansas and Oklahoma, in ppm.

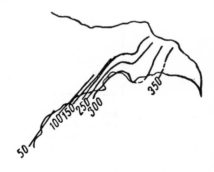

Fig. 111. Map of maximum mineralization of waters of productive zone V in Apsheron Peninsula (according to G. P. Tampazian [26]). Isolines in mg-equiv. per 100 g.

been constructed for Ordivician rocks and other horizons of the North American plateau (23, 24, and others) (Fig. 110). The sections of the horizon where the highest "isocones", "isochlors", etc. are found should be considered as most favorable for finding commercial deposits. Similar hydrochemical maps of the strata have been constructed for the Russian platform (25) and for the Apsheron Peninsula (Fig. 111) (26). Indicators of the degree of metamorphism of the salt composition of water such as Na/Cl, (Cl/Na)/Mg, (Na-Cl)/SO$_4$, etc., can also be used for the construction of hydrochemical maps of strata.

Hydrochemical Investigations in Exploration Work

Hydrochemical investigations can solve a number of problems during exploratory drilling. Here several cases can be distinguished. The first case is when the exploratory drilling is conducted in an area where the oil potential has not been determined.

If the first wells drilled do not indicate a reservoir, this does not mean that none is present in the general area of a given uplift. The determination of hydrochemical indicators in the water-bearing part of a zone can sometimes help to show the presence or absence of a reservoir within the limits of the same structure. The way of making such predictions is not well worked out as yet. So far experience shows that such hydrochemical indicators as soaps and sulfates are the most important for making predictions (according to D. V. Zhabrev in Azerbaidzhan and others). If no soaps are found in alkaline waters and there is a considerable amount of SO$_4$ (more than 1 per cent equiv.), the area may be considered dry. Other indicators (iodine, ammonia, hydrosulfides, dissolved gases) may also be used depending on local conditions. An predictions refer only to the horizons from which the water samples were taken. If commercial oil deposits have already been located in a given area but new, deeper zones are being investigated, the same hydrochemical methods are used.

In another case, additional investigations may be undertaken in a horizon where oil has been found by contouring the productive zone, clarifying the oil potential of individual fault blocks, etc. Here, hydrochemical investigations can be of considerable value and various criteria can be used depending on specific conditions. The determination of even insignificant differences in total mineral content, chloride content, amount of sulfates, metamorphosis of the water, etc. can, in some cases, facilitate the evaluation of oil potential in individual sections of the area and even the estimation of the distance to the limits of the reservoir. A detailed study of the different hydrochemical indicators is necessary to solve such problems. Such work was done for formations on the Apsheron Peninsula by V. A. Sulin and his collaborators. Variations in the hydrochemical indicators within the productive limits of a pool are complicated (see Chapter I). It must be remembered that production processes are likely to exert a strong influence.

Hydrochemical auxiliary investigations are of importance not only in the direct detection of petroleum but also in revealing geological structure. Auxiliary hydrochemical work in exploration for oil can solve different geological problems. A detailed study of the distribution of some hydrochemical indicators over the areal extent of the strata sometimes reveals the presence and location of faults. These faults are revealed by zones of water with anomalous indicators as compared with the background for the given horizon. For example, elongated zones of waters showing a high calcium chloride mineral content indicate a tectonic dislocation (through which waters from other higher or lower beds are flowing) when they occur in the middle of an area characterized by alkaline waters of normal mineral content. Similar cases have been encountered in a number of formations of Azerbaidzhan, Georgia, Dagestan, and in other regions.

Hydrochemical investigations may facilitate finding where beds and lenses wedge out. This problem occurs in exploration and exploitation of stratigraphic traps. An increase in total mineral content and metamorphism of the water is observed along these boundaries (e.g., in Baku and Kuban formations).

In some cases hydrochemical indicators can be utilized to correlate the sections of separate wells within a given formation. Such work was conducted by V. N. Lashenov for oil-bearing horizons in the eastern Kuban, and by L. A. Gulyaeva on the Samar bend. However, such a hydrochemical correlation is not always possible. Uniformity of water composition, a detailed study of the water composition in each horizon, and considerable diversity of hydrochemical indicators in different horizons are necessary.

Hydrochemical maps of individual strata are an important tool in hydrochemical exploration. These large-scale maps of strata should be constructed from a number of the more important hydrochemical indicators. The indicators are plotted on the map in the form of isolines or zones (Fig. 112). Such maps permit detailed studies of the changes in water composition in the area and how they depend on geological structure, oil and gas possibilities, and rate of exploitation.

Unfortunately, detailed hydrochemical methods of exploration are not widely used. These methods can help not only in the solution of purely exploratory problems, but also in exploitation and technical problems.

Hydrochemical Investigations in Production Work

In the exploitation of oil and gas fields, hydrochemical investigations can be used in solving some production problems.

An important use of hydrochemical data during drilling and exploitation is to detect the occurrence and location of an accidental flow of water into the well (through casing leads or bad cement jobs.) This can be done by comparing the properties of the water entering the well with the properties of water from the production zone as well as from higher horizons. If the properties of the water differ from those of the producing zone penetrated by the well, there has been an accidental inflow. Its location can be determined by comparing the analyzed water with waters from higher zones.

In order to determine where the water is entering the well the hydrochemistry of the entire section, the hydrochemical indicators of the various horizons, and the properties of the waters in the pay zones and their areal distribution must be known. If the waters of the various horizons differ only slightly, these techniques, of course, cannot be used. Sometimes the appearance in the well of water of an unusual composition is explained by the inflow of water from other parts of the pay sand, where the hydrochemical indicators may be different.

Another use of hydrochemical investigations in production work which recently has become important is connected with water flooding. In this

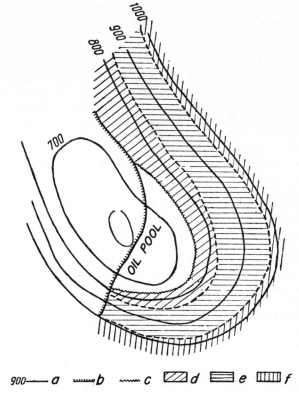

900——— a ˷˷˷˷ b ˷˷˷ c ▨ d ☰ e ⦀ f

Fig. 112. Example of a commercial hydrochemical
map of a geologic stratum. a —isolines within the
stratum; b —edge of sand lens; c —oil-water boundary; d —zone of waters with calcium content less
than 10 percent equiv.; e —zone of waters with calcium content 10 to 20 percent equiv.; f —zone of
waters with calcium content over 20 percent equiv.

case, it is necessary to know a number of the properties of the injection
water and of waters in the productive zones into which the injecting is done.
For the injection water (which itself can come from wells), such indicators
as appreciable quantities of iron, potassium, bicarbonate, and sulfate are
important. For waters of the producing sands, such properties as the
presence of hydrogen sulfide, alkalinity, etc., are important (27). A knowledge of these water properties (and the reactions which can take place during injection) permits selection of the water for injection and the appropriate method of treatment.

A special case is the injection into the producing zone of a solution of
sodium naphthenate to isolate bottom waters (method worked out by G. M.
Panchenkov). Here it is necessary to know the properties of the water in
the bottom layer, particularly the calcium content.

Hydrochemical studies of the well section are also important in predicting the destructive effects of some waters on the casing cement. This
destructive action on cements is especially strong for high sulfate waters
and also waters with a high content of free carbonic acid (28). A knowledge

of the hydrochemical indicators for a particular section of strata makes possible the application of preventive measures.

HYDROCHEMICAL INDICATORS OF STRUCTURE

Hydrochemical methods of investigating geologic structure are typical examples of indirect methods of oil prospecting. In many respects, they are similar to the geophysical methods. The basic purpose of both is to show the subsurface geological structure (mainly the tectonic structures) using surface techniques. Therefore, structural hydrochemical surveys can in a number of cases supplement and sometimes replace geophysical investigations. Like the latter, they are of greatest importance in regions with "buried structures", in regions "geologically closed", where the tectonics of surface deposits differ from the tectonics of deep oil formations. The main problem of structural hydrochemical surveys is the search for buried tectonic uplifts ("structures") and oil traps.

In contrast to the hydrochemical methods considered above, groundwaters and surface waters are studied rather than the waters of oil-bearing and potentially oil-bearing sediments. If deep springs discharge in the area being investigated they are also studied, but the role of such springs is usually secondary. There is also another kind of structural hydrochemical survey, which consists in the study of waters from bed rock and is used in geological mapping if there are few outcrops. If the cover is too thick this method cannot be used. The method is of little value. Area surveys, either detailed or semi-detailed, are also types of hydrochemical investigations that are used for geologic purposes.

Theoretical Concepts of Structure Surveys

As was shown above, the study of groundwaters, and sometimes the waters of surface reservoirs (lakes, etc.) is of basic importance in structural hydrochemical surveys. Such a study may indicate the subsurface structure because the ground and surface waters in a number of cases are connected with the waters in deeper horizons. How closely they are connected depends on tectonic factors. Deep waters can influence the shallower waters both hydraulically and geochemically, and this influence can be exerted in different ways.

The first way in which deep waters affect ground and surface waters is obviously the movement of deep waters towards the surface and their mixing with the ground and surface waters. Deep waters rise to mix with ground and surface waters under the following conditions: (a) there must be sufficient hydrostatic pressure in the deep waters to cause them to reach the water table or the bottom of surface reservoirs and (b) there must be a hydraulic connection between the deep aquifer on the one hand, and the water table and the surface reservoirs, on the other hand. The hydraulic connection is most often present along fractured zones especially where there are faults. It is possible that an important role is played by flow of this type.

As a result of a partial discharge of deep waters into shallow groundwaters and surface reservoirs, the following can take place: (a) replenishment of groundwaters from deep sources and local raising of the groundwater level (formation of a water dome) and, of most importance, (b) a

change in the salt composition of ground and surface waters. The change
is usually in the direction of increased mineralization and chloride content.

Another way in which deep waters reach the shallow zone is by diffusion and, especially, the diffusion of salts and ions from the depths toward
the earth's surface. The nature of this process was considered by K. V.
Filatov (29). The diffusion of water and dissolved salts and ions proceeds
separately. Of primary importance is the diffusion of the dissolved substances. Since deep waters are more highly concentrated, as a rule, the
diffusion usually is directed towards the surface. As a result, the ground
and surface waters can be enriched with salts coming from deep horizons.

Both the upward movement of the deep waters and the diffusion of dissolved substances can lead to an increase in mineralization and to a change
in the salinity of the ground and surface waters. Where these processes
are most intense, hydrochemical anomalies may appear. Hydrochemical
anomalies in the shallow waters occur primarily in sections of deep tectonic uplifts. This is explained by the fact that, in such sections, the deep
aquifers are closer to the earth's surface and also the rocks are more
fractured which facilitates migration (Fig. 113).

The theoretical justification of the structural hydrochemical surveys
of waters as an indirect method of prospecting for petroleum is based upon
the relation between hydrochemical anomalies and deep structures. It has

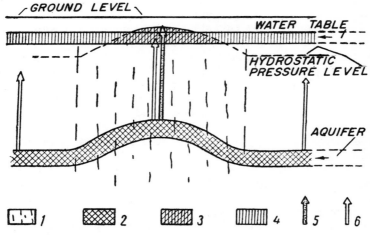

Fig. 113. Formation of hydrochemical anomalies in groundwater.
1—fracture zone; 2—deep brines; 3—groundwaters with high salinity and metamorphism (hydrochemical anomaly); 4—groundwaters of normal composition; 5—rise of water by filtration;
6—diffusion of salts.

been thought that hydrochemical anomalies in groundwaters are the result
of the influence of the oil and gas reservoirs themselves (30). The diffusing stream of gases from the reservoirs passes through various aquifers.
Here it may increase the evaporation of water, just as gas flows from wells
carry with them large masses of water from below the oil reservoir. As
a result of increased evaporation, the mineralization of groundwaters should
increase.

It is thus theoretically possible that the formation of hydrochemical anomalies in groundwaters under the influence of gas and oil reservoirs is independent of tectonic and hydraulic factors. However, the scale of such processes, if they take place, is obviously very limited. There is no basis for explaining the formation of the great majority of hydrochemical anomalies connected with structural highs, as was done by American authors.

Organization and Methodology of Structure Surveys

According to the degree of precision desired, two main types of hydrochemical surveys of ground and surface waters can be distinguished (for others, see below): semi-detailed and detailed. The semi-detailed hydrochemical surveys have as their purpose the discovery of buried structures in a large area where there may be several such uplifts (for instance, the so-called Stavropolskaia depression to the north of the Samarsk bend). A necessary condition for conducting such surveys is the presence of a sufficient number of water sources: springs, small wells and pits, and lakes. There should be no mining work in the area. The water samples are taken from the springs, pits, wells, lakes, etc., and the distribution of the sample points in the area is not necessarily uniform.

Such work is many respects resembles the route or reconnaisance survey work (see above). Deep springs in which direct indicators of oil might be found may also be discovered in semi-detailed work, but this is a secondary goal in structural surveys.

Detailed hydrochemical surveys can be conducted in separate small areas for the purpose of verifying and refining available data on the presence of tectonic uplifts (obtained by other methods, such as geophysical). They can be conducted along with other geochemical surveys: gaseous, bituminous, etc. The area in a detailed survey is, as a rule, approximately equal to the area occupied by a single uplift. In such a limited area, a sufficient number of water sources can be found only in exceptional cases. Therefore, in detailed hydrochemical surveying, shallow wells should be drilled into the groundwater horizon. The area can be covered by a uniform grid of sampling points.

The analysis of water samples in any hydrochemical survey is most conveniently conducted using field laboratories. For detailed surveys, the most suitable equipment is the Reznikov laboratory. A standard water analysis is adequate.

The results of the survey are shown on maps and profiles. In semi-detailed surveys hydrochemical maps are constructed in the same way, in general, as for route hydrochemical surveys. In detailed surveys, profiles and zonal hydrochemical maps are constructed with respect to separate indicators (Figs. 114 and 115). The zonal maps are contour.

Indicators Used and Their Interpretation

The fundamental criterion for the presence of a tectonic uplift (or fault) in the survey of ground and surface waters, as was said above, is the hydrochemical anomaly due to the action of deep waters. A hydrochemical anomaly can be explained only when the hydrochemical background is known: i.e., the composition of ground and surface waters characteristic of the given region.

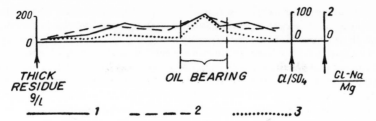

Fig. 114. Hydrochemical profile based on groundwaters (according to V. A. Kovda and P. S. Slavin). 1 —thick residue; 2 —Cl/SO$_4$;
3 —(Cl-Na)/Mg

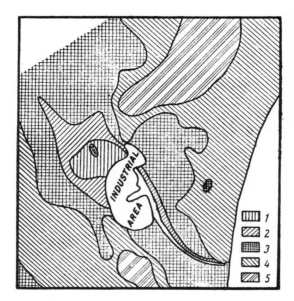

Fig. 115. Example of a detailed hydrochemical
map based on groundwaters (according to V. A.
Kovda and P. S. Slavin). 1 —waters in which
Cl:SO$_4$ exceeds 25; 2 —waters in which Cl:SO$_4$
is 15 to 25; 3 —waters in which Cl:SO$_4$ is 5 to
15; 4 —waters in which Cl:SO$_4$ is from 3 to 5;
5 —waters in which Cl:SO$_4$ is less than 3.

The following hydrochemical indicators are used in constructing profiles and maps to interpret background and anomalies: (1) total mineral
content of the water, (2) Cl/SO$_4$ ratio, (3) (Cl-Na)/Mg ratio and the type of
water in which it is found, (4) MgSO$_4$/MgCl$_2$ ratio, and (5) the water class
defined by Sulin and others. The Cl/SO$_4$ and (Cl-Na)/Mg ratios are more
promising indicators. The relative sulfate content should decrease under
the influence of deep waters. However, there are also exceptions to this
rule. The (Cl-Na)/Mg ratio as an indicator of the metamorphism of salinity
should increase under the influence of deep aquifers. In all cases, the
absolute values of the indicators are not as important as their deviations
from normal background values.

The total mineral content of waters in hydrochemical anomalies caused by the action of deep aquifers should, as a rule, increase. However, in the regions where salts exist in surface beds, it is not always possible to explain such an increase in mineralization.

The hydrochemical background depends mainly upon climate and relief. The composition of ground and surface waters is subject to climatic zonality. With increase in aridity, the salinity of water increases. In uniform climatic zones, the salinity and the composition of groundwaters ·depend on the relief. The highest salinity is associated with depressions having no run-off.

In dry, undrained sections where salt accumulates at the surface, a strong influence of deep brines can also be observed, and the clearest hydrochemical anomalies exist here. In more humid regions, hydrochemical anomalies cannot be expressed clearly since the salts emerging from the depths are carried away by shallow groundwaters or surface streams.

According to V. A. Kovda and P. S. Slavin (31), the following indicators of hydrochemical background and hydrochemical anomalies based on groundwaters are characteristic for two climatic zones: (1) deserts (the Kurinsk Plains) and (2) steppes (Saratov on the Volga) (Table 33).

TABLE 33. Typical Indicators of Hydrochemical Background and Hydrochemical Anomalies for Deserts and Steppes (according to V. A. Kovda and P. S. Slavin).

Zone and Indicator	Values Characteristic for:	
	Background	Anomaly
Desert		
$\Sigma(g/l)$	20-80	30-220
Cl/SO_4	<8	>8
$(Cl-Na)/Mg$	<1	>0.9 (up to 4)
Steppe		
$\Sigma(g/l)$	<0.5	>2
Cl/SO_4	<0.5	>1
$(Cl-Na)/Mg$	<0	>0.3 (up to 1.5)

The data given in Table 33 show: (1) marked differences in the magnitudes of the indicators for different climatic zones, (2) considerable differences between the background and anomaly (least clear are the differences in total mineral content in desert zones), and (3) the presence of calcium-chloride type waters in anomalous sections, which is of great importance. These data are not complete, however. The basis of the majority of hydrochemical anomalies is an enrichment of the water with chlorides. In humid, forest areas (for instance, near Moscow) the preservation of chlorides in groundwaters is almost impossible. Therefore, hydrochemical surveys based on ground and surface waters in such regions are generally not appropriate.

In addition to climate and relief, the nature of the anomalies is also influenced by the composition of buried rocks. Buried salt domes act essentially like other tectonic uplifts but usually their influence is stronger. For this reason the first structural hydrochemical surveys were conducted over salt domes. Thus, in the Gulf Coast region the areas overlying salt domes were contoured by using class S_2 groundwaters (magnesium-chloride type) in a hydrochemical environment of alkaline waters (32 and others). F. A. Alekseev, who first conducted a hydrochemical survey in lakes (on the Emba), found that, in sections over the salt domes, the (Cl-Na)/Mg ratio exceeded 1, while the $MgSO_4/MgCl_2$ ratio was less than 0.25. (In magnesium-chloride type waters such amounts indicate major metamorphism) (33).

A quite special case is the situation where there are layers of gypsum and anhydrite not far from the surface. There the ground and surface waters, as a result of the influence of the deep horizons, can be enriched with sulfates and unusual sulfate hydrochemical anomalies can be observed. This phenomenon was used by A. A. Varovy in Western Bashkiria. He conducted a structural hydorchemical survey for the purpose of explaining the uplifts formed by the Kungur gypsum anhydrite formation.

The shape of the anomalous areas must be taken into account in addition to the magnitudes of the anomalous and background values. This shape may depend on a number of factors. If there are faults in the area, the maxima shown by the indicators may be drawn out along the fault. The hydrochemical anomaly may be completely restricted to this zone or, because of the dip of the fault plane, it may be considerably displaced with respect to the crest of the structure.

The relief of the area and the confluence of deep waters with groundwaters affect the shape of anomalies. Where deep waters flow together and the relief is positive the anomaly is ring shaped. This was observed in the Caucasus (31), on the Emba (34), and in America (32). Groundwaters flow out of the elevated part of the uplift into the lower sectors surrounding it. The maximum accumulation of salt occurs here. In other cases (when the waters do not flow together and when the relief is either flat or negative) the highest mineral content will be directly above the uplift.

V. A. Kovda and P. S. Slavin have observed that the maximum total mineralization and the maximum Cl/SO_4 and (Cl-Na)/Mg ratios do not coincide in the surface salt zone if the hydrochemical anomaly is ring-shaped. If the maximum total mineral content forms a ring, the maximum Cl/SO_4 and (Cl-Na)/Mg ratios are all directly over the structure. This is because the influence of the deep waters predominates over the arch. On the limbs of the structure, where the current is directed, the surface salt factor prevails and sulfates accumulate. Thus it can be seen that climatic, orographic, hydrogeological, and lithological factors must all be considered in interpreting the results of hydrochemical surveys in which ground and surface waters are used to determine the location of structures and faults.

Correlation of Results with Stratigraphic Data

Sometimes hydrochemical criteria can be used to correlate the rocks exposed in a given section. They may be used when it is difficult to differentiate formations and correlate the rocks by other methods. They may also be used when outcrops are covered with talus, vegetation, etc. Hydrochemical surveys may be of help in geological mapping when there are enough springs flowing from the bedrock and when the formations show sufficiently distinct hydrochemical differences. Similar work was done, for instance, by E. A. Bars in Tatariya for the purpose of contouring a tectonic uplift covered on the surface by Tatariya sediments which could hardly be distinguished by other methods (35).

On the southern slope of the Great Caucasus in Eastern Georgia, according to A. A. Kartsev, a clear correlation of a number of hydrochemical indicators with definite stratigraphic horizons may be observed. When outcrops are poor, hydrochemical surveys using data obtained from artesian springs can facilitate geological work. In such surveys, various hydrochemical indicators may be used depending on field conditions. The field methods and the analysis and presentation of results depend on the scale of the survey and do not differ substantially from the methods described above.

BIBLIOGRAPHY

1. A. Potylitsyn. Composition of waters accompanying petroleum and ejected by mud volcanoes. Zh.P.F.Kh.O, vol. IV, issue 7, 1882.
2. K.V. Kharichkov. Determination of petroleum acids in waters of drilling wells. Neft. delo, 3, 1913.
3. V.A. Sulin. Waters of petroleum formations in the system of natural waters. Gostoptekhizdat, 1946.
4. V. Reisner. Examination of drilling fluid for content of naphthenic acids. Az. Nef. Khoz. no. 11-12, 1931.
5. N.H. Butorin and Z.P. Buks. Naphthenic acids in the formation waters of Old and New Grozny regions. Groznen. Neftyanik, no. 5-6, 1935.
6. V.B. Porfiryev and I.V. Grinberg. Geochemistry of the genesis of petroleum. Tr. Lvov. geol. o-va, ser. geol. nefty, issue 1. Izd. Lvovsk. gos. universiteta, 1948.
7. A.P. Vinogradov. Dispersed chemical elements in subsurface waters of diverse origin. Tr. Lab. gidrogeol. problem, vol. 1, ANSSSR, 1948.
8. T.I. Kazmina. Devonian waters of the Western Russian Platform. Tr. VNIGRI, new series, issue 57. Lengostoptekhizdat, 1951.
9. L.A. Gulyaeva. Iodine in Devonian sedimentary rocks. DAN SSSR, vol. LXXX, no. 5, 1951.
10. A.L. Shinkarenko. Gaseous composition and content of microelements in mineral springs of the region of mineral waters of Caucasus. Tr. Lab. gidrogeol. problem, vol. III, AN SSSR, 1948.
11. G.D. Lidin. Zonal distribution of natural gases in Donbass. Izv. AN SSSR, OTN, no. 6, 1944.
12. M.M. Fomichev. Chokrak hydrogen sulfide springs. Tr. Lab. gidrogeol. problems, vol. I. AN SSSR, 1948.
13. A.M. Ovchinnikov. Conditions of formation of the Matsestin hydrogen sulfide waters. Tr. Lab. gidrogeol problem, vol. II, AN SSSR, 1948.
14. A.M. Ovchinnikov. Mineral waters. Gosgeolizdat, 1947.
15. A.N. Buneev and L. P. Kharitonova. Reduction of sulfates in waters of the Krainsk springs in an atmosphere of hydrogen. Tr. Lab. gidrogeol. problem, vol. I, AN SSSR, 1948.
16. G.N. Kamenskii, P.P. Klimentov, and A.M. Ovchinnikov. Hydrogeology of deposits of useful minerals. Gosgeolizdat, 1953.
17. M.V. Sedenko. Hydrogeology of some coal deposits in USSR. Ugletekhizdat, 1951.

18. G.D. Lidin. Gases and mineral waters of Donets basin in the Rostov region and surrounding regions. Materially po geol. i polezn. iskop., Az.-Chern. geol. upr. sb. 6. (Rost) Obl. izd.-vo, 1938.

19. V.A. Sulin. Conditions of formation, basis of classification, and composition of natural waters. AN SSSR, 1948.

20. I.O. Brod and E.F. Frolov. Prospecting and exploration for oil and gas deposits. Gostoptekhizdat, 1951.

21. M.A. Dragomirova. Iodine content in drinking water. Tr. Biogeokhim. Lab. AN SSSR, vol. VII, 1944.

22. G.M. Sukharev. Hydrogeological conditions of formation of oil and gas deposits in Tersk-Dagestan oil province. Groz. obl. izd-vo, 1948.

23. R.H. Dott and R.L. Ginter. Isocon-maps for Ordovician waters. Bull. Am. Assn. Petrol. Geol., vol. 14, no. 9, 1930.

24. L.C. Case. Subsurface water characteristics in Oklahoma and Kansas. Prob. of Petrol. Geology, USA, 1934.

25. A.B. Ronov. Role of vibrational movements of earth's crust in the development of coal formation waters and gas fields along the Volga. Tr. In-ta teor. geofiziki. AN SSSR, vol. III, 1947.

26. G.P. Tatrazyan. The change of chemical composition of waters of the productive layer of Apsheron oil region. Izv. AN SSSR, no. 1, 1954.

27. I.E. Apeltsin and G.K. Maksimovich. Preparation of water for flooding of oil reservoirs. Gostoptekhizdat, 1951.

28. V.A. Priklonskii and F. F. Laptev. Physical properties and chemical composition of underground waters. Gosgeolizdat, 1949.

29. K.V. Filatov. The origin of underground gravitational waters of a depression. Mater. k pozn. geol. stroeniya SSSR, nov. ser. issue 8 (12). MOIP, 1947.

30. E. McDermott. Geochemical exploration. Bull. Am Assn. Petrol. Geol., vol. 24, no. 5, 1940.

31. V.A. Kovda and P.S. Slavin. Soil-geochemical indicators of petroleum. AN SSSR, 1951.

32. H. Minor. Oil field waters of the Gulf. Coastal Plain. Prob. of Petrol. Geology, USA, 1934.

33. F. Alekseev. Hydrochemical mapping applied to the search for salt domes. Razvedka Nedr, no. 5, 1941.

34. G.N. Kamenskii. The hydrochemical environment of regions of the irrigation system of Near Caspian lowlands. Izv. AN SSSR, ser. geol. no. 1, 1952.

35. E.A. Bars and E.S. Itkina. Hydrochemical structural surveys in Aksubaer region of the Tartar ASSR. DAN SSSR, vol. XL, no. 7, 1943.

CHAPTER TEN

Water-Gas Surveys

BASIC INFORMATION ON WATER-GAS SURVEYS

One of the geochemical methods of prospecting for petroleum is the water-gas[1] survey. This consists in analyzing the macro- and microconcentrations of dissolved hydrocarbon gases in shallow and deep groundwaters for the purpose of distinguishing zones having a relatively high hydrocarbon content. These zones may indicate the presence of oil or gas in the region being investigated. The composition of the dissolved gases and their concentration in natural waters depend on the conditions under which the waters exist.

Academician V. I. Vernadskii (1) pointed out the natural aqueous solutions are complex fluid systems of water and gas. The gas dissolved in the water links it very closely to the gaseous medium in which the water is situated; i.e., the gas is in a state of saturation.

Waters in contact with hydrocarbon gas pools contain dissolved methane and heavy hydrocarbons in amounts which depend on the partial pressures of these gases in the stratum, the coefficients of solubility, the temperature, and the mineralization (salt content) of the water. The quantity of gas dissolved at a given temperature in a unit volume of a liquid is proportional to the pressure of the remaining undissolved gas:

$$Q = KP,$$

where Q is the weight of gas in a unit volume of solvent; P is the pressure of the gas over the solvent; K is a constant depending on the type of gas, the liquid, and the temperature.

This law is applicable only to gases having low solubility, such as nitrogen, hydrogen, oxygen, helium, or methane. Easily soluble gases (carbon dioxide and hydrogen sulfide) conform only slightly to this law. Each component of a gaseous mixture dissolves in water in proportion to the fraction of the total pressure which it exerts (law of partial pressures). Consequently, the dissolved gas is relatively enriched in those components of the free gas that have the greatest water solubility. In air, for example, there is relatively less oxygen (20.9% than in water (around 35%) because oxygen is twice as soluble as nitrogen.

All hydrocarbon gases are difficultly soluble in water. The solubility of methane at $+ 20^{\circ}$ and 760 mm. pressure is 0.0331, and that of ethane is 0.0472. The solubility of oxygen under these same conditions is 0.0310; the solubilities of nitrogen, hydrogen, helium, argon, carbon dioxide, and

---

[1] "Vodnogazovoi" has been translated as "water-gas" and refers to the gases that are dissolved in water. This is not to be confused with the water gas (vodyahoi gaz) that results from the high temperature reaction between steam and carbon. Ed.

hydrogen sulfide are 0.0155, 0.0182, 0.0088, 0.0336, 0.878, and 2.582, respectively. The solubility of a gas in mineralized waters decreases abruptly. When 75 g. of NaCl are added to one 1. of distilled water the solubility of methane at $+5^{o}$ and 760 mm. pressure falls to 0.0250; and when 320 g. are added, the solubility falls to 0.0066.

The composition of free gases accompanying water that is emerging at the earth's surface is quite different from that of the gases dissolved in the water. According to A. N. Buneev (2), the content of the free and dissolved gas is expressed by the following data (Table 34).

TABLE 34. Content of Free and Dissolved Gas

Source and type of gas	$Cm.^3$ in one liter of water			
	H_2S	CO_2	CH_4	N_2
Staraya Matsesta Well				
Free gas	0.2	0.7	6.9	9.6
Dissolved gas	34.7	34.3	9.8	48.5
Agura Well				
Free gas	0.1	0.6	4.2	9.6
Dissolved gas	33.3	45.6	17.7	33.2

Much more carbon dioxide and hydrogen sulfide are evolved from water than nitrogen and methane. Carbon dioxide is present in water as dissolved gas and in a semi-bound state in the form of bicarbonates. Bicarbonates are very unstable and decompose with the evolution of CO_2 when environmental conditions change. The decomposition of bicarbonates can occur at a noticeable rate at $+60^{o}$ or even less.

Gases occur in water not only in the dissolved form, but also as gas emulsions, i.e., gas bubbles, and can enter into chemical reactions. This applies especially to waters that rise from great depths into regions of lower pressure near the surface.

Waters lying above a gas-bearing stratum are saturated by hydrocarbons as the gas migrates from the pool though the aquifer to the surface. The overlying waters are very often saturated with hydrocarbon gases as a result of direct migration of the water from oil and gas formations. Migrating mineralized waters mix with the overlying waters of the surface zone, increase their mineral content, and enrich the dissolved gas in hydrocarbons.

Problems of gas migration were discussed in Chapter IV, but here, a few words must be said about the migration of water. Two types of water migration must be distinguished.

1. Migration of water accompanied by free gas, where the gas facilitates the ascent of the water. The gas forces drops of water upward, thus clearing a path for free evolution. Here the gas has the same effect as in the gas drive mechanism in the oil reservoir.

2. Migration of water containing dissolved gases. If the water contains an excess of dissolved gases, these are evolved spontaneously as bubbles from the rising water and may be collected for study. When low concentrations of dissolved gases are present, the gas is extracted by special degasifiers in the laboratory.

Vertical and horizontal migration of water are observed. Vertical migration takes place along tectonic dislocations through fissures in the rocks that are associated with the crests and limbs of folds. In limestones, gypsum, rock salt, and other soluble rocks, water migrates through solution channels and caverns. Horizontal migration of water takes place in a porous stratum when the beds are inclined rather than horizontal.

As a result of this migration, water emerges at the earth's surface in the form of springs. These water outflows may occur singly or as chains where the springs are scarcely separated from one another. In some cases the water spreads out near the surface and may take the form of a substantial stream or lake. When the faults do not reach the surface, water migrating along these paths spreads out near the surface, occupies a certain area, and mixes with the groundwaters. The moving currents sometimes transport these deeper waters, mixed with surface waters, over considerable distances.

A. M. Ovchinnikov (3) distinguishes three types of subsurface waters: waters of the aeration zone, groundwaters, and artesian waters. On the basis of these three types of waters, Ovchinnikov gives the following classification of springs.

1. Springs associated with waters of the aeration zone. In dry periods these springs vanish.

2. Groundwater springs are divided into erosion, contact, and overflowing springs.

3. Artesian springs are divided into two groups: (a) springs at the areal limits of the artesian slope, i.e., at the boundary between the aquifer and the surrounding impermeable rocks; (b) springs at other discharge points in the artesian basin, such as springs associated with local uplifts and springs associated with monoclines.

The water-gas survey must be used in conjunction with the hydrochemical curvey. However, the results of this latter method, such as the total mineral content and the specific salt composition, are only indirect indications and cannot be used alone to determine the presence of petroleum in the depths (see Chapter IX). For example, the presence of calcium chloride waters is a favorable index because it implies a closed structure, which is a necessary (but not sufficient) condition for the accumulation of oil and gas.

Under these conditions, dissolved hydrocarbon gases (as well as iodine, naphthenic acids, etc.) are direct indications of the presence of petroleum that may have accumulated enough to form a commercial pool. The joint use of direct and indirect methods makes possible more reliable prediction of likely areas.

History of the Method

M. V. Lomomosov wrote of the necessity and importance of the study of the chemical composition of natural waters. Gases in waters have been studied frequently. V. I. Vernadskii (1) attached particularly great importance to the study of gases dissolved in water. He even suggested that the classification of waters be based on dissolved gases rather than their salt composition. V. A. Sulin (4) repeatedly pointed out the importance of the study of gases in waters.

Determinations of gases dissolved in water were separately carried out by V. P. Savchenko, A. A. Kozlov, A. A. Cherepennikov, and others (5, 6, 7), however, systematic investigations were begun only relatively recently (E. K. Gerling, I. B. Feigel'son). In 1942-1944 E. K. Gerling (8) used the mercury apparatus of V. A. Sokolov, with which microconcentrations of gas may be determined to an accuracy of $10^{-4} — 10^{-5}\%$, for analyzing hydrocarbon gases dissolved in water. Gerling showed that the so-called heavy fraction of the gases recovered from water usually contains only traces of heavy hydrocarbons, while most of the gas is nitrous oxide.

I. B. Feiger'son introduced the study of the combustible gases that are dissolved in water into the hydrochemical survey. Analysis of total combustible gases (methane, heavy hydrocarbons, and hydrogen) was performed with the VTI apparatus. In view of the low sensitivity of this apparatus and the slight solubility of hydrocarbons in water, only waters containing over 0.1% hydrocarbon gases were taken into consideration.

In 1947 analyses of gases dissolved in water were performed with the TG-5 microanalytical field apparatus, which separately determines methane and heavy hydrocarbons with an accuracy of about $10^{-5}\%$. A preliminary procedure was developed as a result of this experimental work, and a water-gas area survey was carried out in the Saratov region in 1948. The water-gas surveys conducted by L. A. Kuznetsov differed considerably from earlier surveys. New methods of searching for petroleum rely upon the use of waters with low concentrations of dissolved hydrocarbon gases that are usually found in groundwaters. The study of groundwaters makes it possible to conduct surveys of steppe and foothill regions where deep wells and springs are lacking.

Purpose of the Water-Gas Survey

The water-gas survey is a reconnaissance method intended for the preliminary exploration of large territories. After a water-gas survey has been made, the relative prospects of finding petroleum in specific areas can be determined, and recommendations can be made for carrying out more detailed geochemical and other work. The water-gas survey, as a rule, cannot detect the presence of a structure nor determine its individual potential. It can only be used as a comparative guide.

In deep drilling, the study of water-soluble gases makes it possible to determine the composition of waters more precisely and to locate the position of water-bearing levels. The water-gas survey must be carried out in conjunction with a hydrochemical survey in order to obtain both direct indications of petroleum (hydrocarbon gas) and indirect ones (waters with a salt content characteristic of oil pools).

METHODS AND APPARATUS USED IN WATER-GAS SURVEYS

Methods of Field Work

The results of a water-gas reconnaissance survey are recorded on a map with a scale of 1:500,000. The scale is chosen on the basis of the density of the network of springs and wells, which should cover the entire area uniformly. In rare cases, when the density of springs is sufficient (usually in mountainous regions), the map may be drawn to a scale of 1:200,000. Springs and wells are normally scattered irregularly throughout the area.

Within the boundaries of populated areas they are numerous, but between settlements they may be widely scattered.

In the water-gas survey all oil wells and springs must be tested, although not all water wells are examined. In this matter the following principles serve as a guide.

1. The well must be clean and not neglected, with clear water and a clean bottom.

2. In a large settlement (5-6 km. in length), at least five wells are tested if they are all supplied by one aquifer. If more than one aquifer is present, three wells from each one are tested. In small settlements at least two wells from one aquifer are examined and they should be located at opposite ends of the town. Because of the uneven distribution of dissolved hydrocarbon gases in groundwaters, testing one well per settlement is not sufficient.

3. If increased concentrations of hydrocarbon gases are found in any well, additional samples of water are taken from this and adjacent wells to verify the correctness of the determination and to procure further details. In this case the network of sample points becomes more crowded.

Sometimes the evolution of gas is observed in wells. This gas must be collected and its rate of flow must be measured. To collect gas from a deep well, a funnel that is 20-30 cm. in diameter and weighted with lead poured into special grooves in the rim is used. The funnel is placed in a bucket of water and a sample bottle containing boiled water is attached to the end of the spout. The bottle is fastened to the funnel using twine and special clamps.

The bucket, with the funnel and bottle inside, is lowered into the well. When the bucket is submerged in the water, the funnel and bottle are carefully lifted from the bucket by a cord attached to the funnel and drawn to the side until they are opposite the spot where the gas bubbles are originating. When the bottle is full of gas, it is returned to the bucket, and the whole assembly is raised to the surface. The bottle may then be detached from the funnel and corked.

Every water well, spring, or oil well must have a serial number which is marked on the base map. The sampling conditions for each bottle of water that is collected are recorded in a field notebook. The most important of these conditions are the following.

a. The age and lithological characteristics of the rock from which a spring flows or which supplys a well. Special attention is given to the porosity of the rock, degree of fissuring, presence of faults, and caverns. The type of water (surface, artesian or groundwater) and its origin (in accordance with the classification proposed earlier (3) by A. M. Ovchinnikov) are determined.

b. The output of the spring, the taste, odor, color, and turbidity of the water, and the temperature of the water and the air. In determining the taste of the water, the degree of saltiness, the hardness, hydrogen sulfide aftertaste, carbon dioxide content, sweetness, staleness, etc. are noted. In the case of wells, the total depth, the height of the water column, the type of well cover (frame, twig capping, concrete, limestone slabs, etc.) are recorded.

c. The location of the spring or well is described, i.e., river terrace, shore of a lake, in the mountains, etc. In populated areas, the possibility of contamination of the well by impurities (for instance, the possibility of seepage of drainage waters from animal yards, dumps, etc.) is noted.

d. Any seasonal variations in rate of production (as is characteristic of groundwaters) is determined by questioning the local inhabitants.

Sampling Waters for Degasification

Two liters of water are drawn into a special vessel to determine the dissolved hydrocarbons. If a total gas analysis and determination of hydrocarbons must be carried out in a TG-5A apparatus, 3 or 4 1. of water must be obtained. In this case the water is drawn into either a three-liter vessel or two two-liter ones. The water vessels are flasks (Fig. 116) made of galvanized iron which also serve as components of the degasifier.

The flasks are filled with water at the sampling point and hermetically sealed in order to avoid premature degasification of the water and loss of gas in transporting the samples to the laboratory. Experimental investigations have shown that if the water is drawn into bottles and transferred to the flasks just before degasification, nearly 50% of the dissolved gas is lost. A particularly great loss of gas is observed on transferring samples of deep waters containing gases.

It is sometimes useful to determine the hydrogen dissolved in the waters. For this purpose galvanized iron flasks are not suitable, because hydrogen is formed by corrosion when water is kept in them. Formation of hydrogen, however, does not prevent an accurate determination of hydrocarbon gases in the sample. For the determination of hydrogen, either tinned metal or glass flasks are used. The sample flasks must be carefully protected when ever they are transported in the field because of their fragility.

Water for filling the sample flasks is taken from springs by using an open vessel, and a bathometer is used to take samples in wells. There are several types of bathometers of which the most convenient is the two-valve bathometer devised by A. M. Levit. This bathometer is intended for sampling water at a fixed distance from the bottom of the well and below the surface of the water. Taking water from the very bottom is not recommended because particles of sediment from the bottom of the well would be included in the sample. Taking water from the surface is undesirable because the surface is often contaminated by various

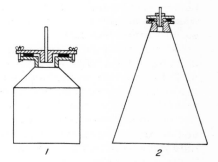

Fig. 116. Flasks for sampling water for degasification. 1—flask with flange; 2—conical flask with screw stopper.

films. Sometimes there are even films of petroleum products which have accidentally gotten into the well because contaminated buckets were used. Furthermore, a rapid exchange of gas between the water and the atmosphere takes place at the water-air interface, and the concentration of dissolved hydrocarbons would be decreased.

The two-valve bathometer (Fig. 117) consists of a cylinder with a capacity of 2.6 or 3.6 liters (depending on the volume of the degasifier flask). At the upper and lower ends of the cylinder, openings are drilled that are closed by valves. Water enters through the lower, wider valve,

and air is expelled through the upper valve. Both valves are attached to a
single rod and the rod is attached at its lower end to a base (see Fig. 117).
At its upper end the rod is attached to a ring which is
used to open the valves to transfer the water sample
from the bathometer to the flask of the degasifier.

In operation, the bathometer is lowered into the
well, tightly sealed with strong twine. When the base
reaches the bottom of the well, the shell sinks down
to the ring under its own weight and open both valves.
The weight of the bathometer shell and the valves is
chosen so that the shell sinks to the required depth in
the well without opening prematurely.

Water may be taken at any depth from the bottom
of the well simply by choosing a rod of the appropriate
length. The water fills the bathometer quietly, without
turbulence, so that premature degasification is avoided.
After the bathometer is filled with water, which takes
about 45 sec., it is lifted out of the well and the water
is transferred to a flask. A funnel is lowered to the
bottom of the flask for this purpose. Before the work
is begun, the bathometer is treated with steam to remove traces of contamination. After sampling water
that is saturated with gas, the bathometer must be
given an especially thorough cleaning.

A. M. Levit has shown experimentally that an ex-
cessive transfer of the water samples reduces the
gas concentration significantly. Water saturated with
butane was poured into flasks and the dissolved gas
was then recovered by boiling. Other portions of the
same water were first poured into measuring cylinders and then poured from the cylinders into flasks
and degasified. The experimental results are given
in Table 35. When the concentration of dissolved
gases in water is low, the losses that occur during
transfer will, of course, be relatively less significant.
A combined bathometer-degasifier flask would be
necessary to eliminate these transfer losses. The
only drawback is that a great number of complex
bathometer-degasifiers would be required.

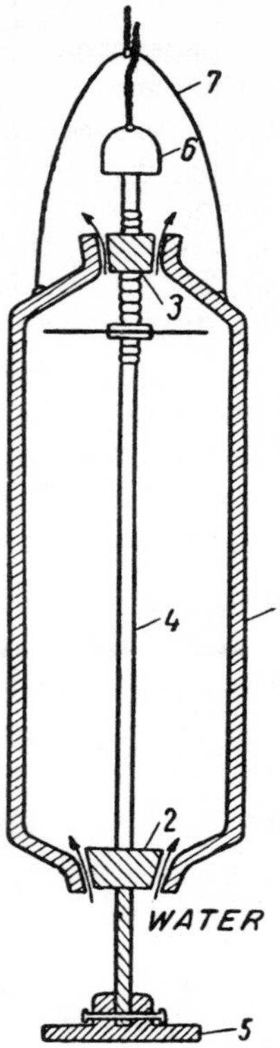

Fig. 117. Two-valve
bathometer for sam-
pling water. 1—shell;
2—lower valve; 3—
upper valve; 4—rod;
5—base; 6—ring for
opening valves; 7—
rib with cord for low-
ering and raising the
bathometer.

Dissolved carbon dioxide and hydrogen sulfide
are determined instead of taking water samples, but it is very difficult to
make accurate determinations of the former. More CO_2 is usually recovered from the water than was actually dissolved in it. This is because
carbondioxide occurs in water in three states: free (dissolved), loosely
bound in the form of bicarbonates ($Ca(HCO_3)_2$, $HaHCO_3$, etc.), and chemically combined ($CaCO_3$, Na_2CO_3, etc.). A mobile equilibrium is established
between the free and loosely bound carbon dioxide:

$$Ca(HCO_3)_2 \rightleftarrows CaCO_3 + CO_2 + H_2O.$$

This equilibrium is temporarily upset during degasification when part
of the CO_2 is removed. Equilibrium is restored by further decomposition

TABLE 35. Effect of Transferring Water Samples on Loss of Dissolved Gas

Experiment Number	Butane recovered from one liter of water, ml.		Difference in butane concentrations, %
	Water poured directly into flasks	Water poured into cylinders and then into flasks	
1	26	21	19
2	25	21	16
3	25	21	16

of bicarbonates. The decomposition of bicarbonates may occur even at room temperature, but is accelerated on heating. Boiling leads to the complete decomposition of bicarbonates. When bicarbonates are present in water, dissolved (free) carbon dioxide can be determined directly only in the water itself.

Recovery of Gas from Water

There are several types of apparatus for the recovery of gas from water. They are all based on the decrease in amount of gas which may remain dissolved in water when there is a decrease in pressure or an increase in temperature. If a strong vacuum is used or if the temperature of the water is raised to boiling, all the dissolved gas may be recovered, provided the recovered gas is continuously removed.

V. P. Savchenko's method (5, 6) is based on the recovery of gas using a vacuum. The apparatus consists of a bottle with a volume of 5-20 liters (Fig. 118), into which is inserted a rubber stopper bearing three glass tubes. One of the tubes (a) reaches nearly to the bottom of the bottle; a football bladder (d) is slipped onto the second tube (b), and the third tube (c) does not extend below the stopper. Degasification of a water sample is carried out in the following manner. A partial vacuum is created in the bottle beforehand by removal of air. The air is removed either by blowing steam through the bottle or by using a Kamovskii vacuum pump. Live steam from a special vessel is passed into the bottle through tube a and passes out, together with air, through tube c. After passage of the steam the tubes are closed with clamps, the remaining steam is condensed and a vacuum is thus produced in the bottle.

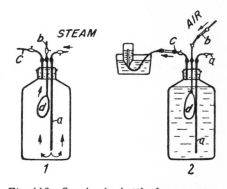

Fig. 118. Savchenko bottle for recovery of dissolved gas from water. 1—removal of air from bottle using steam; 2—transfer of gas from bottle to vessel; a—inlet tube; b—tube for admission of degasified water to the bottle; c—outlet tube; d—football bladder.

Then the water to be degasified is admitted from another bottle into the Savchenko bottle. The water is driven into the bottle with great force and is partially degasified. When the volume of gas over the water to the volume of water in the bottle reaches a ratio of 1:5, the flow of water into the bottle is stopped. The recovered gas is transferred to a vessel (Fig. 118) by inflating the football bladder. During degasification the temperature of the water, the volume of the water and the bottle, and the volume of recovered gas are measured.

Not all the gas dissolved in the water is recovered with the Savchenko bottle. A special formula is used to determine the total quantity of gas dissolved in the water, which is based on the laws of interrelationship between gases and water:

$$V = \frac{V_1(aq + V_2)}{qV_2},$$

where V is the total volume (in liters reduced to 0° C and 760 mm.) of the given component of the gas mixture, present in unit volume of the liquid being studied; V_1 is the volume (in liters reduced to 0° C and 760 mm.) of the given component of the gas in the first fraction recovered; V_2 is the total volume of the gas phase (in liters); a is the coefficient of solubility of the given component of the gas in the liquid being studied at the temperature at which the experiment is performed (data of measurement of water temperature); q is the total volume of the liquid being studied, in liters.

The V. I. Savchenko method of degasification is very crude and does not permit the recovery of small concentrations of hydrocarbon gas from water, but it has been widely used.

A. M. Kravtsov and M. M. Elinson (9) used a thermovacuum degasifier for the degasification of water in 1940. This degasifier (Fig. 119) consists of the following main parts: a roundbottomed flask (1) with a capacity of 1.5 l., a condenser (2), a measuring buret (4), and a receiving vessel for recovered gas (5). The flask is immersed in a water bath. A pressure (leveling) bulb (3) is connected to the condenser. The sections of the apparatus are connected by means of the glass stopcocks (7) and rubber tubing. The water to be tested is poured into the flask, which is connected to the apparatus by means of a stopcock. A vacuum is produced in the apparatus by means of a bulb filled with mercury. Then the stopcock is opened and evolution of gas from the water begins. The gas, together with steam, passes into the condenser, and in order to accelerate the process the flask is heated. The complete recovery of gas from the water takes 3 to 8 hours. Between 38 and 124 cm^3 of gas are recovered from one liter of water. The large amount of glassware in the apparatus, the use of mercury, and the low productivity make this method of degasification very inconvenient in the field. It is used in cases where an accuracy approaching 0.1% is needed.

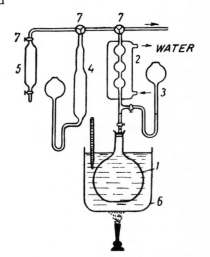

Fig. 119. Thermovacuum degasifier for water.

In 1949 - 1950 A. I. Kravtsov (10) perfected a thermovacuum apparatus for recovery of gas dissolved in the waters of coal formations. The new

apparatus consists (Fig. 120) of a vessel containing the water being examined, a glass bulb condenser, a measuring buret, a bottle for collecting
gas, a water bath, a pressure bottle containing mercury, and a leveling
bottle. The pressure bottle containing mercury
and a specially constructed stopcock are used
to transfer the evolved gases to the measuring buret. To obtain more complete recovery
of gas the water is heated to 70°. This apparatus has the same shortcomings as the
preceding one.

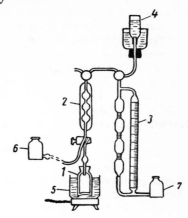

     A thermal degasifier which boils the
water, is also used to recover the gas. This
apparatus (Fig. 121) consists of a 2- or 3-1.
metal flask which holds the water being degasified. The flask may be shaped like a
cone or truncated cone and has an air-tight
seal at the top. Gas leaving the flask passes
into a condenser consisting of a coiled tube
immersed in a tank containing cold water.
The upper end of the tube goes into a special
chamber in which a water-filled bottle for
receiving gas is placed. The method of

Fig. 120. Perfected Kravtsov
thermovacuum apparatus.

operation does not differ in principle from that used with the thermal degasifier for the core-gas survey. Usually from 20 to 80 cm.^{3} of gas are
recovered from one l. of water. The volume of gas depends on the origin
of the water (from an aquifer or the surface) and its physical properties
(temperature, salinity). More complete recovery
of gases (up to 90 - 95%) may be achieved by using
a thermal degasifier. This makes it possible to
study microconcentrations of dissolved hydrocarbon gases in the water-gas survey.

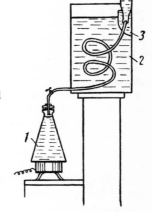

Gas Analysis

Dissolved gases from all sources are first analyzed
for hydrocarbons. Methane and heavy hydrocarbon
are separately determined in the TG-5A apparatus
with an accuracy of 10^{-4}%. If the amount of heavy
hydrocarbons exceeds 10^{-2}%, they are divided
into separate components: ethane, propane, butane,
etc. The heavy hydrocarbons are subdivided by
using either the V. A. Sokolov mercury distillation
apparatus or the P. M. Turkel'taub chromatographic device. A description of these devices is
given in Chapter IV.

Fig. 121. Thermal degasifier for water. 1—metal
flask for water; 2—coil
condenser; 3—receiving
pocket with bottle for collecting gas.

     In addition to the determination of hydrocar-
bons, the nitrogen, carbon dioxide, oxygen, carbon
monoxide, hydrogen, and inert gas concentrations
are also studied. All samples containing high hydrocarbon concentrations must be subjected to total gas analysis. The
total gas analysis is performed in the VTI apparatus, while rare gases are
analyzed with a special apparatus in the laboratory.

The results of analysis of the gas dissolved in water are given in cm.^{3} per l. of water. The content can also be expressed in percent for each gaseous component in the mixture, but in order to do this the actual content of dissolved CO_2 and H_2 must be determined. For an accurate determination of dissolved CO_2 (without partially bound CO_2) and H_2S, the analysis must be made in the field, right at the sampling point.

The determination of dissolved CO_2 is carried out by titrating the water with alkali (NaOH) in the presence of phenolphthalein and a little Rochelle salt ($KNaC_4H_4O_6 \cdot 4H_2O$). The analysis is performed right at the source, since even brief storage and transportation of the sample lead to disturbance of the natural equilibrium between CO_2 and the bicarbonates. A 25 - 50 ml. sample of water is titrated with 0.05$\underline{N}$ caustic alkali (0.1 ml. NaOH is equivalent to 0.114 ml. CO_2):

$$CO_2 + NaOH + H_2O \longrightarrow NaHCO_3 + H_2O.$$

The accuracy of determining CO_2 by this method is approximately equal to the accuracy of analysis of free gas in the VTI apparatus.

The determination of dissolved hydrogen sulfide must also be carried out at the sampling point. Hydrogen sulfide is easily oxidized, even at ordinary temperatures:

$$2H_2S + O_2 \longrightarrow 2H_2O + 2S.$$

When dissolved H_2S is oxidized, the water becomes turbid owing to the formation of very fine crystals and flocs of sulfur. The sulfur falls to the bottom of the spring and is found as a white or slightly yellowish coating which becomes deep black or blue-black in color downstream owing to the formation of iron sulfide (FeS).

Heating the water accelerates the oxidation of the H_2S; hence gas samples recovered from water with a thermal degasifier are usually free of H_2S, even though hydrogen sulfide was originally detected in the water by its odor. Smelling the gas is the most sensitive qualitative detection method for H_2S. It can be detected in this way at a concentration of 0.0014 mg./l., or 0.000009% (by volume). A rather crude determination of H_2S may be also made by using lead paper. Hydrogen sulfide reacts with lead salts to give PbS (lead sulfide), which causes blackening of the paper:

$$(CH_3COO)_2Pb + H_2S \longrightarrow PbS + 2OCH_3COOH.$$

For a quantitative determination of H_2S in water, either the colorimetric or the iodometric method is used. According to A. M. Levit the first method is more convenient in the field, and therefore only the first method is described.

One hundred ml. of the water to be analyzed are put into a volumetric flask, and a pipet which reaches to the bottom of the flask is used to add 5 ml. of sulfide reagent. The flask is then closed with a ground-glass stopper and vigorously agitated. The sulfide reagent consists of 10 g. of Rochelle salt crystals, 10 g. of ammonium chloride, and 0.1 g. of lead acetate, all dissolved in a 5% solution of ammonia. The solution is diluted to a volume of 100 ml. Into a second flask are placed 100 ml. of distilled water and 5 ml. of the sulfide reagent, which serves as a standard.

A dilute solution of sodium sulfide is added dropwise from a microburet until the liquid in both flasks acquires the same light-brown tint. The sodium sulfide solution must always be fresh and cannot be kept more than 3 - 5 hours. The sodium sulfide solution is prepared by dissolving 0.1 g. of Na_2S (to which a few drops of ammonia have been added) in a concentrated solution of sodium nitrate to give a final volume of 100 ml. The concentration of H_2S in the sample under test is calculated from the quantity of Na_2S used. The analysis does not take more than 5 min.

WATER-GAS SURVEY RESULTS AND THEIR INTERPRETATION

Presentation of Results

The results of water-gas surveys are plotted on maps of the gas content of natural waters. Two types of maps are compiled: a map of the hydrocarbon gas content and a map showing the composition of dissolved gases by components. On the first map hydrocarbon gases are shown as circles; the diameter of each circle corresponds to the measured quantity of dissolved hydrocarbons. Since hydrocarbon concentrations vary within wide limits (from 0.0040 to 33 cm.^{3}/l. or more), the circles must be drawn to an arbitrary scale. For instance, concentrations of methane from 0.0040 to 0.0200 cm.^{3}/l. are shown by a circle 3 mm. in diameter; those from 0.0200 to 0.0500 cm.^{3}/l., by a 5 mm. circle; those from 0.0500 to 0.5000 cm.^{3}/., by a 7 mm. circle; those from 0.5 to 1.0 cm.^{3}/l., by a 9 mm. circle; etc.

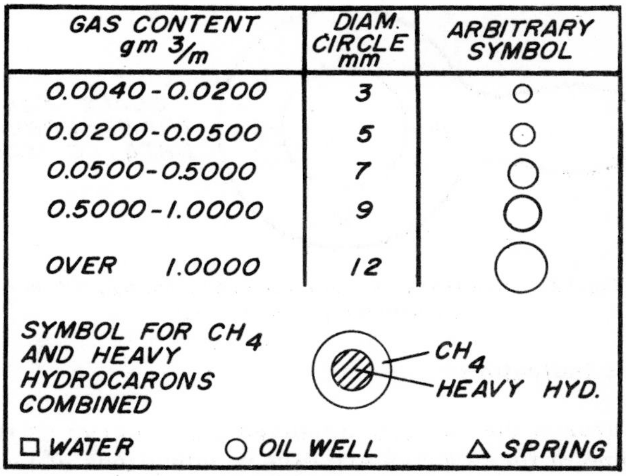

GAS CONTENT gm ^{3}/m	DIAM. CIRCLE mm	ARBITRARY SYMBOL
0.0040 - 0.0200	3	O
0.0200 - 0.0500	5	O
0.0500 - 0.5000	7	O
0.5000 - 1.0000	9	O
OVER 1.0000	12	O
SYMBOL FOR CH_4 AND HEAVY HYDROCARONS COMBINED		CH_4 — HEAVY HYD.
□ WATER	O OIL WELL	△ SPRING

Fig. 122. Arbitrary symbols for representing dissolved hydrocarbon gases on maps.

Circles over 2 cm. in diameter should not be used. The scale for each map depends on the characteristic gas content in the given area. Heavy hydrocarbons are represented by red circles or circles shaded with cross-hatching, while methane is represented by blue circles. An example of arbitrary symbols for gas-content maps is given in Fig. 122. An index denoting the age of the beds from which the water sample is obtained is given either inside or adjacent to each circle, and the type of source (water well, oil well, or spring) is indicated (see Fig. 122). Near each point is placed the serial number of the source.

If many water sources of the same kind are examined in a given area and are found to contain more or less similar concentrations of hydrocarbons, average values are recorded whenever the scale of the map does not permit including individual data. Natural gas seeps are also included on the gas-content map, which is constructed on a geological base map.

The results of the gas analyses are recorded on a second map. The percentage of each gas contained in the water is calculated beforehand, and the analyses are shown on a circular diagram. The diameter of the circle must be from 1 to 2 cm., depending on the density of observation points (Fig. 123).

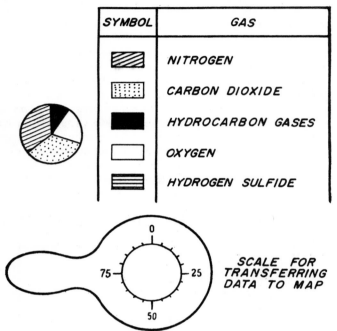

SYMBOL	GAS
	NITROGEN
	CARBON DIOXIDE
	HYDROCARBON GASES
	OXYGEN
	HYDROGEN SULFIDE

SCALE FOR TRANSFERRING DATA TO MAP

Fig. 123. Arbitrary symbols for representing analyses of dissolved gases on maps.

Oil and Gas Indicators

In water-gas surveys the various dissolved gases serve as indicators of petroleum. Some of these gases are direct indications of the presence of hydrocarbons at depth. These may come from a gas field or be part of an oil formation. Among the direct indicators are methane, ethane, propane, butane, and vapors of the higher saturated hydrocarbons. In some instances, however, methane is not a direct indicator of petroleum. This is true when the methane results from contemporary processes of decomposition of organic matter or is associated with other minerals (e.g., coal, bituminous shales, etc.). Heavy hydrocarbons (ethane, propane, etc.) are usually associated only with the gases of oil formations. It must be remembered, however, that these direct indicators of petroleum do not reveal the commercial importance of the pool.

Other indicators are indirect and reflect only conditions that are favorable for the accumulation of hydrocarbons. Hydrogen sulfide that is formed in reactions with the sulfates in water in the presence of hydrocarbons is one indirect indicator. A high percentage of nitrogen of biochemical origin may serve as evidence of closed structures. Carbon dioxide and oxygen indicate that conditions are favorable for oxidation in the depths. Nitrous oxide and ammonia in the waters reveal that the basin being investigated has been contaminated with organic matter of surface origin, often associated with human activity. According to E. K. Gerling (8), nitrous oxide is present in ground waters only to a depth of about 20 m. There is an especially large amount of nitrous oxide near the surface, but none at all in deep waters. According to G. A. Mogilevskii, ammonia is a typical gaseous product of intense microbiological activity in the presence of various organic "wastes".

A hydrocarbon microflora in the waters indicates that hydrocarbon gases assimilated by bacteria are also present in solution. Apparently there are some cases in which nearly all the hydrocarbon gas migrating with the waters is absorbed by bacteria near the surface, and in such cases the only way of detecting the gas is to study the hydrocarbon microflora. Therefore, the water-gas survey should be accompanied by a water-bacterial survey (Chapter XIII).

We have briefly considered the indicators of petroleum in the water-gas survey from the qualitative point of view. However, quantitative indicators are also very important. It is known, for example, that methane is found in very low concentrations in nearly all natural waters. Hence it is necessary to calculate the characteristic gas "background" for the region being investigated, as well as the sensitivity and accuracy of the apparatus employed (degasifiers, analytical devices).

Using previously obtained figures on gas saturations as if they were characteristic for all waters of oil formations is an absolutely unreliable approach. For instance, in investigating the Saratov formations I. B. Feigel'son considers only those concentrations of hydrocarbons which exceed 0.2% of the total volume of recovered gases. He discards all concentrations lying below this limit as untrustworthy.

This approach is basically unsound. Groundwaters seldom contain high concentrations of hydrocarbons; hence, a comparative study of concentrations in different areas wherein limits are not fixed arbitrarily is preferable. The only lower limit that may be set is connected mainly with the accuracy of the analysis. With current techniques this lower limit is 0.0030 cm.^{3}/l. for methane and 0.0010 cm.^{3}/l. for heavier hydrocarbons.

Interpretation of Water-Gas Survey Data

Maps of water-gas survey results are marked so as to show zones where various gases predominate. Thus, nitrogen-oxygen, carbon dioxide-nitrogen, carbon dioxide, nitrogen, methane, methane-nitrogen, and other zones may be distinguished. A distinction is also made between deep, intermediate and surface waters. The nitrogen-oxygen and nitrogen-carbon dioxide zones and the nitrogen-methane and methane-nitrogen zones which are usually associated with contemporary gas formation in marshes and peat bogs, are included in the surface water zone (aeration zone). The nitrogen and nitrogen-methane zones, which are connected with the deep penetration of atmospheric air, are included in the intermediate zone (erosion zone). Methane, heavy hydrocarbons (in waters associated with an oil pool or bituminous rocks), and in some cases nitrogen of biochemical origin and carbon dioxide of metamorphic origin are characteristic of deep waters.

There is undoubtedly a close connection between dissolved gases and salts in waters, but this has not been proven because the gaseous components have been underestimated. The work of I. B. Feigel'son and E. A. Bars around Saratov showed that hydrocarbon gases and nitrogen predominate when the waters are primarily of the calcium chloride and magnesium-chloride types. Carbon dioxide is primarily characteristic of waters of the sodium-sulfate, sodium-bicarbonate, and (rarely) magnesium-chloride types. Waters containing hydrogen sulfide are usually lacking in sulfates, because the latter is converted to hydrogen sulfide.

Zones where there is an increased concentration of hydrocarbons are indicated on the water-gas map as water-gas anomalies. Zones showing low concentrations constitute the gaseous background for the waters of the region. It must be remembered in designating anomalies that the hydrocarbon gas content in natural waters is not uniform even within the limits of an anomaly. This is especially true of groundwaters and may be explained by the fact that migration of gas and gas-bearing water from the depths is not uniform throughout the area. It follows the path of least resistance, such as fissures and zones of tectonic dislocations in folds and domes. For this reason points often occur within the anomaly which do not contain dissolved hydrocarbon gases. Special maps for methane and heavy hydrocarbons and a composite map are also compiled.

In interpreting water-gas survey data, the results are considered in the light of geologic structures, peculiarities of relief, and biochemical peculiarities of the area. When zones of high gas concentration coincide with favorable geological conditions, one has the most reliable criterion for drawing conclusions as to the possibilities of the region being investigated. Hydrochemical data, which necessarily are always collected during a water-gas survey, aid in shedding more light on the possibility of accumulations of oil and gas.

In these interpretations, the displacement of an anomaly caused by groundwater movement must be considered. The direction and rate of flow of the waters have a substantial significance because they alter the true position of the anomaly.

Evidently the seasons affect the gas content of waters. In rainy periods groundwaters are diluted by fresh waters and the concentrations of gases are decreased. Sometimes water-gas anomalies may be associated with small accumulations of gases in lenses or the formation of gases in marshy areas rather than with deeper oil and gas pools.

BIBLIOGRAPHY

1. V.I. Vernadskii. History of the minerals of the earth's crust. Vol. II. History of natural waters. Goskhimtekhizdat, 1933.
2. A.M. Ovchinnikov. Mineral waters. Gosgeolozdat, 1947.
3. A.M. Ovchinnikov. On a new classification of springs. Byull. Mosk. Obshch. Ispytatelei Prirody, nov. ser. otd. geol. 25, No. 6, 1950.

4. V.A. Sulin. Waters of oil formations in the system of natural waters. Gostoptekhizdat, 1946.

5. M.S. Goryunov, V.G. Kleinberg, and V.P. Savchenko. Method of testing natural gases in the field. Gostoptekhizdat, 1940.

6. V.P. Savchenko. Instruction in the investigation of the gas-bearing nature of underground waters in deep rotary drilling. VSEGINGEO, 1940.

7. A.A. Cherepennikov. Direction of testing and analysis of natural gases. Gosgeolozdat, 1951.

8. E.K. Gerling and V.G. Barkan. On the content of nitrous oxide in natural waters. Prikladnaya khimiya 17, No. 6, 1944.

9. A.I. Kravtsov and M.M. Elinson. Toward the question of the influence of underground waters on the gas-bearing character of coal formations in the Donets basin. Tr. Inst. Geol. Nauk, v. 42, ser. geol., No. 12. Publ. Acad. Sci. USSR, 1940.

10. A.I. Kravtsov. Influence of geological conditions on the gas-bearing character of coal formations. Ugletekhizdat, 1950.

CHAPTER ELEVEN

Soil-Salt Methods

Soil-salt methods of prospecting for oil and gas formations are based on the determination of the content and composition of salts (and some other mineral components) in soils. Salts in soils are closely connected with salts dissolved in ground and other waters. Therefore, a close connection also exists between soil-salt and hydrochemical (see Chapter IX) methods.

Soil-salt indicators of petroleum are divided, as in hydrochemical surveying, into direct and indirect categories. In contrast to the hydrochemical methods, however, there is only one direct soil-salt indicator, and that is iodine. All other soil-salt indices are indirect and are divided into two groups. On the one hand, the soil contains those substances that may be formed because of the influence of an oil or gas pool (calcium carbonate, silica). On the other hand, there may be other accumulations in the soil that are due to deep brines rather than to petroleum. These will be mainly chlorides. The influence of deep aquifers on the salt composition of soils (and groundwaters, as well) is chiefly dependent on tectonic conditions. Hence the chloride content of soils may, in turn, indicate tectonic features. Thus, it also may be used in oil prospecting.

The principal, most thoroughly studied soil-salt indicator is the chloride ion. Therefore, soil-salt methods are important mainly as an indirect approach to the search for petroleum because they are used primarily in elucidating geological structure. With regard to general problems, types of indicators studied, and the very nature of the work, soil-salt methods are almost identical with structural hydrochemical surveying of ground waters (see Chapter IX). In a number of cases these surveys have been carried out simultaneously.[1]

However, soil-salt methods also differ fundamentaly from hydrochemical (and other geochemical) methods. In the first place, they use soil, which is peculiar in its nature and qualitatively different from the waters, rocks etc. Secondly, some soil-salt petroleum indicators (e.g., carbonate) have no relation to hydrochemistry. Therefore these methods must be considered separately.

The first soil-salt surveys conducted for the purpose of oil prospecting originated from the gas survey and the diffusion-current theory of V. A. Sokolov. The soil-salt surveys conducted in the USA in 1938 were based on these same ideas. In the USSR soil-salt methods appeared in 1944 (I. I.

---

[1] V.A. Kovda and P.S. Slavin combine indicators of the soil-salt and hydrochemical methods and also soil bitumens in a single group of "soil-geochemical" indicators (1). However, it must be remembered that: first, groundwaters may have no connection with the soil; second, groundwaters belong to a unified system of natural waters, to which soils do not; third, soil-geochemical indicators must include soil gases and soil bacteria which broadens the scope of this concept excessively. Soil-salt indicators have peculiarities of their own; therefore, it is more convenient to consider them separately.

Feofarova). They were developed later under the direction of V. A. Kovda (1). In contrast to the American work, in which soil-salt indicators were studied without considering other factors, these indicators were approached for the first time in the USSR from a soil-genesis viewpoint. In the USSR, soil-salt methods involve careful consideration of geographical environment, hydrogeological conditions, the chemistry of deep aquifers, and other factors. The soil-iodine and soil-gypsum methods were first applied and developed in the USSR.

Soil-salt methods are used chiefly in detailed surveys. Soil maps already on hand are also used. At present the following types of soil-salt methods are known: (1) chloride, (2) iodine, (3) gypsum, (4) carbonate-siallite, (5) radium. All these surveys may be used either separately or combined. The different methods are discussed below in the order of decreasing importance.

VARIOUS TYPES OF SOIL-SALT METHODS

The Chloride Method

The chloride method, as already stated, is the most important and most thoroughly developed of the soil-salt methods. Soil-chloride surveys are most nearly related to hydrochemical ones. Chlorides are salts which are easily soluble in water, and the chloride content of soils is closely connected with the chloride content of ground and stagnant surface waters. Chlorides are found in soils either in percolating solutions, i.e., in the capillary waters of the soil, or as crystals deposited from solution. Chlorides enter the soil mainly from ground waters as a result of capillary action.

Like structural hydrochemical surveys of ground and surface waters, the soil-chloride survey is an indirect method of oil prospecting. Its immediate aim is to reveal the deep geological structure (see above). The theory and method of interpretation of soil-chloride surveys and hydrochemical surveys of ground waters are the same. The principal index of the soil-chloride survey is the soil-chloride anomaly over a structural uplift. The soil background values and local relief must also be taken into account.

The zonal nature of soils is very significant in the soil-chloride method. In a desert zone where "burozems" and "serozems" (brown soils and gray soils) are developed, salty soils are common and salt marshes are developed. Soil chloride anomalies are determined by the following quantities: (1) total water-soluble salts in the soil; (2) the Cl/SO_4 ratio in water-soluble salts in the soil. According to V. A. Kovda and P. S. Slavin, background values for total water-soluble salts in a desert zone lie between 0.3 - 4%, while anomalous values lie between 2 - 15%. Background values for the Cl/SO_4 ratio are between 0.2 - 4 and anomalous values are between 2 - 25 (1). In areas of flat or negative relief soil chloride anomalies over tectonic uplifts may be very distinct, often forming masses of moist, saline soil (Fig. 124). In areas with positive relief the anomaly is more complicated (just as in the case of ground waters; see Chapter IX). It acquires an annular or spotty form that is concentrated in the depressions in the relief.

In a steppe zone where chernozems (black soils) and nut-brown soils

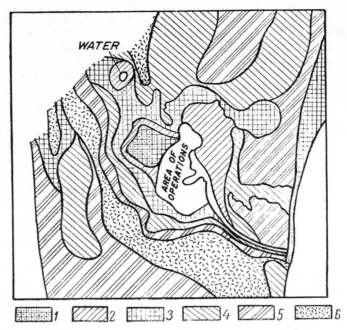

Fig. 124. Example of a soil-chloride chart (according to
V. A. Kovda and P. S. Slavin). 1—Cl:SO$_4$ ratio over 10;
2—Cl:SO$_4$ ratio from 5 to 10; 3—Cl:SO$_4$ from 2.5 to 5;
4—Cl:SO$_4$ ratio from 2 to 2.5; 5—Cl:SO$_4$ ratio from 1.5
to 2; 6—Cl:SO$_4$ ratio less than 1.5.

are developed, the content of water-
soluble salts in the soil is usually negligible. Soil-chloride anomalies over
structural uplifts, as a rule, cannot endure in this zone. Because of abundant
atmospheric precipitation and the dis-
sected relief, soils lose their salts, and
the chlorides are washed away. However,
the disappearance of salt marshes may
result in the formation of a "solonetz",
or soil containing large amounts of sodium carbonate. (The Na cation absorbed by the soil is a residue of the
NaCl which was previously in the soil.)
In a steppe zone, therefore, a solonetz
or an alkaline soil is an important indicator. For example, in the Saratov Volga
region alkaline soils correspond to tectonic uplifts (Fig. 125). Every solonetz,
even if it is quite free of chlorides, must
be regarded as a soil-chloride indicator,
since the solonetz is a vestige of former
chloride salinity. However, it must be
kept in mind that the solonetz may also

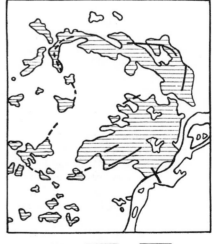

Fig. 125. Correlation between alkaline
soils and the axes of structural uplifts
(according to P. S. Slavin). 1—masses
of moderately and strongly alkaline
soils and solonetz; 2—axes of folds
known to contain oil; 3—axes of folds
believed to contain oil.

be of purely surface origin and may be a residue not of chloride, but of sodium-sulfate salinity.

In forest and forest-steppe zones where podsols, gray forest soils, and degraded chernozems develop, neither saline nor alkaline soils can endure. The soil-chloride method is generally inapplicable there.

The Iodine Method

The soil-iodine method, in contrast to the soil-chloride one, is a direct method of prospecting for oil formations. The significance of iodine in soils for oil prospecting results from its significance in underground waters (see Chapter IX). The normal content of iodine in soils is of the order of $10^{-4}\%$. According to V. A. Kovda and P. S. Slavin, the iodine content of soils over several oil formations reaches $10^{-3}\%$ or even $10^{-2}\%$ (1). Soil-iodine anomalies over oil-bearing structures are more distinct than soil-chloride anomalies. This is explained by the preferential concentration of iodine in the waters within the structure (Fig. 126).

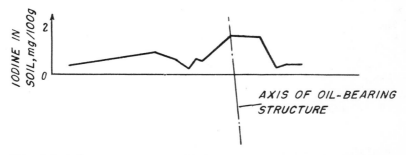

Fig. 126. Soil-iodine transverse profile (according to V. A. Kovda and P. S. Slavin).

Since iodine is directly associated with petroleum, iodine anomalies can only be observed in oil-bearing areas. Hence, if the soil-chloride survey can only reveal the locality of structural highs (or other tectonic features), the role of the soil-iodine survey must be to determine (as with other direct methods) the actual presence of oil in these areas. It must be noted, however, that only limited use of the soil-iodine method has been made up to the present time. Few data have been obtained as yet, and these all are from regions where considerable tectonism has occurred. The iodine method requires considerable development.

The Gypsum Method

In contrast to the soil-salt methods discussed above, the soil-gypsum method is based on the determination in the soil of calcium sulfate, a salt that is difficultly soluble in water. This salt occurs in the soil mainly in the crystalline form. The investigations of V. A. Kovda and P. S. Slavin have extablished that in some oil-bearing areas the distribution of gypsum in the soils is anomalous (1). However, these anomalies are extremely complex and can only be interpreted with the aid of soil-chloride and hydrochemical data on the area. Therefore, gypsum in the soil can be regarded as a supplementary, auxiliary indicator.

The gypsum content of the soil is dependent on an influx of salts from deeper levels, the nature of these salts, and an inflow of hydrocarbons. Chlorides from the depths decrease the relative sulfate content (the value of SO_4/Cl; see above), including gypsum, in the soil. Calcium chloride from deeper strata reacts with the sodium and magnesium sulfate in the soil. This leads to an absolute enrichment of gypsum in the soil according to the reactions:

$$CaCl_2 + Na_2SO_4 \rightarrow 2NaCl + CaSO_4 \downarrow$$

Soda from the depths can react directly with the soil gypsum, and this leads to the transformation of the sulfate to a soluble form and the disappearance of gypsum:

$$2NaHCO_3 + CaSO_4 \rightarrow Na_2SO_4 + Ca(HCO_3)_2 .$$

Lastly, hydorcarbon gases from the depths can reduce sulfates (see the diagram of the process in Chapter I) and may lead to destruction of the gypsum in the soil. Because of the interaction of these processes (and possibly others, as well), the distribution of gypsum in the soils over oil pools is very complex.

If deep waters containing calcium chloride enter the soil, a positive gypsum anomaly may be formed. Nevertheless, the value of Cl/SO_4 (taking all the SO_4 into account) may be decreased with respect to the background. If alkaline waters enter the soil from the depths, a negative gypsum anomaly may be formed; however, the value of Cl/SO_4 may remain high in this case. Hydrocarbons apparently have considerably less effect than the salts, and therefore, it is very difficult, if at all possible, to separate this effect.

It follows from the above that interpreting indicators such as the gypsum content in soils presents very great difficulties. Such interpretation inevitably requires the use of soil-chloride data. The soil-gypsum survey gives no more information than the soil-chloride survey, and its interpretation is considerably more complicated.

The Carbonate-Siallite Method

The soil carbonate-siallite survey is based on the use of three indicators in soils: (1) calcium carbonate; (2) silica; (3) alumina. These indicators have two things in common in that they are insoluble in soil waters and they may result from the same process. However, calcium carbonate on the one hand and silica and alumina (siallite) on the other may be regarded as independent indicators and may be determined separately.

The following essential differences exist between them.

1. Calcium carbonate may accumulate in soils as soda comes from the depths:

$$2NaHCO_3 + CaSO_4 \rightarrow Na_2SO_4 + CaCO_3 \downarrow + CO_2 + H_2O .$$

This phenomenon can take place only where alkaline waters occur in the deeper strata.

2. Calcium carbonate as well as silica and alumina may be formed when hydrocarbon gases rising from the depths are oxidized to carbon dioxide. Calcium aluminosilicates, which form part of the mineral framework of the soil are decomposed by this carbon dioxide.

$$CH_4 + 2O_2 \rightarrow CO_2 + 2H_2O;$$

$$CaAl_2Si_6O_{16} + CO_2 \rightarrow CaCO_3 + 6SiO_2 + Al_2O_3.$$

This phenomenon can occur wherever hydrocarbons rise from the depths, i.e., over oil or gas pools. The decomposition of aluminosilicates in the soil is practically a universal process, usually due to CO_2 of surface origin. However, anomalous accumulations of calcium carbonate, alumina, and silica, may be significant. Thus, an anomalous increase in the calcium carbonate content of the soil may be considered an indirect indicator of petroleum. If alkaline waters are absent, the soil-carbonate anomaly indicates the probability of the presence of oil (or gas) in the given area.

The investigations of V. A. Kovda and P. S. Slavin (1) showed that soil-carbonate anomalies over oil pools are characterized by a contrast between 2 and 5 (Fig. 127). However, the question of calcium-carbonate as an indicator has not yet been adequately investigated. There are still insufficient data. It is particularly important to determine the connection between soil-carbonate anomalies and tectonic fissuring of rocks. The latter, of course, has a marked effect on the magnitude of gas migration.

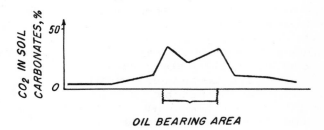

Fig. 127. Soil-carbonate transverse profile (according to V. A. Kovda and P. S. Slavin).

Silica and alumina in the soil are not, strictly speaking, soil-salt indicators. However, there is no point in putting them in a separate category. Anomalous accumulation of silica and alumina in the soil caused by gas or oil pools is not easily ascertained because the content of these substances in soils is not uniform.

According to E. Rosaire in the USA, many soil-siallite anomalies were distinguished in oil areas. The increased density of soil and subsoil horizons caused by these anomalies was so great that it could be detected by geophysical methods such as gravimetry, as well as electrical and seismic exploration (2). However, this claim must be viewed with caution, since it is known that the results of geochemical surveys in the USA are often refined and embellished for advertising purposes before publication.

In any case the carbonate-siallite method of soil surveying requires further development and merits considerable attention. Its special value may consist in its applicability (especially, the siallite variation) in more humid zones (forest, forest-steppe) zones where chloride indicators are entirely lacking.

APPLICATION OF SOIL-SALT METHODS

Soil-salt methods are used primarily in detailed area surveys (scale, 1:50,000 or larger). The field work consists in sampling soils from specially drilled shallow wells (or pits). Sampling points are located in a grid pattern, the peculiarities of the soil cover being taken into account. Sampling is accompanied by description of the soils and compilation of a schematic soil map. Soil samples are taken from every genetic horizon in wells and pits.[2]

The kind of soil analysis depends on the type of survey, but in all cases it is carreid out by the methods usually employed in soil work. In the chloride and iodine surveys, analysis of water extracts with additional determination of absorbed cations in some cases is sufficient. The method of preparation and analysis of the extracts is very simple. All chlorides, the sodium and magnesium sulfates, soda, and iodine pass quantitatively into the water extracts, while other salts and cations are dissolved only to a slight degree. In the water extracts the Cl and SO_4 ions are determined just as in waters (see Chapter IX).[3]

The determination of absorbed cations is more difficult. The soil is usually treated with a solution of ammonium chloride and the resulting filtrate is analyzed for the principal ions, including calcium and magnesium. Sodium is calculated by difference. This method cannot be applied to soils containing much carbonate, and in this case, the determination of absorbed cations is practically an impossible task.

In the gypsum and carbonate surveys, hydrochloric acid extracts must be prepared and analyzed. These are prepared from samples already treated with water. Most of the sulfates and carbonates of calcium and most of the free colloidal silica go into the hydrochloric acid extracts. SO_4, HCO_3 and CO_3 ions are determined in these extracts and then the gypsum and calcium carbonate content of the soil is calculated. The total sulfate content includes the sulfate from both extractions. In the siallite survey, where SiO_2 and Al_2O_3 must be determined, analyses are even more difficult.

Data obtained for specific soil horizons may be averaged for the entire soil section. Profiles and maps are then constructed either on the basis of specific soil horizons or on the averaged data (see examples given above). Soil-salt surveys are also conducted in conjunction with other geochemical surveys, and the interpretation of results is correlated with other surveys.

RADIOACTIVITY SURVEYS

The radioactivity survey should also be included with soil-salt methods of prospecting for petroleum. There are two variations of the method: soil

---

[2] The soil layer (after Vilenskii, 3) is divided into four principal genetic levels constituting the soil profile, which are distinguished according to color, texture, structure, etc.: (1) topsoil or the horizon in which humus collects (A); (2) an eluvial or leached horizon (E); (3) an illuvial or depositional horizon (I); (4) subsoil or bedrock (M). Each horizon in a given section may differ considerably from all other horizons with respect to salt composition.

[3] The analysis of water extracts of rocks, conducted in similar fashion, may give valuable data for paleogeographic purposes (4).

radioactivity and aerial radioactivity.

Soil and aerial surveys conducted in Canada and Texas have revealed the presence of anomalously high radioactivity in soils and air over oil formations in a number of cases. These anomalies were annular in form (5).[4] According to H. Lundberg such anomalies over oil pools are explained by the rise in these places of deep-lying chloride waters enriched in radium and the precipitation of radium sulfate in the soil (5). This explanation is very plausible.

Many metamorphosed chloride brines contain an anomalously high amount of radium, up to 10^{-5} mg./l. (6, 7). Radium chloride accumulates in these brines. This may be because the brine has been in contact with radium bearing rocks over a long period. It may also be because of the high chloride content of the waters and the formation of the one highly soluble radium salt, $RaCl_2$. No direct connection between radium and oil has been established.

The reason for using radioactivity as an indicator of petroleum is its association with chlorine. The ascent of waters and salts may cause the accumulation of radium and chloride in the soil. Actually, it has been shown that soil radioactivity anomalies coincide with soil-chloride anomalies (5). Radium sulfate may be deposited in the soil according to the equation:

$$RaCl_2 + Na_2SO_4 \rightarrow 2NaCl + RaSO_4.$$

However, even when this process does not occur, radium present in the soil solution as radium chloride may give rise to anomaly of radioactivity in the soil.[5]

The radioactivity survey is essentially the same in its theoretical basis and significance as the soil-chloride survey (see above). Anomalies in the soil (and in the air) may be regarded only as indications of tectonic uplifts and faults and not as direct indications of oil formations.

It must be kept in mind that by no means all the water from oil-bearing strata contains increased amounts of radium. Hence, the absence of radioactivity cannot be considered a negative indication. In interpreting the results of aerial surveys, one must also remember that anomalies of radioactivity may be observed over areas of granite (which, as is known, contains the greatest amount of radioactive elements, mainly thorium, of all rocks).

The radioactivity survey, especially the aerial survey, merits close attention, testing and perhaps, considerable use. Evidently, the aerial survey can render considerable aid in geological mapping and understanding the tectonics of extensive, little known, and difficulty accessible territories.

---

[4] The determination of radioactivity in soils and air was carried out with the aid of scintillation counters mounted on automobiles and airplanes. This method is also a geophysical method since it involves direct measurement of physical properties.

[5] The radioactivity of the air is caused by radon evolved in the disintegration of radium.

BIBLIOGRAPHY

1. V.A. Kovda and P.S. Slavin. Soil-geochemical indicators of deep oil-bearing rocks. Akad. Nauk. SSSR, 1951.
2. E.E. Rosaire. Geochemical prospecting for petroleum. Bull. Am. Assn. Petrol. Geol., vol. 24, No. 8, 1940.
3. D.G. Vilenskii. Soil management. Sel'khozgiz, 1950.
4. A.A. Kartsev. Paleogeochemical investigation of the Maikop beds of Georgia. Tr. MNI, No. 13. Gostoptekhizdat, 1953.
5. H. Lundberg. World Petroleum, vol. 23, No. 5, 1952.
6. V.I. Vernadskii. Essays on geochemistry. Gorgeonefteizdat, 1934.
7. V. Chlopin and W. Vernadsky. Z. Elektrochem. 38, 524, 1932.

CHAPTER TWELVE

The Oxidation-Reduction Potential Method

The oxidation-reduction potential method (redox potential or ORP method) was first developed and used for oil prospecting in 1935 by V. E. Levenson (1). The method consists in measuring the electrical potential developed between a natural medium (rock, soil, water) and a hydrogen electrode. This potential shows the degree of oxidation or reduction of the medium, and in general, it is relatively low in the presence of such a strongly reduced substance as petroleum. The more oxidized the medium is the higher the oxidation-reduction potential will be and vice-versa.

The oxidation-reduction potential measured with the hydrogen electrode is expressed by E_H. $E_H = 0.029 \log (H^+)/(H_2)$ (at 18° C).[1] The hydrogen electrode consists of a sheet of platinum immersed in a normal solution of hydrochloric acid (pH = 0) saturated with hydrogen at a pressure of one atm., i.e., $(H^+) = (H_2)$ and consequently, the E_H of the hydrogen electrode is equal to zero. The value of E_H may be measured directly with a potentiometer. From the E_H may be calculated rH_2 (negative logarithm of the molecular hydrogen concentration):[2] $rH_2 = (E_H/0.029) + 2pH$ (T = 18° C). There is no real geochemical difference between E_H and rH_2. The more oxidized the medium is, the greater are its E_H and rH_2 and vice versa. A medium with a large E_H will oxidize a medium with a smaller E_H.

APPLICATION OF THE METHOD

Hydrocarbons, as is known, are relatively reduced compounds in a sedimentary environment. Therefore, the presence of hydrocarbons in the rocks must decrease the redox potential of the latter. The nearer and larger the oil pool, the more pronounced this effect should be. This very idea was proposed by V. E. Levenson as the basis for the redox potential method (1). Levenson and his co-workers determined the E_H of rocks from several horizons in pits and wells. A potentiometer was used for determinations on potassium chloride extracts from rock samples saturated with carbon dioxide, and the rH_2 was calculated from E_H measurements. In a number of cases a regular decrease in E_H and rH_2 along the strike of the strata in the direction of oil-bearing strata was established. In the Troekurovo-Gubinian area, drilling confirmed the presence of oil which had been predicted by a redox survey (2).

However, a number of complications developed which made the

---

[1] The $(H^+)/(H_2)$ ratio (the ratio of ionic to molecular hydrogen) in the given medium, is used for convenience in determination. Numerically $(H^+)/(H_2)$ is equal to $(Ox)/(Red)$, i.e., it is equal to the ratio of all oxidized and reduced forms in the given medium (for example, the forms of iron, sulfur, etc.) and therefore fully replaces this total ratio.

[2] Often incorrectly written as rH.

interpretation of E_H and rH_2 more difficult. It was found that rocks containing hydrogen sulfide, but lacking in oil bitumens, have a much lower E_H and rH_2 than oil-bearing rocks which do not contain hydrogen sulfide. Hydrogen sulfide is a stronger reducing agent than hydrocarbons. This complication is not so serious since hydrogen sulfide is itself an indirect indicator of petroleum (see Chapter X).

It has also been established that solid oil bitumens or heavy oils in rocks do not exert a strong influence on the E_H and rH_2. Even small pools of heavy oil (e.g., in Shubany) do not have any appreciable effect in some cases. Nevertheless, the redox potential method developed by V. E. Levenson merits considerable attention. At the present time further developments and testing are in progress.

I. P. Serdobol'skii et al. developed another variation of the method, the soil-redox potential survey (3). The idea behind this survey is that hydrocarbon gases seeping into the soil from an oil or gas pool must decrease the redox potential of the soil. Consequently, the results of soil-redox potential surveys should correspond to gas survey results.

Similar experimental work was carried out in several oil-bearing areas in Transcaucasia and other regions of the USSR. In this work measurements of redox potential were carried out directly in the soil on the walls of pits (up to depths of 50 cm.) without taking samples by using a potentiometer and a condenser.[3] This work was done in connection with a soil-salt and a soil-bitumen survey. The determinations were conducted at the same points. Negative redox potential anomalies in the soils, evidently caused by oil or gas pools, were shown to occur. These anomalies, like gas

Fig. 128. Transverse soil profile of a redox potential survey (after I. Serdobol'skii).

anomalies, may be annular in form (Fig. 128). However, it has also been found that soil redox potential anomalies over oil pools may also be positive, i.e., values of redox potential may be abnormally high (4). This may be caused by organisms using oil hydrocarbons and associated with them.

It has also been established that the soil redox potential fluctuates considerably depending on moisture, humus content, population of the soil, and other factors. In the opinion of P. S. Slavin the anomalous increase in redox potential values above oil and gas pools may be due to the "influence of such associated elements as iodine and bromine" (5). All this greatly complicates the interpretation of redox potential measurements on soil and seriously diminishes the value of this type of survey.

S. Ya. Vainbaum suggested another use of redox potential methods in the "subsoil survey". In this survey, measurements are made at depths not greater than 2 - 3 m. (within the walls of gas-survey bore holes) with the aid of a special apparatus and a probe (6, 7). Similar work was done in the Middle Volga region.

_____

[3]This direct measurement of a physical parameter of the medium constitutes a link between this method and geophysical methods.

BIBLIOGRAPHY

1. V.E. Levenson. Problems of mud volcanism and geochemical bituminology. Sb. "Rezul'tat. issled. gryaz. vulkanov Krymsko-
   Kavkaz. geol. prov." Akad. Nauk. SSSR, 1939.
2. S.F. Fedorov. Factors in the comparative evaluation of oil-bearing
   rocks. Tr. MNI, No. 2. Gostoptekhizdat, 1940.
3. I. Serdobol'skii. Oxidation-reduction potential of soils. Nov. neft.
   tekh., geol. Izd. TsIMTnefti, 1948.
4. V.A. Kovda and P.S. Slavin. Soil-geochemical indicators of deep oil-
   bearing rocks. Akad. Nauk. SSSR, 1951.
5. P.S. Slavin. On the soil-geochemical method of prospecting for
   petroleum. Sb. "Geokhim. metody poiskov nefti i gaza, No. 1.
   Gostoptekhizdat, 1953.
6. S.Ya. Vainbaum. Probe for the measurement of potential differences
   in oxidation-reduction systems. Polevaya i promyslovaya
   geokhimiya, No. 1. Gostoptekhizdat, 1953.
7. S.Ya. Vainbaum. Apparatus for the measurement of E_H values at the
   bottoms of gas-survey wells. Polevaya i promyslovaya geokhimiya, No. 1. Gostoptekhizdat, 1953.

CHAPTER THIRTEEN

Microbiological Methods

The content of hydrocarbon gases in the subterranean atmosphere, and also in the biosphere as a whole, is determined to a significant extent by the correlation of a number of oppositely directed microbiological processes. One of the latter leads to the formation of hydrocarbon and other fuel gases. The others, on the contrary, lead to rearrangement and destruction of these gases.

It is understood that all these different processes warrant study and concrete consideration to the same extent. Only in this way can serious errors be avoided in the use of geochemical prospecting methods based on the determination of migrating hydrocarbon gases and vapors. The actual magnitude of processes of oxidation of hydrocarbon gases now taking place and their practical significance in oil and gas prospecting were not immediately apparent. It must be noted that even today these phenomena are not adequately studied.

The very first investigations of microbiological oxidation of hydrocarbons were conducted mainly on samples of oil-bearing strata and on those parts of the earth's surface in which there were open outlets of sources of oil and gas (V. O. Tauson). Processes of oxidation of methane and hydrogen formed during the day in lakes, seas, and other bodies of water were also studied. (V. L. Isachenko, V. S. Butkevich, S. I. Kuznetsov.)

The presence in sedimentary rocks over oil and gas pools of a specific bacterial population which oxidized the hydrocarbon gases of the migration current became known relatively recently as a result of the development in the Soviet Union of the microbiological method of prospecting for oil and gas. The origin of this method is connected with research work on gas surveying conducted in 1937 in Isachki (Ukr. SSR). On the basis of this work (1) it was proved that the microquantities of hydrocarbon gases and some incombustible components (nitrous oxide) present in the subterranean atmosphere over oil and gas pools vary throughout the year and sometimes vanish altogether.

This circumstance led to the idea of the possible existence in the deposits of a subterranean bacterial population requiring the hydrocarbon gases of the migration current. Such a hypothesis not only explained seasonal changes in the indicators used for gas surveying, but also revealed the equally important possibility of using the naturally occurring hydrocarbon microflora as a biological indicator in prospecting for oil and gas.

On the basis these considerations a microbiological method of prospecting for oil and gas was proposed in 1937 by G. A. Mogilevskii (2). Research conducted in 1937-1939 by the Department of Microbiology of TSKhA under the direction of Professor V. S. Butkevich confirmed the validity of the proposed hypothesis.

Work in known oil- and gas-bearing areas revealed that in sedimentary rock strata microorganisms are active which subsist by utilizing the gases of the migration current. Depending on the qualitative composition of the incoming gases, these microorganisms are represented by specific forms which oxidize either methane alone, ethane and propane, or other, heavier hydrocarbons. Hydrocarbon gases of the migration current are present in known amounts in the composition of the subterranean atmosphere of sedimentary rocks. Furthermore, in their migration from a pool to the earth's surface they traverse aquifers and dissolve in the waters. Hydrocarbon-consuming bacteria settle wherever hydrocarbon gases and vapors exist, i.e., in native rocks, in the waters of aquifers over oil or gas accumulations, or in soils.

Investigations of subterranean waters and the cores of test wells revealed that biochemical oxidation of hydrocarbon gases can be followed to a considerable depth. However, these processes occur most vigorously in the weathering zone. Thus, various forms of hydrocarbon microflora together form a unique biological filter which can intercept and digest a considerable part of the fuel gases migrating to the surface.

Biological oxidation of hydrocarbons, therefore, cannot affect the indices of gas surveying and other geochemical methods of prospecting for oil and gas. Furthermore, as a result of microbiological oxidation of hydrocarbons in soils, various products of bacterial metabolism accumulate: carbon dioxide, humic substances, etc.

If these products are taken into consideration, new criteria for oil and gas prospecting may be established. At present, several variations of the microbiological method exist. Depending on whether the hydrocarbon-oxidizing microorganisms are sought in water or rock, a soil microbiological survey or an aqueous one is used. If a thick section of sedimentary strata (with aquifers included) is investigated for hydrocarbon-oxidizing bacteria, a third variant of bacterial prospecting arises — biologging.

There are no fundamental theoretical differences among these variants of the microbiological method of prospecting for oil and gas. The most highly developed method at present is the aqueous microbiological survey, used either alone or in conjunction with other types of hydrogeochemical investigations in preliminary survey work in new regions. Less use is made of the soil microbiological survey, the task of which is usually restricted to the examination of structures already discovered by geophysical prospecting or core drilling.

Biologging is ordinarily used in conjuction with gas logging in the examination of geological structure tests. Unfortunately, both geochemical and biochemical investigations of wells drilled with the core bit are as yet poorly developed.

The bacterial yield survey has not been used in practice owing to the unwieldiness of the required operations. It is based on the degree of development of bacterial cultures oxidizing methane, ethane, propane, liquid hydrocarbons, and hydrogen after standing 10 - 12 days in shallow wells of 3 - 5 meters depth.

All variations of the microbiological method of prospecting for oil and gas were first proposed and developed in the Soviet Union. Soviet priority in this field is irrefutably confirmed by the dates of delivery and publication of the author's attestations on the microbiological method (3), given 2 - 3 years earlier (10/XI 1937) than American patents on analogous types of geomicrobiological surveying (4, 5).

The proposals of the American investigators appeared in the USA after a number of reports and articles on microbiological surveying were published, first in the Soviet press, and then as reviews of our work in the American journal, "Geophys. Abstr.," No. 1028 (1938) and No. 2034 (1941). Despite this, only the very latest works of the noted American microbiologist ZoBell have made reference to the work of Soviet authors in the field of microbiological surveying. Even here misrepresentations of factual data on Soviet priority (6, 7) occur.

One of the co-workers of ZoBell – Collins – writes in an article published in 1943 (8) that he does not have sufficient means to test the method of bacterial surveying. This possibility was called "the great hope of the future". At that time a vast amount of work had been done in the USSR on application of the method. Thus, the microbiological survey was not only first proposed, but also first applied in practice in the USSR.

THEORETICAL BASIS OF THE MICROBIOLOGICAL METHOD

The microbiological method of prospecting for oil and gas, as well as gas surveying proposed by V. A. Sokolov (9), is based primarily on the migration of gases through a layer of sedimentary rock. This hypothesis, general for all geochemical methods of prospecting, is set forth in preceding sections of this work. Another, equally important principle of the method is the physiological ability of a limited group of microorganisms to subsist in sedimentary deposits — on the surface of the earth and in the depths — owing to the energy of oxidation of hydrocarbon gases.

Before turning to the discussion of special questions related to the use of biological indicators, the essential difference between the gas and microbiological survey methods of studying the current of migrating hydrocarbons should be stated. Microbiological surveying studies those masses of microorganisms which develop in subsoil and deep-lying deposits owing to biological assimilation of the diffusing gases. Therefore, with the aid of the microbiological method it is possible to determine the presence or absence of that part of the hydrocarbon current which is utilized by the bacterial population of the subsoil in its metabolic processes. In contrast to this, gas surveying fixes only those quantities of hydrocarbon gases which reach the surface without having undergone biological oxidation or sorption on their way.

It follows from this that for accurate evaluation of the intensity of the hydrocarbon current, it is necessary to take into account all of its component parts, of which one is absorbed by the bacterial filter, another is sorbed by water and rock, and a third remains untouched by these processes.

The significance of microbiological investigations in the total complex of geobiochemical methods of oil and gas prospecting is chiefly determined by the character and scale of the subterranean activity of microorganisms and their role in the formation and destruction of hydrocarbon and other gases. The general information given below on microorganisms and their biochemical activity gives an indication of the possible effect of this factor on the basic parameters of geochemical methods of surveying.

General Information on Microorganisms

Microorganisms are living organisms which are all very small (microscopic). The dimensions of microorganisms are usually measured in thousandths and ten-thousandths, and sometimes hundred-thousandths of a millimeter. Most microbes are one-celled organisms. However, particularly types of organisms are encountered, such as some filar bacteria, etc., which consist of a considerable number of cells.

Owing to their small dimensions, microbes easily penetrate the finest cracks, pores, and fissures, and are carried for great distances by dust particles. Because of their small dimensions, microbes have an enormous surface of contact with the surrounding medium. Therefore, encounters of microbes with various molecules occur quite frequently, even when the latter are very highly dispersed in the medium. This permits a number of microorganisms easily to utilize gaseous substances as a source of nourishment.

Under favorable conditions microbes multiply exceptionally rapidly (every 20 - 30 min.). For the majority of forms multiplication takes place by transverse division. Higher forms of filar bacteria, ray fungi, and yeasts multiply by other methods (aerial spores, gemmation, etc.).

Particular notice should be taken of the ability of some kinds of bacteria to form spores (spore-forming bacteria are called bacilli). In contrast to fungi and lower plants, the formation of spores from bacteria is not related to their multiplication. Spores are a definite stage of development of bacteria, permitting them to survive the onset of unfavorable external conditions.

The metabolism of microorganisms can proceed in a relatively wide range of temperatures between a few degrees below zero and 85 - 90° C above zero. However, for concrete types of microorganisms and specific breeds, the temperature intervals between minimum and maximum appear to be narrower. In general the activity of microbiological processes conforms to the rule of van't Hoff, according to which the rate of a chemical reaction increases 2 - 3 times when the temperature increases 10° C.

The microbes are extremely varied. They are subdivided into classes, types, and families according to their morphological peculiarities, physiological properties, and family relations. At the present time, on the basis of study of the evolution and origin of microorganisms (N. A. Krasil'nikov), bacteria are divided into four separate classes (10).

Class I: Actinomycetes
Class II: Bacteria
Class III: Myxobacteria
Class IV: Spirochetae

Actinomycetes or ray fungi are sometimes grouped with fungi. Also, forms are encountered among the Actinomycetes which are difficult to distinguish from bacteria, such as mycobacteria and coccus-like types. A branched cell structure is characteristic of actinomycetes in the early stage of growth. A colony of actinomycetes is sometimes velvety and sometimes powdery in form. The powdery form is caused by spore formation at the ends of the filiments (Fig. 129).

Bacteria include morphologically varied species. Among this group of microorganisms stick-formed bacilli and bacteria, and spiral (vibrios) and filamentary forms (Fig. 130) are found. Among the actual bacteria are included spore-forming bacilli and non-spore-forming bacteria, as well as motile forms and those lacking this capacity.

Myxobacteria are chiefly distinguished by a peculiar structure of the

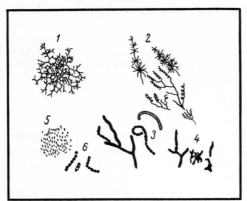

Fig. 129. Actinomycetes. 1 —my-
celium of actinomyces; 2—fruit-
bearing filaments; 3—spore formation; 4—germination of spores;
5—cells of mycobacteria; 6—spore
formation by mycobacteria.

Fig. 130. Basic forms of bacteria and spirochetes. 1 —mi-
crococci; 2—streptococci; 3—
diplococci; 4—staphylococci;
5—sarcinae; 6—bacteria; 7—
bacilli; 8—vibrios; 9—spirilla;
10—spirochetes.

cell envelopes, which consist of an elastic, plasmatic layer. A characteristic peculiarity of myxobacteria is the formation of slime, sometimes of
various colors. Some unstriped myxobacteria are in motion owing to the
unilateral secretion of slime (Fig. 131).

Spirochetes. Organisms of this class
differ in their mode of motion from other
microbes according to cell structure (Fig.
130). Many investigators group these
among the protozoa, while the other three
classes of microbes mentioned above, along
with algae, constitute a group of lower plants
(protophyta).

Fig. 131. Myxobacteria.
1 —slimy pseudo-fruit
bodies; 2—view under
the microscope.

The physiological functions of microorganisms are respiration, feeding, growth,
multiplication, and reaction to external ir-
ritation. An extremely important feature
of the physiology of microorganisms is
their ability to utilize for respiration either
free oxygen from the air (aerobes) or the
combined oxygen of highly oxidized or organic compounds (anaerobes). The degree
of anaerobicity may vary. There are facultative and obligate anaerobes.
The latter cannot develop in a medium in the presence of even insignificant
amounts of oxygen. Facultative anaerobes develop either in the presence
or the absence of oxygen.

Nutrition, like respiratory gas exchange, occurs in microorganisms through the entire surface of their bodies. Water and the substances dissolved in it pass into the cell through the semipermeable surface of a layer of protoplasm, i.e., by osmosis. Waste is also removed from the microorganism by osmosis.

In order to utilize colloidal and water-insoluble substances, as well as some stable compounds, microorganisms secrete specific enzymes (catalysts), with the aid of which they can bring into solution and oxidize the substances they must assimilate. Enzymes influence the course of a wide variety of chemical reactions as catalysts and are independent of the living cells of bacteria, although they are formed by these cells. Desmolases are enzymes which cause fundamental changes in substances, leading to their oxidation or reduction (11).

The physiological activity of microorganisms is exceedingly varied. Microorganisms play an essential role in the nitrogen-carbon-sulfur-phosphorus-iron cycle. They maintain the following processes: nitrification and denitrification, reduction of sulfates and oxidation of hydrogen sulfide, formation of hydrocarbons (methane) and their oxidation.

Depending on the character of the biochemical processes caused by microorganisms and the nature of the resulting substances, microorganisms are subdivided into various physiological groups. According to the type of carbon compounds utilized by them, microorganisms are divided into three groups — heterotrophes, autotrophes, and mesotrophes.

Heterotrophic microorganisms subsist mainly on organic matter already formed, nearly always in the form of carbohydrates and albumins. They cannot utilize carbon or carbon dioxide in processes of photosynthesis or chemosynthesis for the building of their bodies. Several forms of heterotrophic microbes are nourished by organic substances entering into the composition of living organisms, and are parasitic on animals and plants. Others — saprophytes — utilize only dead organic substances.

Autotrophic organisms can oxidize several inorganic compounds (sulfur, ammonia, nitrites, hydrogen), utilizing the liberated energy for the synthesis of organic matter. In this case carbon dioxide is their sole source of carbon. Strictly autotrophic bacteria include the following: thionic bacteria, which oxidize sulfur compounds; nitrifiers, which oxidize ammonia; iron-bacteria and other forms. Facultative autotrophes, or mesotrophes, can oxidize inorganic matter and at the same time can utilize organic matter already formed.

In connection with the questions of interest to us regarding geochemical surveying, let us consider the effect of microbial activity on the composition of the gaseous components of the subterranean atmosphere.

Role of Microorganisms in the Formation of Gases

Biochemical processes in the sedimentary layer of the earth's crust, resulting from the activity of microorganisms, extend to a considerable depth. The activity of microorganisms is the most important factor in the original formation and subsequent transformation, as well as disintegration of pools of oil, gas, and other combustible substances.

The presence of a living and active microflora in oil strata and in waters stiuated at great depths was established in 1926 in the Soviet Union by T. L. Ginzburg-Karagicheva (12) and almost simultaneously in the USA by Bastin and his co-workers.

The vital activity of the microflora discovered was at first attributed to its use of organic compounds of oil in the reduction of sulfates contained in subterranean waters. Hypotheses were offered to the effect that the microflora found in oil-bearing strata is indigenous to the corresponding oil formations from the moment of their origin (13). Although the problem of the origin of this microflora remains unsolved, there can be no doubt that the various forms of microorganisms found in deep-seated sedimentary layers of the earth's crust subsist in these layers for long geological periods. Hence, the composition and physiological properties of the microorganisms may have changed depending on changes in the geological environment. Furthermore, the microflora of deep layers could be partially renewed owing to the movement and percolation of subterranean waters.

These general hypotheses have not as yet been supported by detailed investigations which would serve to establish the relation between the development of specific microorganisms and the presence of particular substances that could be utilized or formed by the microorganisms in the process of their metabolism.

On the basis of the investigations of T. L. Ginzburg-Karagicheva (12, 13), L. D. Shturm (14, 15), S. I. Kuznetsov (16), Z. I. Kuznetsova (17), and other Soviet and foreign microbiologists (18, 19, 20, 21, 22), and also of the combined results of numerous microbiological searches for oil and gas (23, 24), the prevalence in subterranean waters, oil strata, and rocks enclosing the latter has been established of the following groups of bacteria: (1) those reducing sulfates; (2) those reducing nitrates with evolution of gaseous nitrogen; (3) those decomposing cellulose under anaerobic conditions; (4) those causing butyric acid fermentation; (5) those oxidizing sulfur compounds (thionic); (6) those oxidizing gaseous, liquid, and solid hydrocarbons; (7) those decomposing albuminous substances with evolution of combustible gaseous products; (8) ammonizers; (9) nitrifiers.

In general, the activity of the subterranean bacterial population can be estimated from its total number. Under subterranean conditions, with the participation of bacteria, processes of formation, transformation, and decomposition of organic matter occur. These processes, as a rule, are associated with the transition of substances from the solid and liquid phases to the gas phase.

The gases formed again take part in biochemical processes, undergoing further changes down to formation of the final products of mineralization of organic substances. Among the latter may be included nitrogen, carbon dioxide, water, and sulfur. However, every one of these ingredients under known conditions may be involved again in a material cycle and, owing to chemosynthesis, may serve as the beginning of the formation of new sources of bioenergy.

The main role in the decomposition of organic substances with formation of primary gaseous products belongs to heterotrophic organisms (25). As a result of their activity under anaerobic conditions, such gases are formed as methane, hydrogen, carbon dioxide, hydrogen sulfide, and nitrous oxide, and such intermediate products as ammonia and various organic acids.

Actually, the formation of the different components of natural gas may be assumed to be the result of the following heterotrophic anaerobic processes of decomposition of organic substances (26).

1. Decomposition of sugars and hemicelluloses with formation of

carbon dioxide and fatty acids. This process may continue all the way to formation of carbon dioxide and methane or hydrogen.

2. Decomposition of cellulose with formation of carbon dioxide, fatty acids, and methane or hydrogen.

3. Decomposition of albumins with formation of hydrogen, carbon dioxide, and free nitrogen (through a stage of denitrification).

4. Decomposition of fatty acids and amino acids with formation of methane, carbon dioxide, and nitrogen. Under certain oxidative-reductive conditions of the surrounding medium the formation of hydrogen is possible.

5. Decomposition of nitrogen-containing compounds with evolution of free nitrogen and hydrogen sulfide through an intermediate stage of formation of amino and amido groups without formation of nitrates.

6. Decomposition of hydrocarbons due to the reduction of sulfates with formation of hydrogen sulfide.

Among the chief initiators of autotrophic processes must be included the following microorganisms.

1. Bacteria which oxidize hydrogen under aerobic conditions by the use of molecular oxygen, and under anaerobic conditions through the reduction of sulfates and other highly oxidized compounds. The final gaseous product formed by bacteria is hydrogen sulfide; under known conditions methane may be synthesized from hydrogen and carbon dioxide.

2. Bacteria which oxidize methane, ethane, propane, and other hydrocarbons, as well as carbon monoxide by the use of molecular oxygen under aerobic conditions and through the reduction of nitrates and sulfates under anaerobic ones. The final gaseous product of their activity is carbon dioxide.

3. Nitrifying bacteria, which oxidize ammonia to nitrates or nitrites.

4. Denitrifying bacteria, which reduce nitrates to free nitrogen with the possible formation of nitrous oxide in an intermediate stage by some organisms.

5. Thionic and sulfuric bacteria, which oxidize hydrogen sulfide to free sulfur and water, or in some cases, to sulfuric acid.

Thus, as a result of different biochemical processes — heterotrophic on the one hand, and chemoautotrophic on the other — the very same gaseous products may be formed: methane, hydrogen, carbon dioxide, hydrogen sulfide, nitrogen, nitrous oxide, and other gases. Consequently, the concept, "gases of biochemical origin", today includes various gaseous minerals and gaseous associations in relation to their genesis.

Meanwhile, it is important in the study of sedimentary deposits to know not only the chemical composition of the observed gas, but also its genesis. Heterotrophic processes are characteristic, on the one hand, at the top of a sedimentary rock layer, where the first stage of decomposition of buried or dissolved organic matter is not yet completed, and on the other hand, for gas and oil-bearing and bituminous strata lying at a considerable depth, decomposition of oil and gas pools formed earlier may occur.

In contrast to this, the prevalence of autotrophic processes of gas formation and, in part, chemosynthesis, occurring in the absence of already formed organic matter largely characterizes the intermediate rock layer. Here, as a rule, transformation of individual gas components and oxidation of hydrocarbons from the migration current by reduction of highly oxidized mineral salts transported by subterranean waters occurs.

It must be known whether the various components of the subterranean atmosphere are autochthonous with respect to the given stratum, (whether they originated where it was found) or migrated from a deeper stratum of rocks. In the latter case they may be called allochthonous. These questions can be answered in every concrete case in which all gaseous components within the boundaries of a given geological section and, simultaneously, all microbiological associations present in the same deposits are studied.

Up to the present time the most commonly used indicator microorganisms for oil and gas have been different kinds of bacteria. Undoubtedly with further study of microbiological and gas associations, as well as bitumen determination, it will become possible to use the determined proportions of microorganisms characterizing any given geobiochemical situation as indicators of gas and oil.

INDICATOR AND CONTROL MICROORGANISMS IN PROSPECTING FOR OIL AND GAS

Microorganisms determined in oil and gas prospecting may be subdivided into direct and indirect indicators and control organisms. At the present time in microbiological searches for oil and gas, desulfurizing and hydrogen-oxidizing bacteria are used as indirect indicators, while bacteria which oxidize gaseous and vaporized hydrocarbons are used as direct ones. Bacteria which decompose cellulose and produce methane are used as control organisms determining the presence of processes of contemporary decomposition of organic matter in waters and rocks. The characteristics of indicator and control microorganisms are briefly given below.

Sulfate-Reducing Bacteria

Sulfate-reducing (or desulfurizing) bacteria are the most widely studied and most characteristic physiological group found in oil-bearing formations and waters. Furthermore, sulfate-reducing bacteria are widely distributed in ground waters, fresh- and salt-water reservoirs, and soil deposits. A definite relationship has been established between the abundance of sulfate-reducing bacteria and the hydrogen sulfide content. In the sulfate reduction process, bacteria aid in the oxidation of organic matter to carbon dioxide and water under anaerobic conditions. The organic matter is oxidized by the oxygen from the sulfates which, in turn, are reduced to hydrogen sulfide.

According to existing literature data, the reduction of sulfates may proceed in two ways (20, 27): (1) by utilization of organic matter (oil and high-molecular hydrocarbons); (2) by utilization of molecular hydrogen.

The ability of desulfurizing bacteria to utilize hydrogen may serve to explain the relatively rare occurrence of these gases around oil formations. Desulfurizing bacteria cannot reduce sulfates by using gaseous hydrocarbons (methane, ethane, and propane) as a source of carbon.

The most characteristic examples of sulfate-reducing bacteria are Vibrio desulfuricans and Vibrio rubentschikii (Fig. 132). According to the data of Shturm (14), sulfate-reducing bacteria found in the waters of oil formations are characterized either by fine, filamentary form or by a thicker, spirillum-line one. As a typical form, L. D. Shturm selected V. desulfuricans var. granularis (Fig. 133).

An important distinguishing property of sulfate-reducing bacteria in

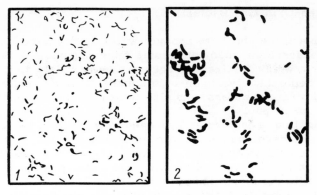

Fig. 132. Bacteria which reduce sulfates. 1 — Vibrio
desulfuricans (x800); 2 — Vibrio rubentschikii (x1200).

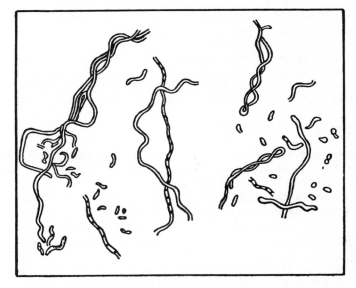

Fig. 133. Sulfate-reducing bacteria of oil-bearing waters.
Vibrio desulfuricans, var. granularis. Vibrios and rod-
shaped forms (x2000).

oil formations in their ability to develop in a medium in which heptane is
the only source of hydrocarbon nourishment.[1] No common desulfurizing
microspira with this ability is known (17). Sulfate-reducing bacteria developing in a medium which contains heptane are the only oil-indicating
microorganisms for waters containing hydrogen sulfide, since bacteria
which oxidize hydrocarbons in an atmosphere containing hydrogen sulfide
cannot exist.

---

[1]A controversial claim. Some workers believe that sulfate reducers grow only on
aliphatic hydrocarbons of greater molecular weight than decane. Ed. (WDR)

Hydrogen-Oxidizing Bacteria

As stated above, the ability to produce water by decomposition of organic matter is possessed by many anaerobic microorganisms. At the same time, bacteria which oxidize hydrogen are quite widely distributed in soil and subsoil deposits. Hydrogen-oxidizing bacteria are encountered in ground- and stratum-waters, and also in sedimentary layers containing gas pockets or oil pools.

The oxidation of molecular hydrogen to water is a basic energetic process for the development of hydrogen bacteria. Hydrogen bacteria use free oxygen to oxidize hydrogen. Under certain conditions they may also utilize the combined oxygen of nitrates and sulfates, and even reduce carbon dioxide with the formation of methane.

Typical and non-typical forms of hydrogen-oxidizing bacteria are distinguished (28). For non-typical forms of hydrogen-oxidizing bacteria, this process is incidental. Noticeable growth of these bacteria occurs only in the presence of already-formed organic matter, which is utilized by them as a source of carbon. In contrast to this, typical forms of hydrogen bacteria oxidize hydrogen under autotrophic conditions. For these the source of carbon is carbon dioxide.

As is known, the relation of hydrogen to oil pools and hydrocarbon gases is not sufficiently clear as yet (29). In biologging work the presence in the cores of hydrogen-oxidizing bacteria is usually considered to be one of the indirect indicators of the oil-bearing nature of the deposits.

Methane-Producing Bacteria

As investigations of subterranean waters conducted in the course of aqueous-biochemical surveys have shown, bacteria which produce methane from fatty acids are widely distributed in ground waters lying at lesser depths, and also in the waters of polluted wells and sumps. Methane-forming or methane-producing bacteria are strictly anaerobic.

There are about ten different kinds of bacteria capable of causing methane fermentation, i.e., producing methane from the salts of fatty acids and various alcohols by the reduction of carbon dioxide to methane in the presence of hydrogen (30). The most characteristic producers of methane are the four kinds of nonspore-forming bacteria given below:

1. Methanosarcina methanica, known mainly because of the work of Söhngen; it is characterized by great size and the formation of sarcinous packets; it does not ferment alcohol;

2. Methanococcus, which causes more vigorous fermentation than sarcina; usually appears in the lower stages of fermentation of ethyl and butyl alcohols;

3. rod-shaped bacteria; there are two morphologically similar forms, Methanobacterium Söhngenii and M. Omelanskii, which have the appearance of long, twisted threads consisting of separate rods. In their physiological properties, however, the two forms differ sharply from one another: one ferments acetic acid with formation of methane, while the other ferments ethyl alcohol.

The two forms of methane-producing bacteria, separable in Barker media with alcohol and with sodium acetate, are extremely important control microorganisms. Cases of contemporary formation of methane in underground waters through decomposition of various organic residues or through reduction of CO_2 by hydrogen are quite definitely established by their presence.

Bacteria which Decompose Cellulose

The non-nitrogenous matter remaining after decomposition of albumins is usually broken down to carbon dioxide and water by microorganisms under aerobic conditions. After this other compounds which make up part of the remains of animals and plants (sugar, starch, cellulose, and other carbohydrates) are decomposed. The most stable of these is cellulose. Its decomposition under anaerobic conditions leads to the formation of methane, carbon dioxide, and water (31, 32).

The cause of anaerobic decomposition of cellulose is a cylindrical rod which forms spores. It is observed in the ground by use of Omelyanskii solution. Decomposition is apparently due to two microorganisms, one of which produces hydrogen and carbon dioxide, while the other brings about the chemosynthesis of these gases with formation of methane.

Cellulose-decomposing bacteria are used as control organisms in surveys in the zone of subsoil deposits. If cellulose-decomposing bacteria are found together with methane-oxidizing bacteria in the soil profile, ground samples must be taken at a greater depth in order to avoid the zone of contemporary formation of combustible gases.

Bacteria which Oxidize Gaseous and Vaporized Hydrocarbons

Hydrocarbon-oxidizing bacteria are of the greatest interest in oil prospecting, since these bacteria are direct indicators of the corresponding hydrocarbons. However, not all members of this widespread group are sufficiently specific with respect to their function — oxidation of hydrocarbons.

In particular, bacteria which oxidize vaporized and liquid hydrocarbons are heterotrophic organisms, i.e., they can utilize already-formed organic matter. A stricter selectivity in relation to the source of carbon nourishment is possessed by bacteria which oxidize gaseous hydrocarbons. The oxidation of hydrocarbons serves as a source of energy, while carbon dioxide serves as a source of carbon. Thus, they may be included among the autotrophic or mesotrophic bacteria.

The occurrence in nature of processes of biological consumption of methane was established in 1905 by Kazerer. At the same time Söhngen discovered bacteria requireing methane for their development.

Bacteria which oxidize methane (according to Sohngen, Bacillus methanicus), have the appearance of short, thick rods having a shape intermediate between an ellipsoid and a cylinder. The bacteria vary in length from 2 - 3 to 4 - 5 μ and are about 1.5 - 2 μ thick (Fig. 134). Methane-oxidizing bacteria related to the type Methanomonas methanica are very widely distributed in nature in comparison with other forms of bacteria which oxidize gaseous hydrocarbons. Methane-oxidizing bacteria are found in surface deposits and in deep-lying ones, as well as in ground and stratum waters.

According to the findings of Münz (33) the methane bacteria isolated by him developed not only in the presence of methane, but also with other organic substances (sodium acetate, glycerol, mannitol, glucose). However,

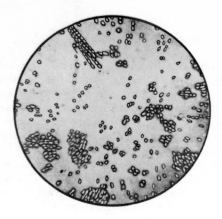

Fig. 134. Cells of methane-oxidizing
bacteria.

in this case the development of the methane-oxidizing bacteria proceeded
much more slowly. It has been shown that the ability of methane-oxidizing
bacteria to assimilate methane after cultivation with other sources of
organic matter usually diminishes or even vanishes.

The investigations of G. P. Slavnina (34, 35) showed that the properties
of methane-oxidizing bacteria stated above are associated with the presence
of the oxidative enzyme peroxidase. This enzyme is absent in other forms
of bacteria which oxidize heavier hydrocarbons.

Bacteria which oxidize ethane were isolated from Tambukanian mud
by Gubin in 1923. Ethane-oxidizing bacteria have the appearance of moving,
sporeless rods measuring 1.5x0.5 . Ultimately, bacteria utilizing ethane
as a source of energy were isolated in a number of regions in the course
of oil-prospecting work. However, in the examination en masse of ground
samples from known oil-bearing regions, ethane-oxidizing bacteria are
found relatively rarely. It may be that these bacteria require special conditions for development. For these reasons ethane-oxidizing bacteria are
not now used as indicating organisms in oil-prospecting work.

Ethane-oxidizing bacteria are identified as Mycobacterium perrugosum
var. ethanicum. They are not able to assimilate methane, but can develop
in an atmosphere of propane and other heavier hydrocarbons mixed with
air (36).

Bacteria which oxidize propane were first isolated in 1939 in the
Maikop region in the course of microbiological prospecting for oil and gas
(37). At present propane-oxidizing bacteria are used as very characteristic indicator organisms in oil-prospecting work. According to the data of
E. N. Bokova (36), propane-oxidizing bacteria belong to the type Mycobacterium rubrum var. propanicum (Fig. 135).

They possess an oxidative enzyme, or catalase (35), and are unable to
assimilate methane or ethane, but can utilize hydrocarbons heavier than
propane (butane, pentane, hexane, etc.). As experiments have shown, most

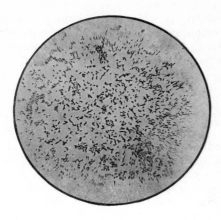

Fig. 135. Cells of propane-oxidizing
bacteria.

varieties of <u>Mycobacterium rubrum</u> utilize only molecular oxygen and cannot subsist by reduction of the oxygen of sulfates and nitrates.

Bacteria which oxidize butane and do not utilize propane are not
described in the literature and have not been studied. Attempts to isolate
these bacteria from samples of oil-bearing regions were made by using a
propane-butane mixture. Therefore, clear results were not obtained. The
question of the existence of butane-oxidizing bacteria as organisms having
distinct physiological properties remains open.

<u>Bacteria which oxidize vaporized hydrocarbons</u>. It has been established
that vaporized and liquid hydrocarbons are accessible to a relatively large
number of heterotrophic microorganisms. In particular, it has been shown
that paraffin hydrocarbons with 10 - 16 carbon atoms are more easily
oxidized by bacteria than those of lower molecular weight (21). Therefore,
bacteria developed in an atmosphere of vaporized hydrocarbons cannot always be considered indicators of the corresponding hydrocarbons.

This group of microorganisms is less significant in the examination
of surface deposits. However, as the depth from which samples are taken
is increased, the finding of bacteria which oxidize vaporized hydrocarbons
acquires definite significance in prospecting. Bacteria which oxidize the
first homologs of liquid hydrocarbons (pentane and heptane) are of great
interest. Different varieties of these, isolated from deep-lying deposits,
are able to utilize the bound oxygen of nitrates. Hexane-oxidizing bacteria
belong to the type <u>Bact. aliphaticum liquefaciens</u>.

As stated above, one of the theoretical foundations of the microbiological
method of prospecting is the specificity of the bacteria used as indicators.
If prospecting for oil and gas pools is to be on the basis of microbiological
indicators, it is necessary to know how widespread within the bacterial
world is the ability to oxidize methane, propane, and higher homologs and
to what extent indicator microorganisms possess the ability to assimilate
different hydrocarbon homologs, as well as other organic compounds.

The great mass of experimental material accumulated during the years of application of the method shows that relatively few groups of micro-organisms have the ability to oxidize methane and especially propane. In the examination of ground and water samples containing methane- or propane-oxidizing bacteria, the bacteria could only develop in an atmosphere of the corresponding gas mixed with air or oxygen.

The indicated forms of microorganisms are easily distinguished in cumulative cultures by the character of the films they form and also morphologically. Methane-oxidizing bacteria in a later stage of development form a brownish, wrinkled film, while propane-oxidizing bacteria form an elastic, sagging film, usually white or light yellow (Fig. 136). The specificity of methane-oxidizing bacteria, in particular, is confirmed by the fact that, after cultivation in media containing prepared organic substances instead of methane, they lost peroxidase.

Propane-oxidizing bacteria have been only rarely observed beyond the boundaries of oil- and gas-bearing regions. Thus, data on bacteria which oxidize gaseous hydrocarbons show that they possess sufficient specialization to permit their use as indicators of the corresponding gases. Vaporized and liquid homologs of methane, beginning with pentane, are available

X

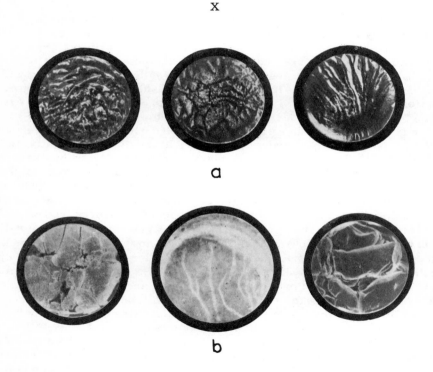

Fig. 136. Films of bacteria which oxidize methane and propane.
a—methane-oxidizers; b—propane-oxidizers (view from above)

to many microorganisms, and hence, the determination of these hydrocarbons in the microbiological way is possible, but without their subdivision into separate fractions. Table 36, compiled on the basis of the investigations of E. N. Bokova (38), shows the difference in selective ability among the various microorganisms which oxidize hydrocarbons.

TABLE 36. Utilization of Gaseous and Liquid Hydrocarbons by Bacteria

Bacterial cultures	Hydrocarbon						
	methane	ethane	propane	butane	pentane	hexane	heptane
Methane oxidizers	+	-	-	-	+	+	+
Ethane oxidizers	-	+	+	+	+	+	+
Propane oxidizers	-	-	+	+	+	+	+
Oxidizers of pentane and higher homologs	-	-	-	-	+	+	+

Conditions Limiting the Propagation and Use of Indicator Microorganisms

Bacteria which oxidize methane and its homologs (propane, butane, and hexane) require atmospheric oxygen, moisture, and sources of mineral nourishment containing nitrogen, phosphorus, potassium, and magnesium besides the hydrocarbons in order to develop. The growth of the bacteria is substantially affected by temperature, hydrogen-ion concentration, and several other environmental conditions. The correlation of the physico-chemical conditions enumerated above changes, upon transition from one climatic or geographical zone to another, and also with change of depth of the layer being studied. Let us consider the change of these conditions with depth.

The earth's crust may be divided into three microbial zones which differ in the nature and abundance of their bacterial populations, and in the peculiarities of biochemical activity of these bacteria. This division, which is somewhat provisional in character, is as follows:

1. The zone with the greatest bacterial population and variety of morphological and physiological groups of bacteria is the soil zone. The thickness of this first zone is very slight in comparison with the other zones distinguished by us. Depending on soil-climatic conditions it varies for specific regions and areas from 0.5 to 1.5 m., or slightly more in a few cases. The soil zone from the viewpoint of bacterial investigations is characterized by the presence of biochemical processes of decomposition of soil organic matter now taking place. As a rule, these processes occur slightly below the soil layer itself.

2. Below the soil zone lies a zone of subsoil deposits which, in a number of cases, is associated with Quarternary deposits. It coincides with the so-called zone of erosion. The peculiarity of this zone is the greater

or lesser degree of aeration of its constituent rocks. Thus, the bacterial population of this zone is characterized by the development of aerobic forms along with anaerobic and facultative ones. The thickness of this zone is measured in tens, and sometimes hundreds of meters.

3. Below the zone of subsoil deposits lies the zone of deep-lying deposits, which is characterized by the presence of poorly aerated and slightly permeable, mainly bedrock deposits. Here are encountered only selected forms of microorganisms, the functions of which are determined by the character of the various organic compounds buried in the depths or diffusing through a sedimentary layer and by the presence of necessary mineral substances.

The practical significance of these zones is that:

1. not all forms of hydrocarbon microflora have the ability to utilize the combined oxygen of nitrates and sulfates; hence, their propagation is limited in depth;

2. specific microorganisms used as bacterial indicators of oil and combustible gases are not good indicators through the full thickness of a stratum because, as the surface is approached, processes of contemporary gas formation resulting from the decomposition of organic residues occur.

For these reasons, neither bacteria which oxidize methane nor those which develop in an atmosphere of vaporized hydrocarbons can be indicative in oil and gas prospecting within the limits of the soil zone. Such additional indicators as hydrogen-oxidizing and desulfurizing microorganisms also lose their significance here. Only propane-oxidizing bacteria may be used to some extent within the soil zone. However, the theoretically admissible possibility of formation of heavy hydrocarbons from organic compounds in the soil must also be kept in mind.

The soil layer can be significant in microbiological surveying if the relationships between morphological groups and the total number of microorganisms are taken into account. In this way the total increase of biogenic activity of the soils over oil and gas pools may be determined.

In the subsoil zone the main indicators of hydrocarbon gases are bacteria which oxidize methane and propane. Here bacteria which develop in an atmosphere of vaporized hydrocarbons are less reliable. Within the limits of the zone of deep-lying deposits, the most important indicator organisms are anaerobes or facultative anaerobes which can utilize the combined oxygen of highly oxidized minerals or organic compounds.

Among the enumerated forms of microorganisms, those which fully satisfy this requirement are the bacteria which oxidize vaporized hydrocarbons and the desulfurizing bacteria. Methane-oxidizing and hydrogen-oxidizing bacteria are detected in well bores to a lesser depth. Propane-oxidizing bacteria are encountered in small numbers, even in deep-lying deposits. Thus, in deep-lying deposits, bacteria which oxidize methane and propane play a minor role in oil- and gas-prospecting work in comparison with bacteria which oxidize vaporized hydrocarbons.

Existing data on the occurrence of a hydrocarbon microflora for a great variety of geographical points show that different climatic conditions do not hinder the development of the microorganisms named above, although they do affect the total number and rate of growth during specific periods of the year. The presence of bacteria which oxidize methane, propane, and vaporized hydrocarbons in subsoil deposits has been established in the north, particularly in the permafrost zone, and in the southern regions of the Soviet Union, particularly in the desert zone.

The lithological composition of the rocks also has a certain effect on the development of a hydrocarbon microflora. It has been established that the mineral compounds necessary for the growth of the hydrocarbon microflora exist in a wide variety of contemporary deposits as well as in ancient rocks. Relatively rarely, cases are observed in which given clay interbeds do not contain the mineral salts necessary for the growth of bacteria or prove unsuitable for their vital activity owing to the acid reaction of the medium. Correlation of the lithology of rocks with the population density of the hydrocarbon microflora shows that, other conditions remaining equal, increase in porosity favors greater development of the bacterial population.

An extremely important element for the metabolism of bacteria is moisture. It has been established that in the southern regions the drying out of the rocks in certain periods of the year may lead to a pronounced diminution of the hydrocarbon microflora. However, the seasonal decrease of moisture in rocks of the central zone of the Soviet Union has no effect on indicators for microbiological surveying.

Thus, if the unfavorable conditions enumerated above are absent growth of the hydrocarbon microflora will be determined mainly by the presence of a source of hydrocarbon nourishment and the qualitative composition of the hydrocarbons. It has been shown that the quantity of gas needed to insure the growth of a hydrocarbon microflora is on the order of 1 - 10 parts per million (39). Similar concentrations of hydrocarbons, according to gas-survey data, are usually found over oil and gas pools. As a result of this, hydrocarbon gases migrating from the depths may be completely oxidized in the presence of a sufficiently developed bacterial filter.

MAIN VARIETIES OF THE MICROBIOLOGICAL METHOD

Microbiological searches for oil and gas may be conducted by examination of subterranean waters and ground samples from various depths below the surface. The following methods may be used:

1. microbiological soil surveys when the samples being examined are taken from subsoil deposits;

2. rock surveys in depth, where samples are taken from rotary-drilled wells;

3. biologging where microbiological analysis is applied to cores from core-drilled wells;

4. water surveys, where formational waters and ground waters are studied.

Each of these varieties of the method covers a different area. The amount of detail in the observations also varies. Historically, the ground survey came into use first; it was followed by biologging and finally the water survey. At present, the water survey is the most widely used.

The Soil Survey

The main type of detailed microbiological prospecting work is the soil survey, which is based on the collection and subsequent analysis of samples of subsoil deposits for methane- and propane-oxidizing bacteria. Two stages of this survey consist of the search for and subsequent localization of the hydrocarbon aureoles which accompany oil and gas pools. Here the samples

may be taken from shallow, specially drilled wells of 2 - 3 m. depth, and
also from pits, clearings, and trenches.

Another type of detailed survey consists of sampling many levels in
rotary-drilled wells to a depth of 15 - 30 m. in conformity with individual
geological profiles. The "deep" survey consists of detailed qualitative
and quantitative analysis of gasobacterial effects through the well section.
Soil surveys are useful when the geological structure of the region has been
studied to a certain extent and the results obtained can be compared with
previously obtained data from geophysical or geological surveying work.

Field method of soil surveying. The points where samples are to be
taken in detailed work are usually chosen on individual profiles at intervals
of 100 - 200 m. and 200 - 300 m. in a reconnaissance survey. The distance
between profiles correspondingly varies from 400 - 500 m. to 1 - 2 km.
The depth of sample-taking assumed for soil-survey wells may change
depending on soil- lithological conditions. In regions with highly developed
terrace and alluvial deposits it must be not less than 3 - 4 m. In areas of
high relief the depth of sampling may be decreased to 2.5 - 3 m. In stony
ground, and also at points where bedrock reaches the surface, it is permissible to take samples from about 2 meters. For wells deeper than 2 m.,
as a rule, two samples are taken at an interval of 0.5 m. In conducting
field work, geomorphological and soil conditions unfavorable for microbiological surveying must be taken into account.

The main containers used to hold soil samples are paper containers
or glass jars. The paper containers have a double bottom and are shipped
to the working site already sterilized in shipping boxes. The size of the
soil sample put into a container must be not less than 250 g. Knives used
in taking soil samples are sterilized in the flame of an alcohol burner.

The soil sample is brought to the surface by means of special core
lifter-sterilizers (Fig. 137). The core lifter-sterilizer consists of a core
separator (1) which is a hollow tube with an internal diameter of 35 mm.
and a length of 250 mm., a core extractor (2), a worm (3), which, when the
handle (7) is turned, ejects the core from the core separator through the
sterilizer of the circular cutter (4); the latter cuts away the outer surface
of the extruded rock. The apparatus is reinforced by a collar (6), fastened
to a hollow shaft (5). The shaft is driven into the ground beforehand. The
sequence of operations in well-sampling with the aid of the core lifter-
sterilizer is shown in the diagram (Fig. 138).

In the absence of a core-lifter and also in cases when the rock is so
dense that it cannot be trimmed by the cutter of the sterilizer, a hollow
cylinder with a sharp outer edge is used.

Microbiological analysis of soil samples. The purpose of microbiological analysis is to establish the presence and abundance in the soil
sample of methane-oxidizing and propane-oxidizing bacteria. Samples in
which methane-oxidizing bacteria are found are further analyzed for cellulose-decomposing bacteria. The same experimental conditions are used
for the isolation of bacteria that ozidize methane or propane. A liquid
mineral medium is inoculated with a portion of the rock being studied and
the hydrocarbon content of the gas mixture is varied depending on the
particular type of bacteria that is to be isolated.

For development of the hydrocarbon microflora, the so-called elective
media, which are most favorable (specific) for a given type of bacteria and
do not secure the growth of other types, are used. The liquid mineral part

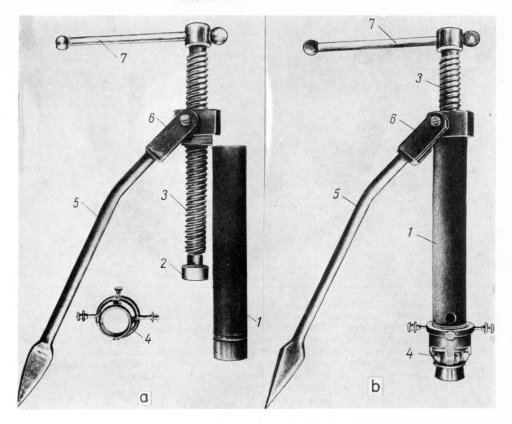

Fig. 137. Core lifter-sterilizer constructed by G. A. Mogilevskii and M. V. Velemitsyn. a—in dismantled form; b—in assembled form. 1—core separator; 2—core extractor; 3—worm; 4—circular cutter; 5—hollow shaft; 6—collar; 7—handle.

of this medium (for the first two groups of bacteria in general and, with slight changes, for cellulose-decomposing bacteria) contains nitrogen, phosphorus, potassium, and magnesium sulfate. The only source of energy and hydrocarbons provided for methane-oxidizing bacteria is methane; for propane-oxidizing bacteria, propane is used; and for cellulose-decomposing bacertia, cellulose is used. Furthermore, the oxygen content must be different for each group, i.e., aerobic for methane and propane bacteria and anaerobic for cellulose-decomposing bacteria.

Bacterial analyses consist of three steps: (1) preparation cultures, (2) incubation of cultures, and (3) analysis of cultures. The technique of making bacterial cultures is described in the following paragraphs (Fig. 138):

Each soil-sample studied is introduced collaterally into five small glass beakers supplied with covers. Correspondingly, five cultures are made of each type of bacteria, i.e., methane- and propane-oxidizing bacteria. The size of the portion of soil-sample may vary for each individual beaker between 5 and 7 g. The portion may be measured by the volume method. After the beakers are loaded with sample material, a thin layer of mineral medium is poured into them. Recently, a method of preliminary

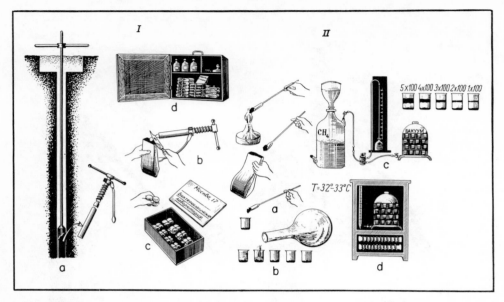

Fig. 138. Diagram of procedures in the soil survey. I—field work: a—extraction of soil-sample from well by core lifter; b—sterile separation of soil-sample with the aid of core lifter; c—packing of samples into shipping boxes for transportation to laboratory; d—field kit with accessories for taking soil samples. II—laboratory work: a—putting soil-sample into beakers; b—pouring mineral medium into beakers; c—charging bell jar, filled with cultures, with gas mixture (1/3 methane + 2/3 air or 1/5 propane + 4/5 air); d—incubation of cultures in thermostat (time of incubation 14 days).

aqueous dispersion of samples has been introduced into laboratory practice. This increases the accuracy of determinations.

Cultures prepared in this manner (observing the requirements of sterility) are placed in groups of 60 - 80 in several layers on a metal platform with a stopcock and covered with a bell jar, the ground base of which is fitted to the platform and sealed with vacuum cement. At first the air under the bell jar is evacuated to a residual pressure of 40 mm. Hg; then it is filled with a gas mixture containing 1/3 methane and 2/3 air (in analyses for methane-oxidizing bacteria, or correspondingly, 1/5 propane and 4/5 air (in analyses for propane-oxidizing bacteria).

The filled bell jars are kept in a thermostat at a temperature of 32° C for 14 days. At the end of the allotted time each beaker is examined. In those cultures in which the soil contained hydrocarbon microflora, a bacterial turbidity or film, quite distinctive in form, appears on the surface of the culture medium (see Fig. 136).

The results of bacterial growth are evaluated according to the thickness of the film formed by the bacteria and the area of the beaker surface to which this film adheres. The intensity of formation of the film and its thickness are evaluated according to the following five-point scale:

1. Turbidity of medium, bacteria observable only with microscope
2. Thin, transparent film
3. Semitransparent, weakly pigmented
4. Dense, opaque, smooth, pigmented
5. Dense, opaque, wrinkled, pigmented

The fraction of the beaker surface covered by the film is also measured. The percent of the beaker surface which is attached to the film is multiplied by its thickness as evaluated by the five-point system. The size of the films in arbitrary units of intensity of growth bears a definite relation to the quantity of hydrocarbon-oxidizing bacteria in the in the ground-samples.

In order to determine what quantity of bacteria can produce a film of given thickness in a given time, E. V. Dianova and L. I. Tarkovskaya conducted special investigations with artificial introduction into experimental beakers of methane-oxidizing bacteria in quantities varying from 2 billion to a few individuals in each culture. As a result of these experiments it was established that the size of the films developed varies directly with the initial quantity of bacteria and the time of incubation (Fig. 139).

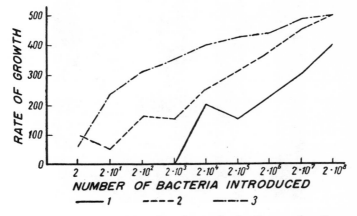

Fig. 139. Diagram of intensity of growth of cultures of methane-oxidizing bacteria in relation to the initial quantity of the latter and time of incubation. 1—incubation time 5 days; 2—incubation time 10 days; 3—incubation time 12 days.

Soil-samples in which methane-oxidizing bacteria have positively been shown to be present must be subjected to a control analysis for bacteria which decompose cellulose. Cellulose-disintegrating bacteria are detected with the aid of a glass test tube into which the ground-sample being tested and a piece of filter paper are placed (Fig. 140). After the test tube has been filled with mineral medium, it is closed with a rubber stopper containing a glass tube. Liquid raising into the tube establishes anaerobic conditions within the test tube. When cellulose bacteria are present in the soil-sample, the filter paper in the test tube begins to decompose with the formation of gas bubbles after two or three weeks of incubation. Anaerobic conditions in the test tubes may be established by the use of 0.75% agar-agar.

The Water Survey

The main type of microbiological work of a reconnaissance nature is the water survey, usually conducted in conjunction with gas and hydrochemical investigations of underground waters. Investigating the bacterial micro-

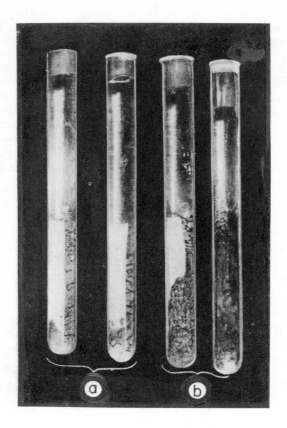

Fig. 140. Detection of bacteria which decompose cellulose. a—filter paper at beginning
of experiment; b—filter paper disintegrated
by bacteria.

flora of underground waters for oil and gas prospecting, also called hydromicrobiological surveying, was developed at the VSEGINGEO Institute during the period from 1944 to 1946 by G. A. Mogilevskii and Z. I. Kuznetsova
(17).

The essence of the method consists in collecting and analyzing sterile
water samples at points of discharge from aquifers. Springs, fountains,
and sumps, as well as artesian wells and other water wells are investigated.
The advantage of the gasomicrobiological survey of waters as a reconnaissance method is that aquifers encounter a current of migrating hydrocarbons at a much greater depth than soil-survey bore-holes.

Underground waters, which dissolve migrating hydrocarbon gases contain these gases in greater quantity and with more uniform distribution in
the area of the investigations than subsoil deposits situated at lesser depths.
Water-bearing strata thus seem to have a check on any given part of the
current of migrating hydrocarbons on its way to the surface. Hency, hydrocarbon gases that can be detected by the water survey may in a number

of cases escape notice in subsoil surveys.

Furthermore, bacterial oxidation of hydrocarbons is extremely active in underground waters. Therefore, analysis for dissolved hydrocarbons should include not only gas analysis, but also analysis of the waters for a microflora which oxidizes these gases. The indicator microflora for oil and gas in hydromicrobiological investigations are: (1) bacteria which oxidize methane; (2) bacteria which oxidize propane; (3) bacteria which develop in an atmosphere of one of the vaporized hydrocarbons, such as pentane, hexane, or heptane.

In conducting a water survey the same methods are used for the determination of hydrocarbon microflora as in the soil survey. A more concentrated Münz (2x) mineral medium is used, and instead of a portion of a soil sample, 3 - 4 ml. of the water being tested are put into the medium.

For waters associated with oil and gas formations, and containing significant concentrations of hydrogen sulfide, the bacterial indicators mentioned above cannot be used. The indicators used in these cases are desulfurizing bacteria, which develop under laboratory conditions in a medium containing heptane which is a source of carbon for them. Desulfurizing bacteria are recovered from the waters by preliminary concentration of the bacteria on membrane filters. The water being tested is filtered through an ultrafilter with the aid of a Seitz funnel, while the bacteria suspended in the water are retained on the filter.

In order to establish the presence of bacteria which oxidize methane, as well as those which are developed in an atomosphere of vaporized hydrocarbons, control analyses must be conducted to determine whether methane is being formed as a result of the activity of methane-producing bacteria which decompose fatty acids under anaerobic conditions. Control analyses are also required since bacteria which develop in an atmosphere of vaporized hydrocarbons may grow in polluted waters owing to the easily assimilated organic substances, while methane-oxidizing bacteria may grow owing to the methane formed as a result of biochemical decomposition of these substances. Analyses for methane-generating bacteria are used in conjunction with hydrochemical analyses of waters for ammonia, nitrites, and nitrates.

Comparison of bacteriological analyses of water with hydrochemical characteristics has shown that such factors as high salinity of the water (up to 7° Bé), the presence of salts of bromine and iodine in quantities as high as 12 mg./l. for iodine and 170 mg./l. for bromine, pH from 6.0 to 10.0, and water temperature up to 40° C do not limit the development of oil- and gas-indicating bacteria. The presence of H_2S in petroleum waters is the only circumstance which inhibits the growth of hydrocarbon microflora. The most favorable locations for gasomicrobiological surveys in waters are where underground waters discharge as wells and springs or where there are a great number of sumps or water wells.

In a microbiological survey of waters, small streams flowing from alluvial deposits should not be tested especially in the absence of any kind of caprock. Sumps and wells with signs of pollution should not be tested either. Colorimetric determinations of nitrates, nitrites, and ammonia conducted on the spot may serve as an index of pollution

Depending on the presence and arrangement of the underground or capping structures, one of the following methods of sampling of wells, springs, and sumps is used.

a. For overflowing wells or those used for water, and also from capped springs, water samples are taken by pouring samples into sterile bottles placed directly under the drainpipe, faucet, or spout.

b. For sumps and recently drilled, as yet únused wells, water samples are taken with the aid of a special bacteriological bathometer (Fig. 141, a and b). The bathometer is lowered into the well or sump on a rope and brought into action with the aid of a traveling weight. The apparatus con-

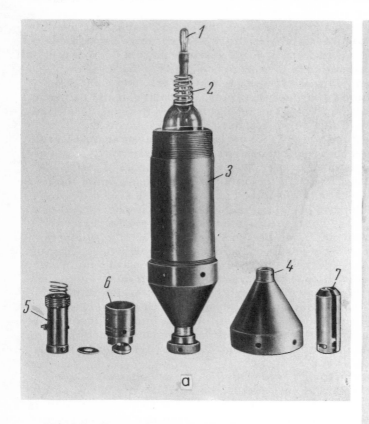

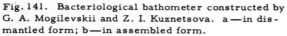

Fig. 141. Bacteriological bathometer constructed by G. A. Mogilevskii and Z. I. Kuznetsova. a —in dismantled form; b—in assembled form.

sists of a glass bulb enclosed in a metallic housing. The lower end of the bulb is hermetically sealed by a glass stopper, while the upper end is sealed by special glass capsule (1). With the aid of the coil spring (2), the bulb is secured to the metallic housing (3), to the top of which is screwed the cap (4) with side-inlets for the admission of water. At the upper end of the cap, secured by a spring, is a block (5), which breaks the capsule in the cap (6) as a result of the action of the traveling weight (7). Water then passes into the bulb through the opening created.

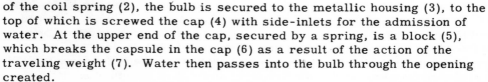

c. In taking water samples from uncapped springs, the water is either poured directly into a bottle at the outlet of the spring or drawn through a rubber hose, previously boiled in water. The first portion of water drawn through the hose is discarded. In cases where the spring flows into a pool of water, the sample is taken by immersing a stoppered bottle. The stopper is removed under water at the outlet of the spring.

In a microbiological survey the time of storage of samples is very important, because the relation between the dissolved gases and hydrocarbon microflora contained in the water bears a dynamic character. In the presence of significant quantities of dissolved hydrocarbons (methane or heavy hydrocarbons) the bacteria originally contained in the water will develop until they have exhausted the entire supply of hydrocarbons and oxygen.

For this reason two samples are taken from every water point for the microbiological analysis of water. One of these is analyzed at once in the field laboratory, while the other is analyzed within 30 - 40 days in the central laboratory. With duplicate analyses it is possible to obtain much more consistent bacterial indices corresponding to areas of maximum gas evolution.

The results of joint gas and microbiological surveys of waters show the definite relationship between gas and bacterial indices. In the majority of aquifers at shallow depths, the dissolved hydrocarbon gases, as a rule, are present in microquantities. If conditions in a layer are unfavorable for the metabolism of bacteria, the concentration of hydrocarbon gases is markedly increased. A relative deficit of dissolved oxygen is observed in areas in which an abundant hydrocarbon microflora is found.

The rules enumerated above indicate the necessity of combining gas and microbiological methods of investigating underground waters in oil and gas prospecting work. Field work in water surveying requires relatively low expenditures, since it does not involve the drilling of wells or other work in the ground.

The water survey is completely dependent on the presence in a region of springs, water-wells, and sumps. If these are absent large portions of a locality remain unsurveyed. If such gaps due to the absence of sample points need to be filled specially drilled wells distributed within a radius of 50 - 100 m. around the designated point may be sampled.

Biologging

Microbiological investigations of rocks may be conducted in deep-lying deposits by means of core-drilled wells. In this case, well cores are examined for the presence of bacterial indicators. Depending on the purpose of the given core-drilling operation, biologging may involve either a reconnaissance or a detailed investigation.

An example of a reconnaissance application of biologging is the examination of cores from a well located on a specific geological profile. In this case the biologging data are used for the comparative evaluation of the extent of microscopic hydrocarbon manifestations in wells and specific parts of the drilled section. The results of biologging may be expressed by curves of the variation of bacterial indices along the section of a well or by isolines of average values of degree of growth of indicator microorganisms, summed up with regard to specific stratigraphic intervals or to the well as a whole (Fig. 142).

The technique of taking samples of rock cores is nearly the same as

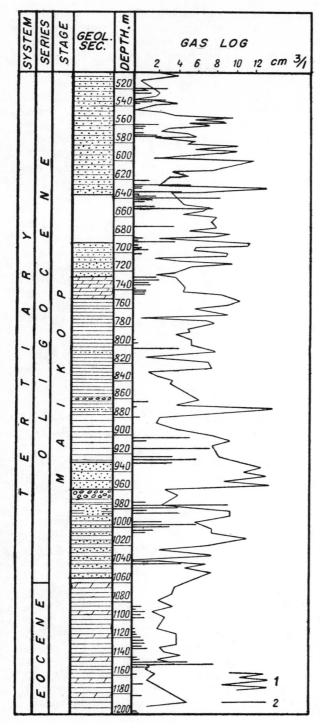

Fig. 142. Comparison of bio-logging results with a gas log in a rotary well. 1—content of hydrocarbon gases in drilling mud; 2—presence of hydrocarbon microflora in cores in arbitrary units of intensity of growth.

that established for the extraction of rocks from shallow wells. The main problem in this work is the separation of the external, contaminated part of the core from its internal part (center), which after trimming is transferred to a sterile package. The sterile treatment of cores is relatively easily accomplished when sandstone-clay rocks predominate in the section. Sterile treatment of carbonate and halide rocks is more difficult. This requires the use of special devices for cleaving and crushing the sample.

The cores are examined for the following types of bacteria: (1) methane oxidizing bacteria, (2) bacteria growing in an atmosphere of pentane, (3) propane oxidizing bacteria, and (4) hydrogen oxidizing bacteria. The first two types of indicator organisms are the most widespread at great depths.

The chief value of biologging work is that it is possible to determine the presence in cores of microquantities of methane, heavy hydrocarbons, and hydroben by using bacterial indicators. This requires preliminary desorption of gas from the cores and the use of complex microanalytical apparatus.

The Bacterial Gas-Output Survey and Other Analytical Methods

All the variations of the microbiological method given above, water survey, soil survey, and biologging, are based on a study of the indigenous bacterial population. The differences among them are mainly determined by the nature of the medium in which these surveys are conducted.

The bacterial gas-output survey is based on a different principle. This method of microbiological investigation involves the use of various bacterial cultures for determining the output of diffusing gases. The technique of bacterial gas-output measurements consists in lowering an assembly of bacterial cultures of definite titer into shallow test wells and allowing it to remain 12 - 14 days. Bacteria which oxidize methane, ethane, propane, liquid hydrocarbons, and hydrogen are used as indicators.

If there is an influx of hydrocarbon gases, development of the corresponding cultures occurs. At the end of the exposure period, the cultures are withdrawn from the wells, fixed, and visually evaluated. An exact estimate of the growth of bacterial cells is made in the laboratory microscopically or with a photometer.

Equipment for bacterial gas-output measurements consists of a duralumin tube and case for lowering test tubes with cultures of bacteria. In the diagram (Fig. 143) the main operations in a bacterial gas-output survey are indicated. Bacterial gas-output measurements may be used in underwater surveys. The bacterial cultures are lowered to the bottom of reservoirs in special bells for this purpose.

The bacterial gas-output survey has not as yet been used in practice owing to the great amount of labor involved in laboratory and field work. However, the technique of bacterial gas-output operations may be applied when it is necessary to investigate shaft air and gases evolved from wells.

Several other methods of distinguishing hydrocarbon-oxidizing bacteria and the microbiological determination of hydrocarbon gases deserve mention.

One of these methods consists in the detection of hydrocarbon microflora with the aid of luminescence microscopy. This is based on the fact that different types of hydrocarbon microflora give different luminescent effects. Bacteria which oxidize vaporized hydrocarbons have a natural

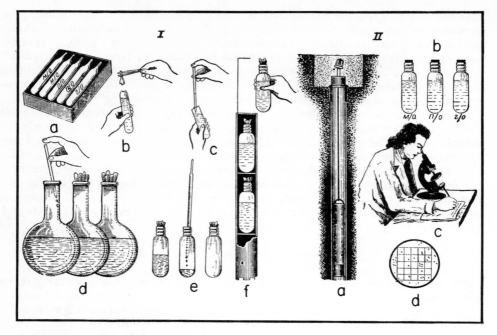

Fig. 143. Diagram of the conduct of a bacterial gas-output survey. I—prepatory operations: a—packing ampules with cultures of bacteria which oxidize methane or propane and liquid hydrocarbons; b—opening ampule with culture; c—taking culture from ampule; d—transferring contents of ampules to flasks containing sterile mineral oil; e—introduction of portion of cultures to sterile test tubes; f—packing test tubes with cultures in case. II—field work and treatment of materials: a—section of bacterial gas-output well (period of exposure of cultures, up to 15 days); b—bacterial cultures fixed on withdrawal from wells; c—counting bacteria under the microscope; d—field of view of microscope with ocular grid for counting bacteria.

luminescence in ultra-violet rays and wood rays. Bacteria which oxidize gaseous hydrocarbons luminesce on application of special dyes. Investigations carried out in this field by G. P. Slavnina and M. I. Meisel (40) showed the possibility of using luminescence microscopy to determine hydrocarbon-oxidizing bacteria in various stages of their development under laboratory conditions and also in the field with the aid of a few fixing accessories.

An evaluation of the biological oxygen demand of the organisms is used to detect the hydrocarbon microflora in underground waters and also to determine the degree of microbiological decomposition of organic matter in the waters. This method is especially important in making analyses under field conditions.

MICROBIOLOGICAL RESULTS AND THEIR INTERPRETATION

Regardless of variations in the method and technique of geobiochemical prospecting for oil and gas, its ultimate purpose is to find zones (within the survey area or in a well section) with anomalous values of hydrocarbon indices and to determine whether or not these anomalies are associated with oil or gas pools of industrial significance. This latter purpose is accomplished in the final stage of the work, the geological interpretation of the obtained data. However, a preliminary treatment of the factual data is required for a complete interpretation and consists of several stages.

Treatment of Factual Data

First of all, the number of observations on the microorganisms is computed and the average development of indicator microorganisms is calculated for the region as a whole, a particular survey area, or for individual wells in biologging. Average data on specific types of microflora are essential in estimating the nature of the source of diffusion. These data are also used in quantitative comparisons of areas where the geological structures are sufficiently similar. In treating biologging data the regularity in variation of microbiological indicators with depth and their association with specific stratigraphic levels is studied.

The next stage in the treatment of the analytical data consists in compiling tables of the relationship between the indices of microbiological surveys and various factors which affect the results (temperature and moisture content of the rocks, their lithological composition, how long samples are kept, etc.).

In a hydromicrobiological survey it is especially important to determine for each water-point being sampled the possible effect of processes of contemporary formation of methane and various impurities in the underground waters on the growth of indicator microorganisms. For this purpose the data of chemical analyses of waters for nitrates, nitrites, and ammonia are compared with the results of microbiological determinations of methane-producing bacteria in the waters or with the index of biological oxygen demand.

For the soil survey, data on the occurrence of methane-oxidizing bacteria are compared with corresponding data for cellulose-decomposing bacteria in the samples. Samples in which simultaneous growth of these two microorganisms is observed are considered doubtful and are not considered to indicate anomalous zones. This restriction is not usually applied to cases in which propane-oxidizing bacteria are found, since heavy hydrocarbons are not formed in the decomposition of cellulose.

The results of microbiological analyses are plotted in terms of population density on a map. The density is expressed as the percentage of positive cultures out of the total number of cultures. The intensity of development of indicator microorganisms, expressed in arbitrary units, is more widely used, especially in water surveys. Anomalous gradations are selected after calculation of average data on observations of indicator bacteria for the main parts of the survey.

For biologging the results of analyses are expressed by isolines of average values of intensity of development of indicator organisms within the limits of the drilled area. Gas and microbiological studies conducted at the same place greatly facilitate the problems of interpretation. With the data obtained in these cases, it is possible to correlate bacterial accumulations and the zones of different concentration from gas surveys.

Evaluation of Bacterial Anomalies

Bacterial or gas-bacterial anomalies detected as a result of preliminary treatment of factual data are not as yet good enough to be trusted. Further evaluation of their qualitative and quantitative nature must be made. The following must be considered: (1) the completeness of the data on bacterial accumulations and the existence of distorting effects of the regional and soil background; (2) the degree of localization of bacterial effects in the survey area; (3) the shape of the bacterial anomaly and its possible correspondence with the location of an oil or gas pool in depth; (4) the qualitative character of the anomaly with regard to the nature of the predominant types of microflora; (5) the values of the quantitative indices of the survey.

If the results of an investigation are negative, the completeness and accuracy of the observations must be determined beforehand because the negative results may be due to various defects in the methods of field and laboratory work, such as insufficient sample taken at the location, inadequate reproducibility of bacterial cultures, keeping samples for a long time, etc. Investigations of underground waters and deep surveys may also be conducted in order to verify negative data.

If the characteristics of the examined area are positive, the possible effect of regional and soil background must be determined. Processes of contemporary gas formation, to which the soil background is due, may be discounted with the aid of control analyses in the presence of cellulose-decomposing bacteria.

Regional background, observed in a number of gas- and oil-bearing provinces in the regions of Maikop, Grozny, and Buguruslan and elsewhere, is due to the shallow deposition of native rocks containing scattered bitumens and gases. In such cases, gas-bacterial anomalies can only be distinguished if a definite pattern of positive points is present. The largest accumulations of indicator bacteria must be adjacent to zones of lower bacterial concentration or points where the value is equal to zero. If this condition is not fulfilled, the results of the survey must be considered inconclusive.

Bacterial anomalies detected in a soil- or water-survey, or from bio-logging data, may be classified according to a number of features. Depending on the degree of localization of positive points, the following may be distinguished:

a. the focal anomaly, where indicator microorganisms are found at separate, disconnected points, but at the same time are grouped in a definite region for which a general boundary may be drawn and within which a particular indicator organism occurs;

b. the continuous anomaly, where indicator organisms within the limits of a definite region are found at all examined points with considerable intensity of development.

In relation to the structural factors of the area being studied, overlying anomalies and peripheral ones are distinguished. Overlying anomalies may be projected over the entire area of an oil or gas pool or only over specific parts of it. Gas-bacterial effects may simultaneously arise along the slopes of the structure — outside the productive limits of an oil reservoir.

As a rule, peripheral anomalies are the result of fissures in the rocks, motion of ground-waters, and geomorphological peculiarities in the structure

of the earth's surface. The deeper the oil or gas pool lies, the more reason there is to expect that the geobiochemical anomaly corresponding to it
will be projected to a wider area and accompanied by peripheral effects.

Deep oil and gas zones in the earth's crust are accompanied in most
cases by focal anomalies, not continuous ones. However, as gasomicrobiological investigations approach the source of diffusion in water-surveys
and biologging work, the separate focal anomalies recombine to form a
general anomalous zone.

As was stated earlier, this is explained by the fact that underground
waters promote more uniform distribution of migrating hydrocarbons over
a pool and also by the fact that at great depth hydrocarbons and the bacteria which oxidize them are encountered in higher concentrations. Thus,
in order to solve the problem of the possible boundaries and location of oil
and gas accumulations, soil-surveys, water-surveys, and biologging work
must be combined.

Classification of microbiological anomalies according to the predomi-
nating types of indicator microorganisms is essential to determine the
possible composition of the source of diffusion.

In a soil-survey, anomalies may be found which contain methane-
oxidizing bacteria, propane-oxidizing bacteria, or both of these types of
microorganisms in various proportions. To a great extent, anomalies containing both types of indicator microorganisms, i.e., methane-oxidizing
and propane-oxidizing bacteria, correspond to oil and gas pools of commercial interest. The growth of propane-oxidizing microorganisms alone
in subsoil deposits is sometimes associated with the occurrence of traces
of oxidized oil at slight depth. Methane-oxidizing bacteria usually predominate over gas fields.

Anomalies detected in the course of a water-survey may contain: (a)
methane-oxidizing bacteria; (b) bacteria which grow in an atmosphere of
vaporized hydrocarbons; (c) propane-oxidizing bacteria; (d) the enumerated
types of microorganisms in various proportions. The most widespread
types of bacteria in soil- and stratum-waters are those which utilize
vaporized hydrocarbons (pentane, hexane, and heptane). They are encountered more often in the waters than methane-oxidizing bacteria.

Propane-oxidizing bacteria are found relatively rarely, especially in
investigations of deep-lying waters. Nevertheless, anomalies in the occurrence of propane-oxidizing bacteria in subterranean waters are of great
practical interest, since the metabolism of these organisms is not associated, as a rule, with processes of contemporary decomposition of organic
matter. Heptane-oxidizing bacteria cannot be used as an index for the determination of the qualitative composition of a source of diffusion, since
different forms of hydrocarbon microflora may develop in an atmosphere
of vaporized hydrocarbons under aerobic conditions.

Examples of the Interpretation of Microbiological Data

Below are given several examples of microbiological anomalies detected
by soil- and water-surveys. The formations differ in depth and in the
nature of the hydrocarbons found in them.

In the Northern Caucasus, microbiological (soil- and water-) surveys
were conducted in several areas where industrially significant gas fields
were finally found. In one of the structures, in which a source of diffusion

at a depth of around 450 m. was indicated by the data of microbiological soil-survey, an intense anomaly was detected, the boundaries of which satisfactorily coincided with the contour of the gas formation ultimately found in the lowest parts of the Maikop deposits (Fig. 144). At the time of

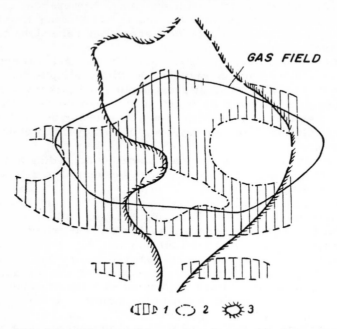

Fig. 144. Schematic map of the results of a soil-survey conducted in 1946 in the area of an anticlinal fold (Northern Caucasus), compared with the results of subsequent survey work. 1—zone of occurrence of hydrocarbon microflora; 2—areas inside the boundaries of a hydrocarbon microflora-bearing region where the microflora is absent; 3—hydrocarbon anomaly according to gas-survey data.

the gasomicrobiological survey, the configuration of the anticlinal structure has not been fully ascertained.

Within the bounds of the anomaly being considered lie several areas which are devoid of indicator microflora. They correspond to surface outcroppings of pyritized clays having an acid reaction which is unfavorable for bacterial activity. A gas soil-survey was conducted simultaneously in the same area. The anomaly detected from the data of this survey only reflected part of the gas-bearing area. The boundaries of the gas anomaly also extended toward the north and south, far beyond the limits of production. It should be noted that the greatest microconcentrations of gases are found in areas where hydrocarbon microflora is absent.

In another area, where a gas-bearing stratum is situated at a greater depth (about 850 m.), a microbiological ground-survey detected only part of the gas pool. Here the propane anomaly was found to correspond with that part of the formation having the greatest output, which in turn corresponded to the sides of the fold (Fig. 145). Closer agreement with the results of subsequent drilling was obtained with biologging data.

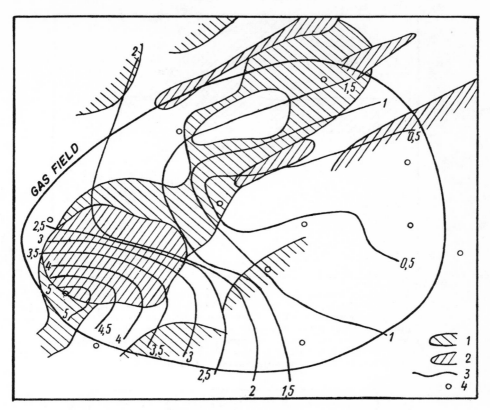

Fig. 145. Schematic map of a microbiological soil-survey conducted in 1948 in an area of brachyanticlinal upheaval (Northern Caucasus) compared with the results of subsequent survey work and biologging. 1—zones of occurrence of methane-oxidizing bacteria; 2—zones of development of propane-oxidizing bacteria; 3—isolines of percent of cases in which propane-oxidizing bacteria were found in the cores of survey wells from the data of biologging; 4—core-drilled wells.

In the third area, under the same geological conditions, a new gas field was located by using the data of a water-survey which involved microbiological testing of springs (Fig. 146). All wells in which edge water was found were outside the boundaries of anomalies, while wells containing industrial quantities of gas, with the exception of two peripheral ones, were inside the boundaries of anomalies distinguished earlier. Microbiological investigations here preceded all other forms of geological prospecting work and made possible the first prediction of the geological structure of the area.

In the Middle Volga region a microbiological (soil- and water-) survey was conducted in several areas. The final surveying has now been completed and oil formations have been discovered. One of these areas is of interest because of the relationship between the gas and microbiological indicators.

In a part of the soil-survey, a focal distribution of methane-oxidizing bacteria was found, and in the western portion of the examined area, a band of propane-oxidizing bacteria was also observed (Fig. 147). The

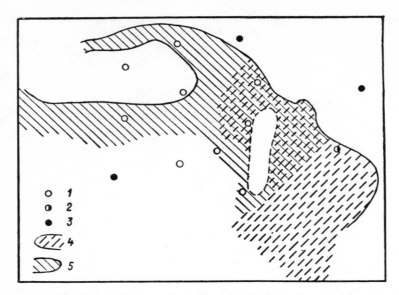

Fig. 146. Schematic map of a hydromicrobiological survey conducted in 1946 and 1948 in a new survey area (Northern Caucasus) compared with the results of subsequent drilling. 1—wells terminating in gas pools; 2—wells encountering gas and water; 3—wells terminating in edge water; 4—zones of hydrocarbon microflora according to data of the water-survey of 1946; 5—the same according to data of the water-survey of 1948.

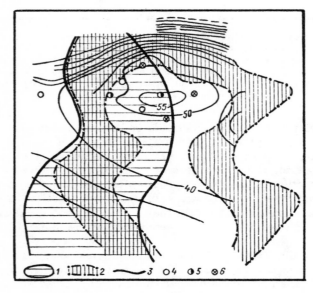

Fig. 147. Schematic map of a microbiological soil-survey conducted in 1943 in a survey area in the middle Volga region compared with data of subsequent drilling. 1—zone of propane-oxidizing bacteria; 2—zone of methane-oxidizing bacteria; 3—geologic structure contours; 4—projected wells; 5—oil-producing wells; 6—dry holes.

stability of the anomaly detected was confirmed by repeated biochemical surveys. For this reason a negative prediction was made on the basis of gas survey data alone. The gasomicrobiological survey, taking the established zonality of distribution of bacterial and gas indicators into account, made possible the recommendation of this area for further survey work.

In subsequent structure drilling in the northern part of the anomaly, an anticlinal uplift was found. Test wells located over the crest of the anticline revealed a commercial oil pool at a depth of about 1,000 m. in Carboniferous strata. The oil has a negligible gas-oil ratio.

A map correlating microbiological and gas indicators for the area

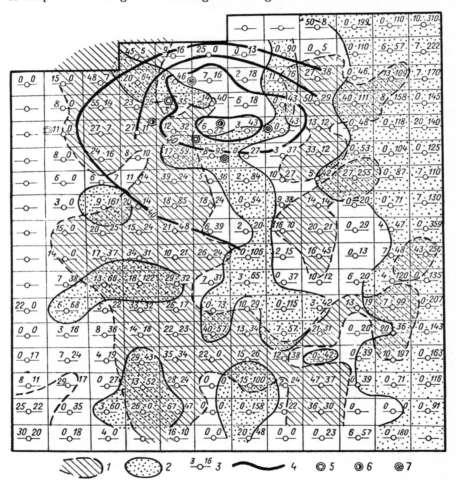

Fig. 148. Map comparing average values from microbiological soil-surveys and gas-surveys conducted jointly in 1943 in a survey area in the Middle Volga region. 1—zones of increased population density of hydrocarbon microflora in subsoil deposits; 2—zones of increased concentration of methane and heavy fractions in subsoil deposits from gas-survey data; 3—figures on the left are average population density of hydrocarbon microflora in ground-samples, figures on the right are average concentration of methane and heavy fractions; 4—geologic structure contour; 5—wells projected; 6—oil-producing wells; 7—dry holes.

being considered was constructed by averaging six points in each square
(Fig. 148). On the basis of these averages, isolines of methane and the
heavy fraction content are shown for the gas-survey, and isolines of the
average population density of methane- and propane-oxidizing bacteria are
shown for the microbiological results (Fig. 148). Zones of higher micro-
concentration of heavy fractions and methane and zones of development of
hydrocarbon microflora are shown separate from one another. It should be
noted that the zone of development of methane-oxidizing bacteria borders
on an oil-bearing area while the band of development of propane bacteria
overlaps a considerable part of the formation.

A water-survey was conducted by microbiological examination of
springs throughout this same area, and an extensive anomaly was detected.
Within the boundaries of the water anomaly, further survey work revealed
two oil formations located side by side (Fig. 149). One of these (the
eastern one) was examined by means of a soil-survey (Fig. 147). The area
of the second formation was not fully covered in this work.

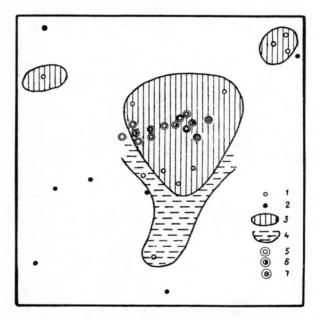

Fig. 149. Schematic map of part of a hydromicrobiological survey conducted in 1947 in the territory
of the Middle Volga compared with results of subsequent drilling. 1 —springs containing hydrocarbon
microflora; 2 —springs giving negative results; 3 —
zone of hydrocarbon microflora with average population density of 20% or more; 4 —the same with population density of 10%; 5 —wells projected; 6 —oil-
producing wells; 7 —dry holes.

In one of the regions of the Kuibyshev Transvolga, a microbiological
soil-survey was conducted in an area where the presence of an anticlinal
structure in the Permian layers was assumed. The anomalous development of a complex hydrocarbon microflora which the survey revealed, was

found to be shifted considerably to the southeast in relation to the assumed structure in the Permian layers (Fig. 150).

The detected anomaly, which was distinguished by a uniform growth of indicator microflora, was recommended for test drilling. As a result of this work it was ascertained that the indicated anomaly corresponds to the central part of a new oil formation situated in Carboniferous layers. The crude oil is characterized by a significant gas-oil ratio.

Thus, with specific formations examined in the Northern Caucasus and the Second Baku serving as examples, several regularities may be noted in the correlation of microbiological and gas indices in soil- and water-surveys. The gas-survey (in cases where the source is at a considerable depth) and biologging give a more complete "reflection" of the pool than the soil-survey does.

Hydrocarbon effects in subsoil deposits, due to the influence of an oil pool with a low gas-oil ratio, take the form of discrete foci for the

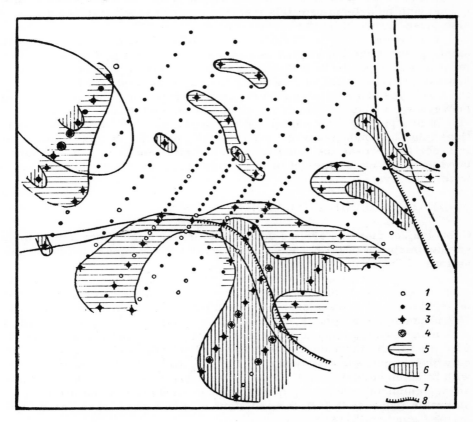

Fig. 150. Schematic map of a microbiological soil-survey conducted in 1943 in a survey area of the Kuibyshev Transvolga compared with results of subsequent drilling. 1—untested soil-survey wells; 2—soil-survey wells with negative results; 3—the same in the presence of hydrocarbon microflora; 4—the same in the presence of cellulose-decomposing bacteria; 5—zones of growth of hydrocarbon microflora with intensity of growth up to 150 arbitrary units; 6—the same with intensity of growth over 150 arbitrary units; 7—structure contours outlining an uplift; 8—contour of oil bearing strata according to data from drilling operations of 1951-1953.

accumulation of hydrocarbon microflora. When the gas-oil ratio is high, the development of microorganisms in subsoil deposits forms a continuous anomaly (when the oil pool lies at a depth not exceeding 750 - 1,000 m.). For portions of the subsoil, and also for underground waters more densely populated with hydrocarbon-oxidizing bacteria, the microconcentrations of hydrocarbon gases are lower than for portions where the bacterial filter is less strongly developed.

When the influx of hydrocarbon gases is intense, complete or partial superposition of gas maxima on the microbiological ones is observed. With a feeble gas source, on the contrary, the zones of microbiological and gas anomalies may fail to coincide within the boundaries of a given gas field. Therefore, for correct interpretation of geochemical anomalies it is necessary to take into account not only the microbiological and gas indices separately, but also the specific way they are related in space. Only on the basis of these data can the actual output of hydrocarbon gases at any given depth be determined; this includes not only freely evolved gases, but also those absorbed by the bacterial filter.

Furthermore, for a correct understanding of the geochemical situation existing within the boundaries of an area under investigation, soil-surveys must be accompanied by a study of aquifers involving microbiological, gas, and salt analyses. Gasomicrobiological water-surveys must be used as the main type of reconnaissance investigation, because they precede soil-surveys and establish objectives for the latter method.

In prospecting for deep oil and gas pools, gasobiochemical investigations must be conducted at great depth, i.e., near the source of diffusion, in order to increase the sensitivity of the determinations. Under these conditions the main types of investigations must be gasobiologging and deep water-surveys.

GEOBOTANICAL INDICATORS

Geobotanical methods are, as yet, only of minor importance among the various methods of oil prospecting. These methods are based on observations of the plant cover.

In the literature there are several references to the fact that many substances of the bitumen group induce changes in the external appearance of vegetation. Thus, for example, when lignite fertilizer (containing up to 79% bitumens) was applied, vigorous growth of a number of cultivated plants took place owing mainly to increases in the sizes of individual plants (41, 42). Significant increase in the green parts of plants growing in soil treated with bitumen was also observed in experiments in the treatment of sand with bitumen emulsion (43). D. M. Guseinov in Azerbaijan used as fertilizer spent "gumbrin" containing a large amount of bitumens and obtained a considerable increase in the size and vigor of plants growing in areas fertilized by the "gumbrin" (44).

In geobotanical investigations conducted at the same time, the appearance of special forms of plants was noticed on the bituminous ejecta of mud volcanoes as a result of adaptation of the plants to the peculiar conditions of volcanic mud. Thus, M. G. Popov found special forms of wormwood (Artemisia limosa H. Koidz), primrose (Primula sachalinensis), and gentian (Gentiana paludicola) (45), native to these mud ejecta alone. P. D. Yaroshenko has described the saltwort Salsola rigida var. foliosa, found in the mud volcanoes of Kara-Chal, and only known to occur on mud ejecta (46).

During the period from 1949 to 1951 this matter was investigated by geobotanists of the All-Union Geological Trust (S. V. Viktorov, E. A. Vostokova, and N. G. Nesvetailova). It was shown by these investigations that in bituminous soils, plants usually have peculiar forms, being distinguished by some gigantism (i.e., sizes significantly greater than the normal average value for the given type) and deformity. The normal proportions of the organs of the given plant are altered and its external appearance is changed.

In the same investigations it was also found that plants growing in bituminous soils quite often develop a capacity for repeated blooming. Many forms normally blooming once a year, when situated at the margins of kir[2] fields or in other soils rich in bitumens, bloomed again in the autumn; some forms did not bloom, but began to vegetate again (i.e., to form new leaves and stems). This capacity for repetition of the flowering cycle appeared in forms belonging to various families and genera: grasses, thistles, irises, roses, etc. One case is also recorded in the literature of mass reblooming of brushwoods near a gas seep (47), although there were no indications of bitumen in the soil in this case.

The causes of all these phenomena are not entirely clear, since the physiological action of bitumens on plants has been studied very little as yet. It is known that the presence of a large quantity of bitumens suppresses nitrification (i.e., the conversion of ammoniacal nitrogen to nitrate nitrogen) and thus brings about some nitrogen hunger in the plants (48, where the literature on the question is reviewed). It has also been shown that several substances similar to bitumens upset normal cell division in plant tissues and lead to the appearance of deformed, giant cells. However, the latter facts were all ascertained by laboratory investigations and have not been confirmed by observations in the field. Thus, the action of the bituminous substrate on plants is obscure.

Furthermore, all observations of the plant cover of bituminous soils were conducted in the semidesert and desert zone (in West Kazakhstan, southwestern Turkemenia, Fergana, and Transcaucasia). Observations in more northerly zones are lacking, with the exception of the above-mentioned work of M. G. Popov.

Despite the fact that the origin of the peculiarities of vegetation in bituminous soils is not quite clear, these peculiarities are so great that with their aid it is very easy (in areas such as Central Aisa and Kazakhstan, in any case) to recognize the presence of bitumens in the soil within the limits of extension of the root systems of plants growing in the area under study. For detection of bituminous soils by means of the plant cover, the following very simple and practicable method of field observations may be recommended.

1. Take note of areas where plants are distinguished by especially large size, luxuriance, or deformities of any kind, particularly those areas in which such peculiarities are found, not in rare isolated instances, but in many cases.

2. In cases where it is necessary to determine how pronounced these peculiarities are, the dimensions of two or three of the most conspicuous

---

[2]"Kir" is an indurated asphaltic substance associated with earthy materials. Ed.

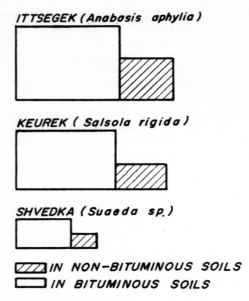

Fig.151. Average sizes of plants in
soils with and without bitumens.

types in the area may be measured (selecting 25 - 50 examples of each
type); the height of the plant and the greatest diameter of its crown are determined. For control, measurements in any area where the plants have
normal average sizes is recommended. Comparative results of measurements are shown in the diagram (see Fig. 151).

   3. When the investigator conducts his observations in summer or
autumn, it is recommended that he take note of cases of second (especially
in the late autumn) blooming of plants. This phenomenon is often observed
in areas where gigantism appears. Second blooming of a plant is revealed
by the presence on the plant of flowers together with the (mostly withered)
remains of flowers and fruits of this year, left over from the first flowering cycle.

   In the desert and semidesert regions of the USSR, special reconnaissance surveys for bituminosity may be conducted by geobotanists in areas
of interest to geologists. Such reconnaissance is conducted by several geological organizations and gives positive results.

BIBLIOGRAPHY

1. G.A. Mogilevskii. On the possibility of biochemical conversion of hy-
      drocarbon gases in the erosion zone. Sb. rabot po gazovio s'emke.
      GONTI, 1939.
2. G.A. Mogilevskii. Microbiological investigations in connection with
      the gas-survey. Razvedka nedr, No. 8 - 9, 1938.
3. G.A. Mogilevskii. Method of surveying oil and gas formations. Avt.
      svid. No. 55154 (June 30, 1939) (applied for Nov. 10, 1937).
4. L.W. Blau. Processes for determination of the location of valuable
      underground oil pools. 2, 269, 889 (applied for Feb. 27, 1939).

5. G.L. Hassler. Microbiological method of surveying. 398, 635, Aug. 12, 1941.
6. C.E. ZoBell. Journal of Bacteriology, No. 4, 1949.
7. C.E. ZoBell. Assimilation of hydrocarbons by microorganisms. Advances in Enzymology, vol. X, 1950.
8. I. Collins. Bacteria make good oil prospectors. Petroleum World, vol. 40, pp. 46, 48, 50, 1943.
9. V.A. Sokolov. Direct geochemical methods of oil prospecting. Gostoptekhizdat, 1947.
10. N.A. Krasil'nikov. On the classification of bacteria. Mikrobiologiya, v. XVII, No. 2, 1948.
11. B.S. Aleev. Introduction to technical microbiology. Pishchepromizdat, 1944.
12. T.L. Ginzburg-Karagicheva. Microbiological essays. ONTI, 1932.
13. T.L. Ginzburg-Karagicheva. On the origin of microflora in oil and gas bearing layers. Sov. geologiya, sb. No. 13, 1947.
14. L.D. Shturm. Microscopic investigation of the waters of oil-bearing layers. Mikrobiologiya, v. XIX, No. 1, 1950.
15. L.D. Shturm. Materials on microscopic investigation of oil formations of the Second Baku. Tr. Inst. nefti Akad. Nauk. SSSR, v. 1, No. 2, 1951.
16. S.I. Kuznetsov. Study of the possibility of simultaneous formation of methane in gas- and oil-bearing environments of the Saratov and Buguruslan regions. Mikrobiologiya, v. XIX, No. 3, 1950.
17. Z.I. Kuznetsova and G.A. Mogilevskii. Development of a method of investigation of the bacterial population of underground waters in the oil regions of the USSR for oil-prospecting purposes. Izv. VGF, No. 1. Gosgeolizdat, 1946.
18. B.L. Isachenko. Sulfur-bacteria from oil wells. Mikrobiologiya, v. XV, No. 6, 1946.
19. M.A. Messineva. Biochemical processes in mud volcanoes. Mikrobiologiya, v. XVII, No. 1, 1948.
20. V.O. Tauson and V.I. Aleshina. On the reduction of sulfates by bacteria in the presence of hydrocarbons. Mikrobiologiya, v. I, No. 3, 1932.
21. C.E. ZoBell. Action of microorganisms on hydrocarbons. Bacteriol. Reviews, vol. 10, No. 1 - 2, 1 - 49, 1946.
22. C.E. ZoBell. The role of bacteria in the formation and transformation of petroleum hydrocarbons. Science, vol. 102, No. 2650, 368 - 369, 1945.
23. G.A. Mogilevskii. Bacterial method of prospecting for oil and natural gas. Razvedka nedr, No. 12, 1940.
24. G.A. Mogilevskii. Microbiological method of prospecting for oil and gas pools. Gostoptekhizdat, 1953.
25. V.O. Tauson. Heredity of microbes. Izd. Akad. Nauk. SSSR, 1947.
26. S.I. Kuznetsov. Role of microorganisms in the material cycle in lakes. Izd. Akad. Nauk SSSR, 1952.
27. C.E. ZoBell. Microbial Transformation of Molecular Hydrogen in Marine Sediments. Bull. Am. Assn. Petrol. Geol., 1947, No. 10, 1709 - 1751.
28. M.I. Belyaeva. Physiology and ecology of hydrogen bacteria. Author's abstract of dissertation. Inst. mikrobiologii, Akad. Nauk SSSR, 1951.

344   GEOCHEMICAL PROSPECTING FOR PETROLEUM

29. V.A. Sullin. Hydrogeology of petroleum formations. Gostoptekhizdat, 1948.
30. H.A. Barker. Studies upon the methane-producing bacteria. Arch. Microb., Bd. 7, 420 - 438, 1936.
31. V.L. Omelyanskii. On the methane fermentation of cellulose. Arkh. biol. mauk, v. IX, No. 3, 1902.
32. V.L. Omelyanskii. On the hydrogen fermentation of cellulose. Arkh. biol. nauk, v. VII, No. 5, 1899.
33. E. Münz. Zur Physiologie der Methanbacterien. Inaugural-Dissertation, Halle, 1915.
34. G.P. Slavnina. Detection of methane-oxidizing bacteria by the fermentation method. Izv. GUGF, No. 3, Gosgeolizdat, 1947.
35. G.P. Slavnina. The peroxidase of methane-oxidizing bacteria. Doklady Akad. Nauk SSSR, v. LVI, No. 2, 205 - 227, 1947.
36. E.N. Bokova. Study of the main properties of bacteria which oxidize liquid and gaseous hydrocarbons evolved from deep-lying strata and underground deposits, and elucidation of several conditions limiting their growth. Izv. GUGF, No. 3, Gosgeolizdat, 1947.
37. G.A. Mogilevskii, V.S. Butkevich, E.V. Dianova, A.A. Voroshilova, and I.V. Bogdanova. Method of prospecting for oil and gas formations (by application of propane-butane bacteria). Avt. avid. No. 57933 (applied for March 25, 1940, published Sept. 30, 1940).
38. E.N. Bokova, V.A. Kuznetsova, and S.I. Kuznetsov. Oxidation of gaseous hydrocarbons by bacteria as a basis for microbiological oil-prospecting. Doklady Akad. Nauk SSSR, v. LVI, No. 7, 755 - 757, 1947.
39. S.I. Kuznetsov, V.A. Kuznetsova, and Z.S. Smirnova. Study of processes of bacterial oxidation of hydrocarbon gases under the conditions of their diffusion through sedimentary rocks. Izv. GUGF, No. 8. Gosgeolizdat, 1947.
40. Byulleten'. Geomikrobiologicheskaya razvedka. Novosti neftyanoi tekhiniki. Geologiya. TsIMTneft', 1947.
41. R. Lieske. Untersuchungen über die Verwandbarkeit von Kohlen als Düngemittel. Brennstoff-Chemie, Bd. 12, H. 5, 1931.
42. F. Fischer. Biologie und Kohle. Angewandte Chemie, No. 9, 1932.
43. A. Gael', N. Zakharov, and E. Malyugin. Cementation of sands by bitumen emulsions. Sb. "Problema rastenievodcheskogo osvoeniya pustyn'", No. 3, 1935.
44. D.M. Gusseinov. Application of spent gumbrin for the purpose of increasing the yield of agr. crops. Izv. Akad. Nauk AzSSR, 1950.
45. M.G. Popov. Endemic species of the Maguntan mud volcano. Botan. Zhurn., No. 5, 1949.
46. P.D. Yaroshenko. Toward the genesis of mud volcanoes near the Kara-Chal State Farm in southeastern Shirvan. Botan. sb. AzGNII, No. 1, 1932.
47. Khokhlov. Repeated blooming of fruits and other peculiarities of behavior of plants in the vicinity of gas wells in the environs of Saratov. Sov. botanika, v. 15, No. 1, 1947.
48. N.P. Remezov. Conditions of nitrogen supply in pine forests. Sov. botanika, No. 6, 1938.

CHAPTER FOURTEEN

The Role of Geochemical
Methods in Petroleum Prospecting

The previous chapters of this book have shown that geochemical methods of prospecting and exploration for oil and gas formations vary considerably. The role of these methods in the search for petroleum is also quite varied. Geochemical methods are used in all stages of prospecting and exploration work under very diverse conditions and may serve entirely different functions.

In the first stage of exploratory geological reconnaissance, the main tasks of geochemical methods are: (a) general evaluation of the possibilities of a region, (b) distinguishing oil-bearing strata, (c) selecting the most promising regions or sometimes, specific areas. The route survey is used primarily for these purposes. A combination of hydrochemical, water-gas, and hydromicrobiological surveys is most useful in evaluating the oil possibilities of a region and in choosing the most likely regions.

Bitumen methods (route bitumen and bitumen luminescence surveys) are used primarily in prospecting for oil-bearing strata. Bituminological determinations and investigations of waters are important, but the results must be coordinated through studies of the dissolved bitumens. The results of geochemical reconnaissance surveys must be in close agreement with geological data. This is particularly true of the hydrochemical surveys which, by their very nature, must agree with geological results.

In this first stage aerial-radiometric surveys, geobotanical investigations, etc. may be used. Test drilling may also be used. Bituminological examinations of cores, the study of the gas content and gas composition of cores, the hydrochemical investigation of well sections, and gas and luminescence logging are conducted in supporting wells.

In the second stage of detailed geological surveys, the task of geochemical methods is to select areas for detailed exploration and to evaluate prospects selected by other methods. Detailed and semi-detailed area surveys are the chief forms of prospecting and exploration used. The hydrochemical (structural) survey is the most practical method and may also be helpful in geological mapping. Geochemical surveys are conducted in areas selected on the basis of geological and geophysical data. The methods that may be used include the gas, gas-core, water-gas, bitumen and bitumen-luminescence, hydrochemical, soil-salt, redox-potential, and microbiological surveys.

These various methods may be and usually are conducted jointly as a combined chemical survey. The combination of methods used may be varied depending on geological and geographical conditions and the purposes of the work or for technical reasons. Gas surveys, for example, are impossible in marshy localities. On the other hand, water-gas and hydrochemical surveys cannot be used in the case of very deep ground waters. Hydrochemical and soil-salt surveys (except the carbonate-siallite method) are impossible in humid climates.

In a combined geochemical survey the area is traversed using a network of sampling points. Samples of subsoil air and soils are taken to determine sorbed gases, bitumens, bacteria, and salts, while samples of ground waters are collected to determine dissolved salts, gases, and bacteria, all from the same boreholes.

The purpose of the gas, core-gas, bitumen, water-gas, redox-potential, and microbiological surveys is to evaluate the petroleum potential of a given area or, in other words, to predict the presence or absence of oil or gas pools below the area surveyed. Hydrochemical surveys are usually conducted for a rather different purpose to confirm data on the geological structure of the area obtained by other (non-geochemical) methods and to improve these data if possible.

Soil-salt surveys are conducted for various purposes. The soil-chloride survey fulfills the same function as the structural hydrochemical survey, while the soil-iodine and soil-carbonate-siallite surveys serve nearly the same purposes as the gas survey, bitumen survey, etc.

The evaluation of results from each type of geochemical survey must be coordinated with the data of other geochemical methods and also with geological and geophysical data.[1] Some geochemical methods (e.g., the core-gas survey and biologging) may also be used in combination with test drilling for mapping purposes.

TABLE 37.   Role of Geochemical Methods in Prospecting and Exploration

Stages of work	Principal tasks	Principal types of geochemical methods
1. Geological prospecting reconnaissance work	General evaluation of the oil-bearing prospects of large regions, prospecting for oil-bearing strata, selecting the most likely regions	Route surveys: hydrochemical, water-gas, bitumen, and bitumen-luminescence. Geochemical study of the sections of supporting wells
2. Detailed geological prospecting and preliminary exploration	Prospecting for exploratory areas and evaluating their possibilities	Hydrochemical surveys. Detailed area surveys: gas, core-gas, bitumen and bitumen-luminescence, bacterial, hydrochemical, soil-salt, redox-potential
3. Exploration work (drilling for prospecting and structure purposes)	Discovery of pools that have been penetrated by the drilling well. Obtaining supplementary data for detailed determination of the geological structure and other secondary tasks	Gas and luminescence logging. Hydrochemical investigations

---

[1] For examples of complex geochemical area surveys see the collection, "Geokhimicheskie methody poiskov nefti i gaza" (No. 1, 1953), articles by V. A. Lobov and A. A. Geodekyan.

In the third stage of exploratory work (which includes deep exploratory drilling), geochemical methods are particularly valuable. The principal use of these methods at this stage of the work is to discover pay sands (pools) during drilling in areas where production exploration is being carried out as well as in areas where the oil potential is not yet determined.

The principal geochemical exploration methods are gas logging and bitumen-luminescence logging (using the drilling mud and drill cuttings). It is most expedient to conduct and interpret these surveys jointly. The data from geochemical methods of logging must be coordinated with electric logging data, hydrogeological observations made during drilling, and drilling data

In exploration and pre-exploratory work, hydrochemical methods are also very important. They can be helpful in solving the problem of predicting oil at a given horizon in adjacent areas, determining the geological structure of a formation, correlating well sections, as well as solving certain production problems. Hydrochemical investigations can also give information of much value in the drilling and development of an oil formation.

All the material of this chapter is presented schematically in Table 37.

Appendix

Generalized Geologic Column for the Oil Producing Regions of the USSR

Era	System	Series	Stage
Cenozoic	Quaternary		Khvalynian Khazarian Baku
	Tertiary	Upper Pliocene	Apsheronian Akchaghylian Balakhan
		Lower Pliocene	Pontian
		Upper Miocene	Maotis Sarmatian
		Middle Miocene	Tortonian Konk Karagan Chokrak Tarkhan
		Lower Miocene	Maikop*
		Oligocene	Kharkov
		Eocene	
		Paleocene	Saratov
Mesozoic	Cretaceous	Upper Cretaceous	Danian Maestrichian Senonian Turonian Cenomanian
		Lower Cretaceous	Albian Aptian Neocomian Barremian Balanzhan
	Jurassic	Malm	Upper Volga Lower Volga Kimmeridgian Oxfordian Callovian
		Dogger	Bathonian Bajocian Aalen
		Lias	
	Triassic		
Paleozoic	Permian	Upper Permian	Tatarian Kazanian Ufa
		Lower Permian	Kungurian Artinskian Sakmarian
	Carboniferous	Upper Carboniferous	Uralian Gshelian Kasimovian
		Middle Carboniferous	Moscovian Bashkirian
		Lower Carboniferous	Namurian Viséan Tournaisian
	Devonian Silurian Ordivician Cambrian		
Precambrian.			

SOURCE: Compiled by the editors from the following sources: (a) Istoricheskaya geologia s osnovami paleontologii, Ya. M. Levites, Gosgeoltekhizdat, Moscow, 1956; (b) Istoricheskaya geologia, G.P. Leonov, Moscow Univ. Press, 1956; (c) The geological map of the USSR, D. V. Nalivkin, editor, Ministry of Geol., USSR, 1956.

*The Maikop is a transitional stage between Lower Miocene and Upper Oligocene.

[349]